Bill Keine

VAN TUYL'S

MATHEMATICS OF BUSINESS

VAN TUYL'S

MATHEMATICS OF BUSINESS

VAN TUYL'S MATHEMATICS OF BUSINESS

by

GEORGE H. VAN TUYL

Evander Childs High School, City of New York; Formerly Instructor, School of Commerce, Accounts and Finance, New York University; Columbia University; and Packard Commercial School, City of New York

AMERICAN BOOK COMPANY

NEW YORK CINCINNATI CHICAGO BOSTON

ATLANTA DALLAS SAN FRANCISCO

E. P. 1
VAN TUYL'S MATHEMATICS OF BUSINESS
MADE IN U. S. A.

PREFACE

Mathematics of Business has been written primarily for students in the business course. The subject matter has been selected and arranged on the basis determined by a country-wide survey of school requirements. The book covers a range of subjects that will make it interesting and helpful to those who study the mathematics of business with either a personal or vocational objective.

The text consists of four parts. Part One emphasizes the important matter "How to Solve Problems." The student learns from the beginning to select the known facts of a problem and how to proceed to find the unknown fact or facts. As he progresses from principle to principle he is constantly reminded of correct analysis by illustrative solutions of problems. The problem material in Part One is built around such subjects as percentage, commission, commercial discounts, profit and loss, interest, bank discount, taxes, insurance, and various forms of credit. At the end of Part One abundant material is provided for reviewing the fundamental operations of arithmetic.

Part Two contains a variety of topics that are to a degree unrelated to each other, yet all of them require a thorough working knowledge of the fundamental principles presented in Part One. All the subjects treated in Part Two are in current usage in various types of business. The application of all the subjects is not to be found in any one business, but each subject is used in one business or another. It is not intended that every class study all the subjects in Part Two unless a class finds some interest in, and has the necessary time allotted for, all the subjects. The teacher can determine the topic or topics that will best meet the needs of the class.

Part Three comprises four series of narrative problems covering types of business such as wholesale merchandising, real estate and building, manufacturing, and farming. These narratives provide an excellent review of the most important subjects covered in the text. They will furnish a test of the student's ability to maintain a sustained interest in a business activity. Technical data and statements of fact in these narratives have been furnished, or approved, by experts connected with the several kinds of activity represented in the narratives.

Part Four is devoted to a testing and remedial program. In it is a considerable variety of tests furnished by, or taken from the examinations of, large business firms, educational examining boards, the University of the State of New York, and from the author's writings. The remedial problems are classified under specific subject heads so that a teacher can turn to any type of exercise or problem desired for review work.

The author wishes to thank business men, professional men, teachers, and others who have contributed so generously of their time, counsel, and subject matter, toward the preparation of this text. Without their assistance many important topics and features could not have been included in the book.

THE AUTHOR

CONTENTS

PART ONE: ESSENTIAL SUBJECTS

PART TWO: OPTIONAL SUBJECTS

PART THREE: NARRATIVES

PART FOUR: REMEDIAL PROBLEMS AND TESTS

PART ONE

ESSENTIAL SUBJECTS

INTRODUCTION

Arithmetic plays a large part in the everyday life of the average citizen. Whether you go to a grocery store, a drugstore, a dry-goods store, a real-estate office, a newspaper office, or engage in farming, arithmetical calculation is required.

Apportioning the income to be allowed for the family needs and spending the income in such a way as to keep within the budget allowance require careful planning and a working knowledge of arithmetic.

There are calculating machines of various kinds that perform several arithmetical operations rapidly and accurately. But with all these calculating devices, there is still a vast number of operations in arithmetic which must be made daily without these aids.

Numbers, known as arithmetic, have a place in almost everything we do; even from earliest times arithmetic has been very necessary in the onward march of the human race.

PROGNOSTIC TEST — PART I

It is assumed that students in this course have already some knowledge of the fundamental principles of arithmetic, but from the reports of various surveys and daily observations, it cannot be assumed that students know *how to apply the principles of arithmetic to actual personal or business situations which they probably will encounter.* While no test will point out all the deficiencies of all students or all the capabilities of any one student, the problems in Part I of the following test will tend to show how the student's present knowledge of arithmetic functions in personal situations and the problems in Part II will show how it functions in business situations.

The figure in the parentheses after each problem is the credit allowed for the problem.

Problems

1. Add $9\frac{1}{6}$ and $7\frac{3}{4}$. (5)

2. Divide $47\frac{1}{4}$ by 7. (5)

3. A man worked $13\frac{1}{2}$ hr. and received $.28 an hour. How much did he earn? (5)

4. A dealer had on hand $\frac{5}{6}$ of a dozen shirts and bought $3\frac{1}{2}$ dozen more. He sold 41 of them. How many shirts had he left? (5)

5. How much is the interest on $450 at 4% for 6 months? (5)

6. $36 is 9% of how many dollars? (5)

7. A baseball team won 9 games and lost 3 games. What was the "standing" of the team? (That is, what was the percentage of games won?) (7)

8. In laying out a baseball diamond the boys did not have a tape measure or measuring rod with which to make measurements. One boy said he could measure the distances (90 feet between bases) by pacing the lines. He said his paces (steps) were $2\frac{1}{2}$ feet each. How many paces must he take to lay off each side of the diamond? (5)

9. From the home plate to the pitcher's box is 60 ft. 6 inches. How many paces must the boy take to measure that distance? (5)

10. In an art class the pupils were drawing from still life. Their object one day was an elm tree on the school ground. The tree was 60 feet high. They were making a sketch of the tree which was to be 6 inches from the base to its top. What was the ratio of the height of the sketch to the height of the tree? (7)

11. A publisher wished to reproduce a photograph 9 inches by 12 inches in size to a picture 3 inches by 4 inches, for publication in a book. What was the ratio of the area of the reduced picture to the area of the original picture? (8)

12. Tom and Fred planned a vacation trip in Tom's car. Tom said, "I will furnish the car if you will buy the gasoline, and we will share equally all other expenses." Their trip was to cover 1000 miles, and they were to take two weeks for the trip. Fred asked, "How much gasoline will it take?" Said Tom, "I average about 16 miles on a gallon of gasoline." After a moment's thought, Fred said, "All right, I will pay for the gasoline." At \$.19 a gallon, how much did the gasoline for the trip cost? **(8)**

13. Referring to problem No. 12, Fred said to Tom, "How much do you estimate is the 'wear and tear' on your car for the trip?" Tom said, "I figure it this way. Depreciation on the car this year will be \$250; insurance costs me \$38.50 a year, and my garage rent is \$50 for the year. For this trip I will need to buy 2 quarts of oil at \$.25 a quart, and have the car greased at a cost of \$1. I drive an average of 8000 miles a year, so this trip will be one eighth of my year's driving." Did it cost Tom more or less to furnish the car than it did Fred to buy the gasoline? **(12)**

14. Referring again to problem No. 12, and to problem No. 13, if other expenses of the vacation trip were \$130, for how many weeks must each of the young men have laid aside \$5 a week to have saved enough to cover his share of the cost of the trip? **(10)**

15. The balcony of a school was on three sides of the auditorium. It measured 120 feet along the railing in front of the first row of seats. To decorate the front of the balcony, the members of the graduating class — 6 boys and 8 girls — agreed to buy the bunting, each paying an equal share of the cost. If the total length of the bunting was twice the length of the balcony, and cost \$.10 a yard, how much should each member of the class pay? **(8)**

PROGNOSTIC TEST — PART II

It is now quite common procedure for large business concerns and also for not a few smaller concerns to require appli-

G. A. Douglas from Gendreau

A section of a large office in which each person's job requires a special type of calculation. Each employee passed a standard test in arithmetic to prove his or her knowledge of the subject, before being accepted.

cants for positions to pass a simple test for the job they are seeking. Some knowledge of arithmetic is required of practically every clerk, salesperson, stenographer, bookkeeper, and of many other classes of employees. Many applicants, therefore, face the prospects of being tested in arithmetic as well as in some special subject such as stenography, typewriting, or bookkeeping.

The problems in the following test have been taken from actual examination papers of different large business houses that require their applicants to know at least the fundamentals of arithmetic. It must be understood, however, that jobs in the higher-wage brackets frequently call for a correspondingly greater working knowledge of business arithmetic.

The figure in the parentheses on the right margin is the credit allowed for each problem.

Problems

1. Find the total value of the following:

4 buttons at	\$.36 a dozen	=	???
6 yd. of lace at	.19 a yard	=	???
4 doz. bars of soap at	.09 a bar	=	???
$\frac{1}{2}$ yd. of lace at	.54 a yard	=	???
18 glasses at	1.44 a dozen	=	???
	Total	=	???

(6)

2. A customer purchased a pair of gloves at \$1.89. She returned the gloves and selected a pair selling at \$2.27, and handed the clerk a half dollar. How much change should she receive? (4)

3. A customer made a purchase for \$6.69. She gave the clerk a ten-dollar bill in payment. Indicate the change she should receive in pennies, nickels, dimes, quarters, half dollars, and dollar bills. (3)

4. A sales slip shows that a customer bought an article for \$1.54, and that she handed the salesperson \$2. Calculate the sales tax of 2% and state how much change should be returned. (4)

5. An insurance company charges \$.10 weekly on an industrial policy of \$225. How much would be the charge on a similar policy of \$1800? (4)

6. The weekly wages of A is \$18; of B, \$20; of C, \$35; of D, \$27; and of E, \$40. What is their average weekly wage? (4)

7. A company employing the men referred to in Problem 6 distributed a bonus of \$280 among them in proportion to their weekly wages. How much did each employee receive? (7)

8. Find the interest on \$780 at 6% for 1 month and 24 days. (4)

9. (*a*) Multiply 156 by $4\frac{1}{3}$. (2) (*b*) Divide 156 by $4\frac{1}{3}$. (2)

10. In a certain city there are 195,000 people. Of that number 28,275 persons are attending school. What percentage of the population is in school? (4)

11. On a bill of goods amounting to $2356.75, the terms are 4/10, N/60. Find the cash discount, and the amount required to pay for the goods at the expiration of the ten days. (4)

12. A manufacturer offers a retailer an electric kitchen stove for $198, less a trade discount of $16\frac{2}{3}$% and 10%. Find the net price of the stove. (4)

13. A piece of cloth measuring $7\frac{1}{2}$ feet long was cut from a piece (bolt) of cloth measuring $14\frac{3}{4}$ yards. How many yards were left in the bolt? (4)

14. From $384\frac{1}{3}$ subtract $68\frac{3}{4}$. (3)

15. How much is $1\frac{1}{4}$% of $3268.80? (4)

In the yard-goods department you sell the following goods. What is the amount of each bill?

16.

18 inches at $1.28 per yard
24 inches at .32 per yard
48 inches at .40 per yard
45 inches at 1.00 per yard (7)

17.

$3\frac{3}{8}$ yd. at $1.44 per yard
$4\frac{1}{4}$ yd. at 2.24 per yard
$2\frac{5}{8}$ yd. at .56 per yard
$5\frac{1}{2}$ yd. at .72 per yard (5)

Find the amount of each bill. (16 ounces = 1 pound)

18.

1 lb. 2 oz. at $.50 per pound
3 lb. 8 oz. at .32 per pound
6 lb. 4 oz. at .12 per pound (7)

19.

$1\frac{3}{4}$ lb. at $.08 per pound
$4\frac{1}{2}$ lb. at .36 per pound
$5\frac{1}{8}$ lb. at .16 per pound (4)

20. Find the amount of each bill.

a

14 oranges at $.20 a dozen
20 oranges at .25 a dozen
32 oranges at .40 a dozen (7)

b

$1\frac{1}{2}$ doz. items at $.04 each
$3\frac{3}{4}$ doz. items at .12 each
$2\frac{1}{3}$ doz. items at .16 each (7)

SOLVING PROBLEMS

Underwood and Underwood

Much of the information your employer will ask you to provide either in statement or report form, or even orally, will probably involve figures. Inaccurate answers are not only valueless but may even result disastrously to your employer, to say nothing of the embarrassment you must suffer. Your worth to your employer as well as to yourself will depend largely on your ability to see the correct relations between the elements of all problems that are presented to you. Learn to think straight!

The main object in studying arithmetic is to learn how to make computations and solve the arithmetical problems that arise commonly in daily routine and work, whether of a personal or business nature. The needs of people differ, so a text should provide different types of problems with varying degrees of difficulty. All problems, however, whether easy or difficult, are solved by the application of a few simple principles.

The purpose of the following pages is to present the fundamental principles required, and to show their application to the solution of problems.

Determining the Facts in a Problem

Every problem in arithmetic contains at least **two known facts** and at least **one unknown fact.** The solution of the problem consists in so combining the known facts that the unknown fact, or facts, may be determined. In combining the known facts one must use one or more of the operations of *addition, subtraction, multiplication,* and *division.* (For special drills in the fundamental operations, see pages 150–170.)

In solving a problem the student needs, then, to classify the facts of the problems as follows:

1. *The known facts or values that are stated in the problem*
2. *The unknown fact or facts that are to be found*
3. *How the known facts may be treated, or combined, to find the unknown fact or facts.*

The *method* of combining the known facts to determine the unknown fact is important. One of the simplest plans is to state the problem in one or more equations. An **equation** is an expression of equality. Thus, (*a*) $3 \times 8 = 24$; (*b*) ? (what part) of $56 = 8$, (*c*) $5 \times ?$ (what number) $= 35$, are all equations.

TYPES OF PROBLEMS

There is little difficulty in solving problems in which addition and subtraction are the principal operations. The chief difficulties in solving problems arise more often in those problems that involve multiplication and division. Problems involving these latter operations may be grouped under three headings, or types, as follows:

Type 1. Finding the product of two numbers or factors. As $4 \times 7 = ?$

Note. The term "factor" as used here means one of the two or more numbers which, when multiplied together, will give a certain product. Thus, 4 and 7 are factors of 28 because $4 \times 7 = 28$.

Type 2. Finding what part one number is of another. As $6 = ?$ (what part) of 12.

Type 3. Finding a number when a part of it is known. As $9 = \frac{3}{4}$ of ? (what number).

Finding the Product of Two Factors

Mental Drill

For further drill on addition, subtraction, and multiplication of fractions, see pages 171–183.

How much is

$\frac{1}{2}$ of $\frac{1}{3}$?	$\frac{2}{3}$ of $\frac{1}{2}$?	$\frac{2}{3} - \frac{1}{9}$?	$\frac{1}{4} + \frac{1}{3}$?
$\frac{1}{3}$ of $\frac{2}{3}$?	$\frac{3}{4}$ of $\frac{1}{2}$?	$\frac{3}{4} - \frac{1}{3}$?	$\frac{1}{3} + \frac{4}{9}$?
$\frac{1}{4}$ of $\frac{2}{3}$?	$\frac{1}{4}$ of $\frac{7}{8}$?	$\frac{5}{8} - \frac{1}{4}$?	$\frac{2}{3} + \frac{3}{4}$?

Illustration. A man had $\frac{3}{4}$ of an acre of land. He sold $\frac{1}{3}$ of it for a building lot. What part of an acre had he left?

The known facts:

1. He had $\frac{3}{4}$ of an acre of land
2. He sold $\frac{1}{3}$ of it

The unknown facts:

1. The part of an acre he sold
2. The part of an acre he had left

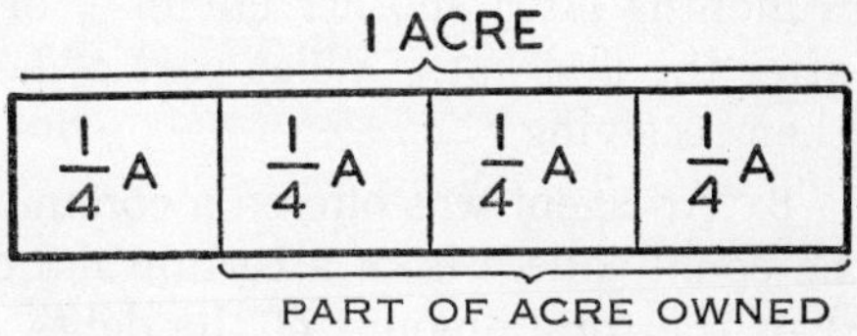

If we know how much land he sold, it will be easy to find how much land he had left. The first unknown fact to discover, then, is how much land he sold.

The problem states "he sold $\frac{1}{3}$ of it."

"It" is "$\frac{3}{4}$ of an acre."

Therefore, the equation is,

$$\tfrac{1}{3} \text{ of } \tfrac{3}{4}A = \text{part sold}$$

Multiplying, $\frac{1}{3}$ of $\frac{3}{4}A = \frac{1}{4}A$, part sold.

Obviously, if a man had $\frac{3}{4}$ of an acre, and sold $\frac{1}{4}$ of an acre, he had left the difference.

$$\frac{3}{4}A - \frac{1}{4}A = \frac{2}{4}A = \frac{1}{2}A, \text{ left}$$

Problems

---

1. A man owned $\frac{3}{5}$ of a mill, and sold $\frac{1}{3}$ of his share. What part of the mill did he still own?

2. A farmer had $\frac{5}{8}$ of his crop of potatoes on hand, February 1. He then sold $\frac{3}{5}$ of his stock on hand. What part of his entire crop of potatoes did he have left?

3. A woman bought $3\frac{1}{2}$ yards of ribbon and used $\frac{3}{7}$ of it to tie a Christmas parcel. How much ribbon had she left?

4. A bookkeeper spent $\frac{5}{8}$ of his wages for living expenses. He gave $\frac{1}{3}$ of the remainder to his mother, and put the rest in the savings bank. What part of his wages did he put into the savings bank?

5. An automobile depreciated $\frac{1}{4}$ of its value the first year. In the second year it depreciated $\frac{1}{5}$ of its value at the end of the first year. What part of its original value was it worth at the end of two years?

6. A man's salary was reduced $\frac{1}{3}$. Afterward his reduced salary was increased by $\frac{1}{3}$. What part of his original salary did he then receive?

7. A stenographer received a cut of $\frac{1}{10}$ of her salary, and 6 months later another cut of $\frac{1}{6}$ of what she was receiving after the first cut. What part of her original salary was she then receiving?

8. An agent was offered a commission of $\frac{1}{10}$ of the amount he could collect from a certain list of debtors. He collected $\frac{7}{8}$ of the total amount of the debts. What part of the total debts did he receive as commission? What part of the total debts did his employer receive?

9. A firm became bankrupt and could pay only $\frac{4}{5}$ of its debts. Before the firm could make payment, a fire destroyed $\frac{1}{8}$ of their available resources. What part of their debts could they pay then?

Finding What Part One Number Is of Another Number

Mental Drill

For further drill on division of fractions, see page 183.

Practice on these exercises before solving the problems.

$\frac{1}{3}$ of $\frac{1}{8}$ =	$\frac{1}{4} - \frac{1}{8}$ =	$\frac{1}{2} + \frac{2}{3}$ =	$15 \div \frac{5}{6}$ =
$\frac{1}{2}$ of $\frac{2}{3}$ =	$\frac{3}{4} - \frac{2}{3}$ =	$\frac{1}{3} + \frac{3}{4}$ =	$12 \div \frac{3}{4}$ =
$\frac{3}{4}$ of $\frac{3}{8}$ =	$\frac{5}{8} - \frac{1}{2}$ =	$\frac{3}{4} + \frac{3}{8}$ =	$16 \div \frac{4}{7}$ =
$\frac{3}{4} \div 2$ =	$4 \div 8$ =	$6 \div 8$ =	$16 \div \frac{3}{4}$ =
$\frac{5}{8} \div 3$ =	$5 \div 7$ =	$7 \div 9$ =	$17 \div \frac{1}{2}$ =
$\frac{2}{3} \div 4$ =	$3 \div 5$ =	$12 \div 16$ =	$11 \div \frac{4}{5}$ =

In exercise No. 1, below, the product and one factor are given. The product, 65, divided by the factor, $\frac{5}{7}$, gives the other factor. $65 \div \frac{5}{7} = 91$, the other factor. Check: $\frac{5}{7}$ of $91 = 65$.

Make a statement like the foregoing for each of these exercises and solve the equation.

1. $\frac{5}{7}$ of ? = 65
2. $\frac{3}{8}$ of ? = 96
3. ? × 72 = 108
4. ? × 91 = 13
5. 46 × ? = $11\frac{1}{2}$
6. ? × 17 = 102
7. $3\frac{1}{2}$ × ? = 105
8. ? × 48 = 64
9. ? × 64 = 48
10. 72 × ? = 9

Illustration. What part of 12 is 4?

In equation form the problem is expressed as

? (what part) of 12 = 4

It is recognized at once that 4 is $\frac{1}{3}$ of 12. To show the solution, it appears this way:

$$4 \div 12 = \frac{4}{12} = \frac{1}{3}$$

In the equation ? of 12 = 4, one known factor (12) and the product (4) are known. The principle to be applied is stated as, **The product of two factors divided by one of the factors gives the other factor.**

Illustration. A building insured for $14,400, was damaged by fire to the extent of $2400. The insurance company paid the loss promptly. The loss paid was what part of the amount of the insurance?

The known facts are:

1. The amount of insurance ($14,400)
2. The amount of the loss ($2400)

The unknown fact is:

What part of the total insurance was the loss

In equation form the question is
The loss paid = ? (what part) of the insurance
Substituting figures, we have

$2400 = ? of $14,400

That is, $2400 ÷ $14,400 = $.16\frac{2}{3} = \frac{1}{6}$, part of insurance paid

Problems

1. Two college students earned during the summer vacation $840. John earned $480, and Henry $360. What part of the total earnings did each earn?

2. Two sections of pavement 72 rods long are to be rebuilt. One section is 48 rods long. What part of the entire length of pavement was each section?

3. An article cost $12. It was sold at a profit of $4. What part of the cost was gained?

4. The product of two numbers is 72. One of them is 144. What is the other number?

5. An accountant's salary was increased from $3600 to $4000. What part of the original salary was the increase?

6. Owing to lowered interest rates a man's income was reduced from $4500 to $4000. What part of his original income was the reduction in his income?

7. If $7.50 was gained by selling an article for $22.50, what part of the selling price was gained?

8. From a bolt of cloth containing $46\frac{1}{2}$ yd. a piece containing $15\frac{1}{2}$ yd. was sold. What part of the cloth was sold?

9. A house rents for $1320 a year. Of that amount the owner spends $550 a year for the taxes and upkeep of the property. What part of the gross rental is he able to save?

10. A man agreed to work a day of 7 hours for \$4.60. If he worked only $5\frac{1}{4}$ hr., what part of the agreed time did he work? How much should he be paid for the time he worked?

Finding the Whole of a Number When Part of It Is Known

The fundamental operation to be performed in the following problems is division.

To divide an integer by a fraction, multiply the integer by the reciprocal of the fraction. The **reciprocal** of a fraction is the fraction inverted. Thus the reciprocal of $\frac{2}{3}$ is $\frac{3}{2}$. For further drill in division by a fraction, see page 186.

Mental Drill

Find the result of each of the following indicated operations:

$4 \div \frac{1}{2} =$	$9 \div \frac{3}{4} =$	$5 \div \frac{3}{4} =$	$15 \div \frac{2}{5} =$
$6 \div \frac{2}{3} =$	$12 \div \frac{6}{7} =$	$8 \div \frac{5}{6} =$	$14 \div \frac{5}{6} =$
$8 \div \frac{4}{5} =$	$16 \div \frac{4}{9} =$	$7 \div \frac{3}{5} =$	$18 \div \frac{4}{5} =$

Illustration. A man worked $\frac{5}{8}$ of a day and received \$3.50 as wages. At that rate, how much would he have received if he had worked all day?

The known facts are:

1. He worked $\frac{5}{8}$ of a day
2. He received \$3.50 as wages

The unknown fact is:

The amount he would have received if he had worked all day

Thus, $\frac{5}{8}$ of a day's pay $= \$3.50$
Then, $\frac{1}{8}$ of a day's pay $= \frac{1}{5}$ of $\$3.50 = \$.70$
Therefore, $\frac{8}{8}$, or a whole day's pay $= 8 \times \$.70 = \$5.60$.

This solution is called the unitary analysis solution. For further drill on unitary-analysis exercises, see page 186. It is very simple and readily applied to problems in which the number to be divided is exactly divisible by the numerator of the fraction. It is called the "unitary-analysis" solution because the first step in solving the equation is to find the value of a *fractional unit* of the unknown value. In the equation $\frac{5}{8}$ of a day's pay $= \$3.50$ the first step is to find $\frac{1}{8}$ of a day's pay, which is $\frac{1}{5}$ of \$3.50, or \$.70.

$\frac{1}{8}$ is called a fractional unit because it is 1 of the 8 fractional parts of a unit (a whole day's pay).

Since $\frac{1}{8}$ of a day's pay is \$.70, $\frac{8}{8}$, or a whole day's pay, is 8 × \$.70, or \$5.60.

In other problems in which the number to be divided by a fraction is not exactly divisible by the numerator of the fraction the unitary-analysis solution is not advisable. In such cases the method of dividing an integer by a fraction as shown in the following illustration is advised.

Illustration. A merchant, admitting a partner, sold him $\frac{3}{7}$ of the business for \$5500. How much was the whole business worth?

The known facts are:

1. A man sold $\frac{3}{7}$ of his business
2. He received \$5500 for the part he sold

The unknown fact is:

1. The value of the whole business

Stating the known facts in equation form,

$\frac{3}{7}$ of the value of the business = \$5500.

This means that $\frac{3}{7}$ of \$? = \$5500.

\$5500 is the product obtained by multiplying some number of dollars by $\frac{3}{7}$. To find the number of dollars that was multiplied by $\frac{3}{7}$ to get \$5500, divide \$5500 by $\frac{3}{7}$.

Thus,

$\$5500 \div \frac{3}{7} = \$5500 \times \frac{7}{3} = \$12{,}833.33$, value of the business

Equations in the form of $\frac{3}{7}$ of \$? = \$5500 consist of two factors and a product. The factors are $\frac{3}{7}$ and an unknown number of dollars indicated by the question mark (\$?); the product is \$5500.

The principle governing the solutions of the preceding problems may be illustrated in the following simple exercises.

In the equation 4 × ? (what number) = 28, we know that the missing number is 7, because 28 ÷ 4 = 7. That is, the product (28) is divided by the known factor (4).

In the equation $\frac{3}{4}$ of ? (what number) = 10, as in the preceding illustration, the unknown number is found by dividing the product, 10, by the known factor, $\frac{3}{4}$.

Thus, $10 \div \frac{3}{4} = 10 \times \frac{4}{3} = \frac{40}{3} = 13\frac{1}{3}$, the number

The principle governing the solution of such equations is stated in these words: **The *product* of two factors divided by one of the factors will give the other factor.**

As a formula, the principle may be stated this way, $F \times F = P$; consequently, $P \div F = F$.

Problems

It will be helpful if questions like these are asked for each problem:

Which number is the product?
What is the known factor?
What principle will solve the equation?

1. $\frac{3}{4}$ of what number is 12?

2. $\frac{5}{6}$ of what number is 15?

3. $\frac{7}{8}$ of what number is 28?

4. $\frac{3}{7}$ of what number is 18?

5. $\frac{7}{9}$ of what number is 21?

6. $\frac{2}{3}$ of what number is $\frac{1}{2}$?

7. $\frac{3}{4}$ of what number is $\frac{2}{3}$?

8. $\frac{5}{6}$ of what number is $\frac{1}{6}$?

9. An agent sold 480 bu. of potatoes, which was $\frac{6}{7}$ of a given shipment. How many bushels of potatoes were in the shipment?

10. A fire caused a loss of $\frac{3}{8}$ of the value of a house. If the loss amounted to $2400, what was the value of the house?

11. A man was allowed $375 for his car when he turned it in for a new car. If the amount allowed for the old car was equal to $\frac{3}{8}$ of the cost of the new car, find the cost of the new car.

12. A man's income was reduced to $4500. If his income now is $\frac{9}{10}$ of what it was before the decrease, how much was it before it was reduced?

13. What is meant by stating a problem in equation form?

14. Show graphically how you would find the whole value of a piece of land if $\frac{5}{8}$ of it is worth $250.

15. How would you use, or explain, the unitary analysis plan of solution in this equation?

$$\tfrac{4}{5} \text{ of a number} = 44$$

Finding a Number When It Is a Part More (or a Part Less) than a Given Number

Mental Drill

Practice on these exercises before solving the problems:

$27 \div \frac{9}{8} =$	$45 \div \frac{3}{4} =$	$\frac{9}{5}$ of what number $= 54$
$24 \div \frac{8}{5} =$	$21 \div \frac{7}{8} =$	$\frac{3}{8}$ of what number $= 27$
$35 \div \frac{7}{5} =$	$36 \div \frac{6}{7} =$	$\frac{8}{5}$ of what number $= 32$
$\frac{6}{5} \div \frac{6}{5} =$	$\frac{1}{2} \div \frac{8}{7} =$	$\frac{5}{9}$ of what number $= 15$
$\frac{5}{8} \div \frac{3}{2} =$	$\frac{2}{3} \div \frac{5}{3} =$	$\frac{8}{9}$ of what number $= 40$

Illustration. Your arithmetic-test mark in January was 88. That is $\frac{1}{10}$ more than your mark is in February. What was your mark in February?

The known facts are:

1. The mark for January, 88
2. The mark in January is $\frac{1}{10}$ greater than the mark in February

The unknown fact is:

The mark in February

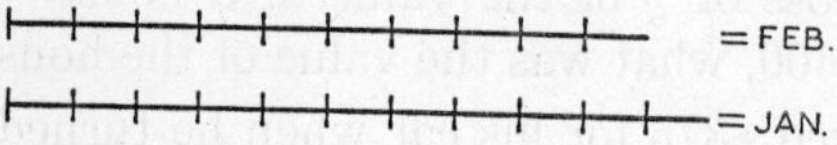

February mark $= \frac{10}{10}$

January mark $= \frac{11}{10}$

February mark $= \frac{10}{10}$ of itself

January mark $= \frac{1}{10}$ of the February mark more than the February mark

That is, the January mark $= \frac{11}{10}$ of the February mark

Therefore, $88 = \frac{11}{10}$ of the February mark

Hence, $88 \div \frac{11}{10} = 80$, the February mark.

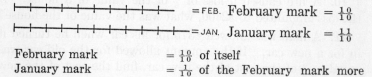

Illustration. By paying cash for a piano, instead of buying it on the installment plan, a man was allowed a discount of $\frac{1}{12}$ of the installment price. If he paid $550 for the piano, how much would he have paid on the installment plan of purchase?

The known facts are:

1. The cash price, \$550
2. The discount allowed, $\frac{1}{12}$ of the installment price

The unknown fact is:

The installment price

$$\begin{aligned}
\text{Installment price} &= \tfrac{12}{12} \text{ of itself} \\
\text{Discount} &= \tfrac{1}{12} \text{ of installment price} \\
\text{Cash price} &= \tfrac{11}{12} \text{ of installment price} \\
\text{Therefore,} \quad \$550 &= \tfrac{11}{12} \text{ of installment price} \\
\$550 \div \tfrac{11}{12} &= \$600, \text{ installment price}
\end{aligned}$$

Problems

1. A real estate dealer sold a parcel of land for $\frac{1}{10}$ less than his asking price, because the buyer paid all cash. If the amount received was \$810, how much was his asking price?

2. Mr. Gray's business profits this year are $\frac{1}{5}$ more than they were last year. If this year's profits are \$2400, how much were the profits last year?

3. The horse power of an auto engine this year is 80. If this is $\frac{1}{3}$ more than the horsepower in last year's cars of the same make, find the horsepower of last year's cars.

4. Mr. Gale's rent this year is $\frac{1}{8}$ less than it was last year. If this year's rent is \$910, how much was his rent last year?

5. An article which sold for \$2.80 was sold at a profit of $\frac{1}{3}$ of the cost. Find the cost.

6. By selling a book for \$.60, a bookseller lost $\frac{1}{7}$ of the cost. How much did the book cost him?

7. What number increased by $\frac{1}{6}$ of itself is 91?

8. When working overtime a man received $\frac{1}{2}$ more than his regular wages. If he received \$.96 an hour for overtime work, how much was his wage per hour for regular time?

9. Two boys earned \$4.20 picking berries. Arthur earned $\frac{1}{10}$ more than Fred did. How much did each earn?

The known facts are:

1. Both boys earned \$4.20
2. Arthur earned $\frac{1}{10}$ more than Fred did

The unknown facts are:

1. How much Fred earned
2. How much Arthur earned

Construct a diagram like the diagram on page 18.

If we knew how much Fred earned, it would be easy to find how much Arthur earned, because he earned $\frac{1}{10}$ more than Fred did.

Fred's earnings were $\frac{10}{10}$ of themselves.

Since Arthur earned $\frac{1}{10}$ more than Fred did, he earned $\frac{11}{10}$ of what Fred earned.

Both together earned $\frac{21}{10}$ of what Fred earned.

Therefore \$4.20 $= \frac{21}{10}$ of what Fred earned.

Hence, \$4.20 $\div \frac{21}{10} =$ \$2, amount Fred earned.

Then, $\frac{11}{10}$ of \$2 $=$ \$2.20, amount Arthur earned.

Check: \$2.00 + \$2.20 = \$4.20.

10. A watch and chain cost \$11.50. The watch cost $\frac{3}{10}$ more than the chain. How much did each cost?

11. A farmer sold 2 sheep for \$9. For one of them he received $\frac{1}{4}$ more than for the other one. How much did he receive for each?

12. A merchant's sales for two years were \$47,598.20. The sales for the second year were $\frac{1}{6}$ greater than for the first year. Find the sales for each year.

13. A man said, "In two years I have raised 650 bushels of beans. This year's crop is only $\frac{2}{3}$ as much as last year's crop." How many bushels of beans did he raise each year?

14. The neighbor of the man in Problem 13 said, "In two years my crop of beans has been 560 bushels, but this year's crop is $\frac{1}{3}$ greater than last year's crop." Find how many bushels of beans he raised each year.

Courtesy of Monroe Calculating Machine Co.

MACHINE ARITHMETIC

On the preceding pages emphasis has been placed on the method to be employed in solving problems. The actual work of performing many of the operations may often be done mentally; that is, without the use of pencil and paper.

Many operations of this type can be performed accurately and quickly on a calculating machine, such as illustrated above, if a machine is available and if the operator knows how to operate it skillfully.

To solve problems with the use of a machine, however, the operator must possess two skills.

1. He *must know* arithmetic. That is, he must be able to interpret problems and decide what operations have to be performed.

2. He must know how to operate the machine and be able to read the results obtained on the machine. In reading the answer, it is very essential that the operator be able to *estimate results*, particularly with reference to the use of decimal points.

For example, a mechanical device is provided on the machine for locating the decimal point in a given operation, but the operator should, in most cases, be able to locate the point by inspection. For instance, in finding the cost of $17\frac{3}{4}$ yd. of cloth at $\$.16\frac{1}{2}$, the machine calculation appears like this $1775 \times 165 = 292875$.

The time required to set the decimal pointers on the machine may be saved if the operator will estimate the result by thinking of $\$.16\frac{1}{2}$ as nearly $\$\frac{1}{6}$ and then mentally estimating the cost of $17\frac{3}{4}$ yd. at $\$\frac{1}{6}$, obtaining approximately \$3. He then knows that the result shown above should be pointed off to give \$2.93.

In division, also, placing the decimal point by inspection will save time. Thus in dividing 23.4278 by 3.406, the machine operation will show this

$$234278 \div 3406 = 687839$$

The decimal point in the quotient is readily located by dividing 23, the integer in the dividend, by 3, the integer in the divisor. The result is 7. Hence the quotient must be approximately 7, and the point must be placed after the 6 in the quotient. Thus, 6.87839.

In finding the interest on \$7234.96 at $3\frac{1}{2}\%$ for 37 days, the ability to estimate the approximate result is important. The steps in the solution are:

1. $.035 \times \$7234.96 = \$253.2236$, interest for 1 year
2. $37 \times \$253.2236 = \$9369.2732$
3. $\$9369.2732 \div 360 = \$26.03$, interest

In this operation the points have all been located by inspection. Study the separate steps and see if you understand how they were located.

In the following pages there are a number of exercises for practice in estimating the results. The estimated results are to be checked by actual calculation. Practice not only on those exercises but make also a mental estimate of the probable result in all problems as they arise in the text. The habit once formed will be invaluable.

ESTIMATES AND APPROXIMATIONS

ESTIMATES

In many cases it will be helpful to make a rough estimate of the answer to a problem before solving for the exact result. Errors are often made in placing the decimal point, thus giving results that are ridiculous. The following examples will illustrate.

Illustration. Find the cost of $3\frac{3}{4}$ yards of cloth at $1.13 a yard.

First, estimate the cost by thinking of 4 yards at $1 a yard, which gives an estimate of $4.

Then by actual calculation the result is found to be $4.24.

By estimating in advance, such results as $.42 or $42.38 are recognized as wrong.

```
  $1.13
   3.75
  -----
   5 65
  79 1
 3 39
 -------
 4.23 75 = $4.24
```

Illustration. At $2.75 a day, how many days must a man work to earn $45.38?

By thinking first of a wage of $3 a day, and total earnings of $45, one sees at once the number of days is approximately 15.

Then dividing $45.38 by $2.75, gives the actual result as $16\frac{1}{2}$ days.

The advance estimate prevents such answers as 165 days.

```
         16.5
2.75)45.38.0
     27 5
     -----
     17 88
     16 50
     ------
      1 380
      1 375
```

Mental Drill

Before solving these exercises make a mental estimate of the result:

$2\frac{1}{2} \times 3\frac{1}{2} =$	$23 \times 3\frac{3}{4} =$	$28\frac{2}{3} \div 7\frac{1}{2} =$
$4\frac{1}{4} \times 3\frac{3}{4} =$	$31 \times 4\frac{1}{2} =$	$34\frac{1}{2} \div 6\frac{1}{4} =$
$6\frac{1}{2} \times 5\frac{1}{2} =$	$27 \times \$.07\frac{1}{2} =$	$\$2.00 \div \$.16\frac{1}{2} =$

Problems

In each of the following problems, first estimate the result, then solve for the exact result. See how nearly you can estimate the correct answer.

1. Find the cost at $1.10 each of 22 pairs of gloves.

2. A man worked 42 hours in a week. His hourly wage was $.56. How much did he earn?

3. At $125 an acre, find the cost of a farm of 75 acres.

4. A man sold 96 acres of land for $5280. Find the average price per acre.

5. A motorist paid $2.22 for gasoline at $.18$\frac{1}{2}$ a gallon. How many gallons did he buy?

6. A young man wished to buy a used car for $247.50 cash. He earns $4.50 a day and spends $1.75 a day for living expenses. How many days will it take him to save enough to buy the car?

7. Find the cost of 17$\frac{1}{4}$ yards of muslin at $.13$\frac{1}{4}$ a yard.

8. At $25.15 a share how many shares of stock can be bought for $4124.60?

APPROXIMATE RESULTS

Many problems have answers that are called **approximate results.** The approximate result is very nearly the exact result and is spoken of as being "to the nearest cent," "to the nearest inch," "to the nearest tenth per cent," or "to the nearest hundredth."

Illustration. To the nearest tenth of a yard, find how many yards of ribbon can be bought for $2, at $.13$\frac{1}{2}$ a yard.

```
          14.81
.135)$2.000.00
      1 35
        650
        540
        110 0
        108 0
          2 00
          1 35
```

In cases of this kind the result must be found to one decimal place beyond the number of decimal places called for in the result. If the extra place is 5 or more, then the place to its left must be increased by 1. If less than 5, that place-figure is dropped. Thus, in the example the result called for is 14.8 yards. If the result had been 14.86, the final result would be 14.9.

Illustration. A chair cost a furniture dealer $8.45. He sold it for $\frac{1}{3}$ more than he paid for it. Find his selling price.

The cost	=	$ 8.45
The profit is $\frac{1}{3}$ of $8.45	=	2.8166
The selling price	=	$11.2666 = $11.27

Since the figure next beyond the cent-figure is more than 5, the number of cents in the answer is increased by 1: that is, $11.2666 is called $11.27.

Problems

1. An automobile tire cost $13.75. It had been run 24,740 miles when it was worn out. Find, to the nearest hundredth of a cent, the tire cost per mile for that tire.

2. The circumference of any circle is 3.1416 times its diameter. If the diameter of a given circle is 75 inches, find its circumference, to the nearest inch.

3. For an examination you have ratings on four distinct parts of the test, as follows: 1st part, 89.75; 2d part, 84.5; 3d part, 76.75; and 4th part, 62.5. Find, to the nearest tenth, your final mark.

4. Divide 43.17 by 34.73, and give the result, to the nearest thousandth.

5. Multiply .043 by 6.58, and state the result in the nearest hundredth.

6. Find the sum of 5.147 and 31.0287. From the sum subtract 34.578, and give the final result in the nearest hundredth.

7. Add 4.08, 73.5, .0276, and 54.078, giving the result in the nearest tenth.

8. Find to the nearest cent the value of $\frac{3}{4}$ of a pound of tea at $.65 a pound.

PERCENTAGE

Fractions and Per Cents Compared

The wording of every problem in percentage and its applications can be in terms of ordinary fractions. In other words, **there is no principle of arithmetic found in percentage that is not, or may not, be found in problems of fractions.**

The only *new* thing in percentage is the term "per cent" and its representation by the symbol (%). The use of the term "per cent" and its symbol (%) is a mere convenience.

1. A man had 600 shares of stock.

(*a*) He sold $\frac{1}{4}$ of them. How many shares did he sell?

(*b*) He sold 25% of them. How many shares did he sell?

How do questions (*a*) and (*b*) differ in form? in meaning?

2. A man's sales were $20,000. His net profit was $2000.

(*a*) What part of his sales were the profits?

(*b*) What per cent of his sales were the profits?

How does question (*b*) differ from question (*a*) in form? in meaning?

3. (*a*) $\frac{1}{3}$ of a store's sales for one month were from telephone and mail orders.

(*b*) $33\frac{1}{3}$% of a store's sales for one month were from telephone and mail orders.

How does statement (*b*) differ from statement (*a*) in form? in meaning?

Expressing a Per Cent as a Decimal Fraction

Illustration. Change 12.5% to its decimal form.

$$12.5\% = .125$$

"Per cent" means "hundredths." That is, 8% means 8 hundredths, which, expressed decimally, is .08; $1\frac{1}{4}\% = .0125$.

First, drop the per cent sign and move the decimal point 2 places to the left.

Express each of the following rates as a decimal.

Thus, $5\frac{1}{2}\% = .055$

a. 5%	*d.* 50%	*g.* $1\frac{1}{2}\%$	*j.* $\frac{1}{2}\%$	*m.* .5%
b. 15%	*e.* 2%	*h.* $5\frac{1}{2}\%$	*k.* $\frac{1}{4}\%$	*n.* .25%
c. 25%	*f.* 1%	*i.* $3\frac{1}{4}\%$	*l.* $\frac{1}{10}\%$	*o.* 2.5%

Changing a Fraction to a Per Cent

Illustration. Change $\frac{1}{8}$ to its per cent form.

$$\frac{1}{8} = .125 \quad \left(8\overline{)1.000}\ \ .125\right)$$
$$.125 = 12.5\%$$

First, change the common fraction to its decimal equivalent. Then move the decimal point 2 places to the right and annex the per cent sign (%).

Change the following fractions to per cents:

a. $\frac{3}{8}$	*d.* $\frac{1}{3}$	*g.* $\frac{7}{8}$	*j.* $\frac{2}{11}$	*m.* $\frac{4}{9}$	*p.* $\frac{5}{9}$
b. $\frac{4}{5}$	*e.* $\frac{1}{4}$	*h.* $\frac{5}{6}$	*k.* $\frac{1}{16}$	*n.* $\frac{3}{7}$	*q.* $\frac{3}{16}$
c. $\frac{3}{4}$	*f.* $\frac{5}{8}$	*i.* $\frac{2}{7}$	*l.* $\frac{1}{15}$	*o.* $\frac{3}{11}$	*r.* $\frac{4}{15}$

Definitions of Terms Used

The subject of percentage includes the groups of problems that are most frequently solved by using $\frac{100}{100}$ (or 100%) as the basis of comparison.

Base. The base is the number or quantity represented by 100%.

Rate. Expressed as per cent (as 5%, 30%), the rate is the number by which the base is multiplied to find the percentage, or by which the percentage is divided to find the base.

Percentage. In an individual problem, the percentage is the product obtained by multiplying the base by the rate.

Amount. The amount is the sum of the base and the percentage.

Difference. The percentage subtracted from the base gives the difference.

In percentage the three terms, **base, rate,** and **percentage,** always bear the same relation to each other, as shown in the following equations and their corresponding formulas.

Base × Rate = Percentage	$B \times R = P$
Percentage ÷ Rate = Base	$P \div R = B$
Percentage ÷ Base = Rate	$P \div B = R$
Base + Percentage = Amount	$B + P = A$
Base − Percentage = Difference	$B - P = D$
Amount ÷ (100% + Rate) = Base	$A \div (1 + R) = B$
Difference ÷ (100% − Rate) = Base	$D \div (1 - R) = B$

TYPES OF PERCENTAGE

There are three distinct kinds or types of problems in percentage. They are stated as follows:

Type I. Finding a per cent of a number.

Illustration. A young man paid $300 for a used car and sold it a year later for 75% of its cost. How much did he receive for it?

Type II. Finding what per cent one number is of another.

Illustration. On a sale, a coat which had been selling for $25 was sold for $20. What per cent of the original selling price was the discount?

Type III. Finding a number when a per cent of it is known.

Illustration. After a flood a merchant sold a damaged chair for $32. This amount was 64% of its cost. How much did the chair cost?

It is important that the pupil

(*a*) fully and thoroughly understand these three type forms;

(*b*) be able to recognize the type form to which any problem belongs.

TYPE I. FINDING A PER CENT OF A NUMBER

The only difference between finding a *per cent of a number* and finding a *fractional part of a number* is that in percentage a per cent or decimal fraction is used, and in finding a fractional part a common fraction is used. Thus, finding 25% or .25 of a number is the same as finding $\frac{1}{4}$ of the number.

When base and rate are known, the base is always multiplied by the rate. That is **Base × Rate = Percentage** $(B \times R = P)$

Mental Drill

Find the percentage for the following indicated operations:

1. $11\frac{1}{2}\%$ of \$478
2. $13\frac{3}{4}\%$ of \$960
3. $12\frac{1}{4}\%$ of \$1260
4. 15% of \$1440
5. $16\frac{1}{2}\%$ of \$1620
6. $22\frac{1}{2}\%$ of \$642.60
7. $33\frac{3}{4}\%$ of \$875.20
8. $27\frac{1}{2}\%$ of \$1150
9. $42\frac{1}{2}\%$ of \$125
10. $36\frac{3}{4}\%$ of \$1728

Problems

1. In a school of 450 students 22% were absent one day due to a heavy snow storm. How many students were absent?

2. The assessed valuation of a house was reduced 4% from \$15,000. Find the amount of the reduced assessment.

3. A man's house cost him \$6500. He sold it at a loss of 15% of cost. How much did he receive for it?

4. An automobile cost \$1750. The first year of its use it depreciated 25%. Find the depreciation for the year.

5. The population of a city was 28,450. Five years later the population had increased 8%. How much was the increase in population?

6. The net profits of a business for one year were \$190,000. The next year they were $4\frac{3}{4}\%$ greater. How much was the increase in profits the second year?

7. A sales tax of 2% is charged in some places, for relief purposes. Find the tax paid by a family whose taxable purchases one year amounted to \$748.50.

8. A book agent who received 40% commission on sales, made sales one day as follows: To Mrs. Arden a book for \$2.75; to Mr. Edgerly a book for \$5.50; and to Mrs. Cummings a book for \$3.25. How much were his total commissions?

9. A real estate agent charged $2\frac{1}{2}\%$ commission for selling a business block for \$375,000. How much was his commission?

10. A commission merchant received a shipment of 1150 baskets of peaches. 6% of the peaches spoiled. As a result, the entire shipment had to be sorted and repacked. The cost of sorting and repacking was five cents a basket. Find

(*a*) How many baskets of peaches were spoiled.
(*b*) The cost of sorting and repacking.

11. A house valued at \$14,100 was taxed 3.68%. Find the amount of tax.

12. James Rodney bought a factory for \$28,500. Sales of manufactured goods the first year amounted to \$269,875. His expenses were: taxes, $2\frac{1}{4}\%$ of the cost of the factory; insurance, $\frac{1}{2}\%$ of the cost of the factory; heating, light, and power, 3% of the value of the sales; salaries, wages, and other office expenses were 12% of the sales. His gross profit for the year was \$51,276.25. How much was his net profit?

13. A merchant invested his surplus cash of \$62,500 as follows: 30% of it in first mortgages; 45% of it in railroad bonds; and the remainder in government bonds. Find the amount invested in each. Show these facts in a bar graph.

For construction of bar graph, see page 244.

14. A contractor agreed to build a house for \$9500. His estimate was based on the following costs: plumbing, 9%; electric wiring, 6%; building materials, 33%; labor, 32%; and incidental expenses, 4%. The remainder of the price of construction was to be his profit. Find the cost of each type of expense, and the contractor's profit.

Per Cents of "Increase," "Decrease," "More Than," "Less Than," "As Much As"

These expressions cause pupils much trouble in interpreting problems. As each expression is used in the following problems, its meaning and use should be carefully noted.

Illustration. In a pre-inventory sale, the price of suits selling usually at \$22.50 was decreased by 10%. Find the sale price.

"Decreased by 10%" means that the usual price of \$22.50 was decreased by 10% of \$22.50.

10% of \$22.50 = \$2.25, the decrease.
\$22.50 − \$2.25 = \$20.25, sales price.

Illustration. A merchant's stock of goods valued at \$18,000 was increased by $16\frac{2}{3}\%$. Find the value of the stock after the increase.

"Increased by $16\frac{2}{3}\%$" means that the stock of \$18,000 was increased by $16\frac{2}{3}\%$ of \$18,000.

$16\frac{2}{3}\%$ of \$18,000 = \$3000, increase
\$18,000 + \$3000 = \$21,000, value of stock after the increase

Illustration. A large department store used 65 delivery trucks last year. This year the number of trucks used was 20% more than last year. How many trucks were used this year?

"20% more than" means that the number of trucks used last year was increased by 20% of 65 trucks.

20% of 65 trucks = 13 trucks, the increase.
65 trucks + 13 trucks = 78 trucks, the number of trucks used this year.

Problems

1. Find the value that is 13% more than \$68.
2. Find the value that is 17% less than \$92.
3. Find the number equal to 125 increased by 30%.

4. What number is equal to 160 decreased by 40%?
5. Find the number that is 53% as much as 250.
6. 32% more than 55 is how many?
7. 23% less than $1400 is how much?
8. $\frac{1}{2}$% more than $1600 is how much?
9. $2400 decreased by $\frac{3}{4}$% is how much?
10. $3200 increased by $\frac{1}{10}$% is how much?
11. How much is 10% less than $10? more than $15?
12. How much is 12% more than $25? less than $30?
13. $280 increased by 25% is how much?

Finding a Fraction of 1 Per Cent of a Number

Illustration. How much is $\frac{1}{8}$% of $2400?

$\frac{1}{8}$% means $\frac{1}{8}$ of 1%.
1% of $2400 = $24.
$\frac{1}{8}$ of $24 = $3.

First find 1% of the number by pointing off 2 places in the number, and then find the fractional part of the result.

Problems

1. How much is $\frac{1}{4}$% of $2200? of $2700? of $3220?
2. How much is $\frac{1}{8}$% of $4000? of $2800? of $4200?
3. How much is $\frac{1}{10}$% of $3000? of $1750? of $100?
4. How much is $\frac{1}{2}$% of $690? of $560? of $124.50?
5. How much is $\frac{1}{16}$% of $4800? of $320? of $120?
6. How much is $\frac{1}{20}$% of $3000? of $346? of $6400?

7. A bank charged $\frac{1}{20}$% for collecting a note of $6600. How much was the bank's commission?

8. The assistant manager of a chain store received a salary of $150 a month, plus a commission of $\frac{1}{2}$% of the net profits of the store. If the net profits for the year were $42,750, find the total amount received by the assistant manager for his year's work.

9. At $\frac{1}{4}\%$ a month, how much is the interest on $1860 for one month?

10. Which is greater, $13\frac{1}{3}\%$ of $450, or $\frac{2}{15}$ of $450?

11. Compare $8\frac{3}{4}\%$ of $240 with $\frac{7}{80}$ of $240.

12. Compare $\frac{7}{40}$ with $17\frac{1}{2}\%$. Which expression conveys to your mind more readily its real value?

Comprehensive Test — Type I

1. The normal speed of a train between two cities was 45 miles an hour. On a given day the train was delayed by an accident for 1 hour. To reach its destination on time, the engineer was directed to make a 20% increase in his speed. At what speed did he finish the run?

2. A sales girl's sales in one week were $840. The second week her sales decreased by $12\frac{1}{2}\%$. The third week her sales increased by 20%. Find the amount of her sales for the second and third weeks.

3. Two salesmen were in a contest to see which one could sell the greater amount of merchandise. In January, A's sales were $12,375, and B's were 92% as much as A's. How much were B's sales?

4. The output of a factory last year was $84,950; it was increased this year by $8\frac{1}{2}\%$. How much was this year's output?

5. In a certain family the cost of clothing was 58% as much as the cost of food. If the cost of food was $528.50, find the cost of clothing.

6. One kind of automobile tire costs 88% as much as a better kind. If the better tire costs $13.75, how much does the cheaper tire cost?

7. Mr. Bentley's house was assessed at $12,500. Owing to improvements in the house the assessment was increased by 15%. Find the new assessment.

8. John Letteri is employed by the Larson Suit and Coat Company. His wages the first year were $17.50 a week. At the beginning of each year for the next five years he received a 10% increase in wages. How much were his weekly wages each year after the first year? (Reckon the wages in nearest quarter of a dollar.) Show the increase in wages by means of a line graph. See Line Graphs, page 248.

9. An automobile which cost $2250 was valued as follows: 2d year, at 25% less than the first year; 3d year, at 20% less than the second year; and the 4th year, at 15% less than the third year. Find the value of the car the fourth year. Using a line graph show the value of the car at the end of each year.

10. On his 21st birthday, John had $1560 in the savings bank. His father made him a birthday present of 15% as much as he (John) had in the bank. How much did his father give him?

TYPE II. FINDING WHAT PER CENT ONE NUMBER IS OF ANOTHER

Comparing Fractions and Per Cents

1. (*a*) 5 is *what part* of 20?
(*b*) 5 is *what per cent* of 20?
How do (*a*) and (*b*) differ in form, wording, and meaning?

2. A hat which had been selling for $3 was sold on "dollar day" for $1 less than the regular price.

(*a*) The reduction in price was what part of the regular price?

(*b*) The reduction in price was what per cent of the regular price?

How do the questions (*a*) and (*b*) differ in wording and meaning?

In both illustrations the questions (*a*) and (*b*) are identical in meaning. The answers differ in form only. In 1 (*a*) the answer is $\frac{1}{4}$; in 1 (*b*) the answer is 25%.

In 2 (*a*) the answer is $\frac{1}{3}$; in 2 (*b*) the answer is $33\frac{1}{3}$%.

These simple problems illustrate that percentage problems may be stated in terms of common fractions.

The term "per cent" is used because it expresses relationships much more readily than do common fractions. Per cents are based on the number 100. The number 100 is a number with which everybody is familiar because the dollar contains 100 cents. Parts of a dollar expressed as cents (as 25¢, 50¢, 75¢, etc.) have a very definite meaning to all. For that reason relationships expressed as per cents (as 17%, 38%, 81%, etc.) are readily understood. To illustrate, $6\frac{1}{2}\%$ has a readily recognized value, but the value of its common fraction equivalent, $\frac{13}{200}$, is not so readily understood.

Illustration. An automobile salesman received $77 for selling an automobile for $1400. What was the rate of commission?

The known facts are:

1. The selling price of the automobile (the base or one factor).
2. The commission received for selling the car (the percentage or product).

("Commission" is always the product of two factors of the problem and is called the percentage.)

The unknown fact is:

The rate per cent of commission (the rate).

The **base, rate,** and **percentage** always bear the relation to each other as expressed in the equation

Base × Rate = Percentage

Interpreting this relationship we find that percentage is always the product and the base is always one of the factors. Percentage is therefore always divided by the base to find the other factor, the rate, as expressed in the equation

Percentage ÷ Base = Rate See page 28.

As a formula it is written $P \div B = R$.

Using the facts and figures in our problem, we have

Selling Price × Rate = Commission

That is, $1400 × rate = $77
Therefore, $77 ÷ $1400 = .055 = 5.5%, rate of commission

To check the solution, the simplest method is to multiply the base by the rate.

5.5% of $1400 = $77, commission

Mental Drill

Express each of the following results first as a decimal and then as a rate per cent:

$4 ÷ $16 =	$12 ÷ $200 =	$7.50 ÷ $6000 =
$5 ÷ $40 =	$27.50 ÷ $1375 =	$4.50 ÷ $1500 =
$125 ÷ $250 =	$114 ÷ $2400 =	$13.50 ÷ $5400 =

Problems

In each of the following problems select the known facts and the unknown fact, and then apply the principles used in the illustration. There should be no difficulty in solving the problems.

1. A house valued at $14,400 is mortgaged for $9600. The mortgage is what per cent of the value of the house?

2. The operating expenses of a factory were $19,200. Of that amount $13,440 was for labor. What per cent of the total expenses was for labor?

3. A store rented for $375 a month. The owner paid interest on a mortgage, taxes, insurance, and other expenses amounting to $2700 a year. The expenses were what per cent of the total income? If the store cost the owner $36,000, his net income was what per cent of the cost of the store?

4. In a given city there are 1380 teachers employed in the schools. Of that number 207 are men. What per cent of the teachers are men?

5. A man owed $7200 and paid $2700. What per cent of his debt did he pay?

6. A fruit dealer bought a crate containing 96 oranges for $2.40. He sold the oranges at $.40 a dozen. His profit was what per cent of the cost?

7. A new car cost $1600. At the end of one year the depreciation was $320. What was the rate of depreciation?

8. A grocer's sales for the year amounted to $69,482.60. His expenses for the year were $10,432.39. The expenses were what per cent of the sales?

9. An allowance of $1700 was made when Mr. Holt exchanged his car for a new car. What per cent less than cost did Mr. Holt receive for a car that had cost him $2000?

10. On April 1 the price of coal was $12 a ton. On Sept. 1 the price had advanced to $13.50 a ton. What was the per cent of increase?

11. Mr. Brown's profits for two years were $13,200 and $15,048 respectively. What per cent greater were the second year's profits than the first year's profits?

12. A large department store advertised the following articles in a "May Sale." Find the per cent of reduction on each article.

a. $20 coats for $12
b. $28 dresses for $16
c. $19.95 suits for $10
d. $69.50 coats for $39.95

Many business men wish to have a graphic picture of the results of their business. By means of a graph they are enabled to see not only the results, but they can compare various facts or results with one another, and with the total results.

Illustration. A man kept an accurate record of the cost of running one of his trucks for one year. The results were as follows: cost of gasoline, $120; cost of oil, $15; repairs, $45; garage rent, $75; insurance, $45; and depreciation, $300. The total is $600.

He made a graph (called a box, or rectangle, graph) like the following:

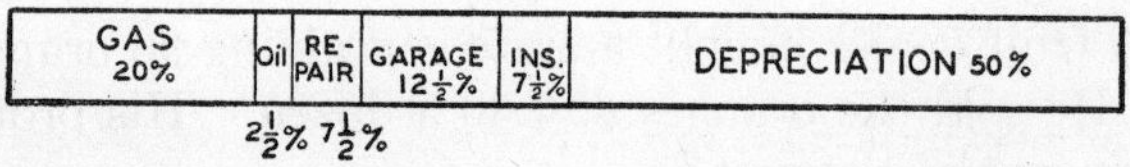

To determine what part of the whole graph should be given to each item, he reckoned the per cent of the total cost for each item of cost. Thus,

$120 ÷ $600 = 20%, cost of gasoline
$15 ÷ $600 = $2\frac{1}{2}$%, cost of oil
$45 ÷ $600 = $7\frac{1}{2}$%, cost of repairs
$75 ÷ $600 = $12\frac{1}{2}$%, cost of garage
$45 ÷ $600 = $7\frac{1}{2}$%, cost of insurance
$300 ÷ $600 = 50%, cost of depreciation

13. An automobile sales agency employs four salesmen. Their total sales for a period of six months were 240 cars. Of that number Adams sold 72; Brown sold 60; Douglas sold 66; and Lundgren the remainder. What per cent of all the sales did each man make? Show the facts in a box graph.

14. Six months later the men in Problem 13 reported the following sales: Adams, 45; Brown, 55; Douglas, 70; and Lundgren, 80. What per cent of the sales did each salesman make? Make a graph of these sales.

15. The revenues of a certain railroad for a given year were as follows: passenger service, $17,500,000; Pullman and dining car service, $2,500,000; freight service, $20,000,000; express service, $6,500,000; mail service, $3,500,000. What per cent of the total revenue was derived from each source of income? Show these facts in a box graph.

16. Over a weekend the price of beefsteak increased from $.33 a pound to $.38. Find the per cent of increase, to the nearest tenth per cent.

The known facts are:

1. The price of beefsteak last week (the base, why?)
2. The price of beefsteak this week

The unknown facts are:

1. The increase in price (the percentage, why?)
2. The per cent of increase (the rate)

The increase in price is the difference between $.33 and $.38, or $.05. What is the per cent or rate of increase?

In finding the rate of increase the second step of the problem must answer the following question.

What per cent of $.33 is $.05?

Solution, $.05 ÷ $.33 = .1515 = 15.2%, rate of increase.

In finding results to the nearest tenth per cent, it is necessary to find the decimal value of the rate to the fourth decimal place. If the fourth decimal place is 5 or more, the third decimal place is increased by 1. If the fourth decimal place had been less than 5, the fourth decimal figure would have been ignored and the rate per cent stated as 15.1%.

In a similar manner, find the per cent of increase or decrease, to the nearest tenth per cent, for each of the following commodities:

	Price Last Month	*Price This Month*
17. Pork chops	$.29	$.32
18. Coffee	$.31	$.33
19. Canned tomatoes	$.07	$.08
20. Ham	$.26	$.30
21. Canned peas	$.19	$.17
22. Oranges	$.35	$.30
23. Lemons	4 for $.11	3 for $.10
24. Eggs	$.34	$.30

Comprehensive Test — Type II

1. What part of 24 is 8?

2. What per cent of 24 is 8?

3. What part of 36 is 9?

4. What per cent of 36 is 9?

5. 12 is what part of 24?

6. 12 is what per cent of 24?

7. 15 is how many times 5?

8. 15 is what per cent of 5?

9. Express in per cent the relation of 8 to 48.

10. A football cost $4. After being used for a time it was sold for $3. The selling price was what per cent of the cost?

11. Mr. Lundstrom's sales for one month were $45,000. His overhead expenses were $5000. The expenses were what per cent of the sales?

12. A young man earned $120 a month. His living expenses were $80 a month. What per cent of his earnings could he save?

13. An article which cost $6 was sold for $7.50. The profit was what per cent of the cost? Of the selling price?

14. At a fire sale a chair which was usually sold for $16 was sold for $12. The sale price was what per cent of the usual price?

15. Find the per cent of increase in the price of butter if last week the price was $.40 a pound and this week the price is $.42 a pound.

TYPE III. FINDING A NUMBER WHEN A PER CENT OF IT IS KNOWN

Fractions and Per Cents Compared

Illustration. (*a*) $\frac{1}{6}$ of how many dollars is $15?

(*b*) $16\frac{2}{3}\%$ of how many dollars is $15?

In each of these simple problems one factor ($\frac{1}{6}$, or $16\frac{2}{3}\%$, respectively) and the product ($15) are given; one factor is missing.

Use the formula $F \times F = P$ (See page 17.)

Substituting figures gives $\frac{1}{6} \times ? = \$15$

and $16\frac{2}{3}\% \times ? = \$15$

Since the product, $15, is known and one factor, $\frac{1}{6}$ or $16\frac{2}{3}\%$, is known, the other factor may be found by dividing the product by the known factor.

That is, $P \div F = F$

Hence, $\$15 \div \frac{1}{6} = \$90$, the amount of which $15 is $\frac{1}{6}$

and $\$15 \div 16\frac{2}{3}\% = \$90$, the amount of which $15 is $16\frac{2}{3}\%$

Illustration. During a given year a factory employed 975 men, which was 65% of its capacity. How many men should be employed to run the factory at full capacity?

The known facts are:

1. The number of men employed — 975 (the percentage, why?)
2. The per cent of full capacity — 65% (the rate)

The unknown fact is:

The number of men required to run the factory at full capacity (the base)

The simplest statement for this problem is

65% of men required for full capacity = 975 men

The percentage (975 men) and the rate (65%) always have the same relation to each other — that is the percentage must be divided by the rate to find the base.

Percentage ÷ Rate = Base. $P \div R = B.$

Therefore, 975 men ÷ .65 = 1500 men, number required for full capacity.

NOTE: It should be observed that the formulas

$$F \times F = P \quad \text{and} \quad B \times R = P$$

are identical in meaning. $B \times R = P$ is a formula that is used only in percentage problems. $F \times F = P$ is a formula that may be used in all kinds of problems in which multiplication or division is involved.

Mental Drill

Change the rate per cent to its decimal form and then divide:

\$24 ÷ 6% =	\$57.50 ÷ 5% =	\$17.50 ÷ $\frac{1}{2}$% =
\$35 ÷ 20% =	\$43.75 ÷ 25% =	\$33.75 ÷ $\frac{1}{4}$% =
\$48 ÷ 8% =	\$92.80 ÷ 12$\frac{1}{2}$% =	\$75 ÷ $\frac{1}{20}$% =

Problems

1. The value of merchandise returned for exchange to a department store, the week following Christmas, amounted to $4025. If the amount returned was 7% of the sales made during the week, find the amount of sales for the week.

2. A young man 21 years old desired to have enough savings at the age of 60 so that his interest return would be $2400 a year, if the savings were invested at 4%. What amount of savings should he accumulate?

3. 750 is $3\frac{1}{3}\%$ of what number?

4. On January 1, two young men decided for the next six months to lay aside 9% of their salaries, to pay for a vacation trip which would cost them $87.50 each, plus $25 each for miscellaneous expenses. Assuming their salaries were the same, find the monthly salary of each.

5. The return from an investment was $2137.50. If the rate of return was $4\frac{1}{2}\%$, find the amount of the investment.

6. Mr. Bowes pays taxes on his home amounting to $310.50. The tax rate is $2\frac{1}{4}\%$ of the assessed value of the home. Find the assessed valuation. If the taxes are equal to $7\frac{1}{2}\%$ of Mr. Bowes's salary, find the amount of his salary.

7. In a shipment of strawberries, $17\frac{1}{2}$ crates had to be thrown away. If that was $2\frac{1}{2}\%$ of the entire shipment, find the number of crates in the shipment.

8. The net amount of cash required to pay for an invoice of goods was $4027.81 after a discount of 5% had been deducted for prompt payment. Find the amount of the invoice before the discount was deducted.

9. Mr. Harkness had his automobile insured against fire and theft for $900. If that amount was 25% less than the valuation he placed on the car, at what price did he value it?

10. An automobile dealer sold a used car for $361.25. This price was 15% less than the allowance he made on it when he took it in exchange for a new car. What did he allow for the car when he received it?

COMPREHENSIVE TEST — TYPE III

1. In an importation of glassware 517 pieces were broken. If the breakage was $3\frac{3}{4}\%$ of the entire number of pieces how many pieces were in the importation.

2. By taking advantage of 3% cash discount on an invoice a merchant saved \$509.40. Find the face value of the invoice.

3. A bankrupt concern paid its creditors $36\frac{1}{2}\%$ of the amounts due them. One creditor received \$547.50. How much did that creditor lose?

4. A salesman received \$516.60 for selling a quantity of merchandise for his firm. If he received $4\frac{1}{2}\%$ of the value of the goods sold, for how much did he sell the merchandise?

5. A man who raised poultry has an order for 260 lb. of dressed chickens and 390 lb. of dressed turkeys. He knows from experience that, on the average, both chickens and turkeys lose 35% of their weight in dressing for the market. Find the weight of live chickens and turkeys required to fill the order.

6. It is desired to leave funds to ensure the giving of two prizes annually. Each prize will cost \$5. What sum must be invested at 4% to provide for the cost of the prizes?

7. \$30 divided by 1.5% is how much?

8. An investment yields an annual return of $6\frac{1}{2}\%$. What amount must be invested to yield an annual income of \$1430?

9. In one year the General Clothing Company sold goods amounting to \$37,765.80, which was at an advance of $33\frac{1}{3}\%$ over the cost of the goods. Find the cost of the goods.

10. From each dollar of his income a man gave \$.16 for benevolent purposes. If he had \$4662 left, find his income.

COMMISSION

The group of problems spoken of as "commission problems takes its name from the fact that when a person is "commissioned" or directed to do some particular kind of work for another person or firm, the compensation is called **commission.** The commission is based usually on *cost, sales price,* or *unit* of quantity, such as bushel, sack, ton, etc.

The person performing the work is known as an **agent, commission merchant,** or **broker.** The person for whom the commission merchant, agent, or broker buys, sells, or performs other services, is called the **principal,** or **client.**

A man sells goods for a firm, and is allowed to keep one dollar out of every ten dollars' worth sold.

(*a*) What name is given to the man who does the selling? (*b*) What is his compensation called? (*c*) What name is applied to the firm for whom the goods are sold? (*d*) $1 is what per cent of $10?

This type of problem is distinctive in that the agent is paid in proportion to the service performed. If, for instance, a real-estate agent is commissioned to sell a piece of real estate, he may work very hard trying to sell the property, but if he does not make a sale, he has earned nothing, and is paid nothing.

In many cases the reason for the employment of an agent to buy or sell merchandise, or other property, is that the person who has goods to sell, or who wishes to buy goods, is not qualified by training or experience to perform that type of service for himself, or has not the time to do it.

Commission merchants and brokers are trained in the particular kind of work they do. If a person has stocks or bonds to sell, he employs a stock or bond broker to sell them for him. The broker knows how and where to sell them. The owner of the stock or bonds could sell them himself if he knew anyone who wished to buy them. In the same way, a person who wishes to buy stocks or bonds applies to a broker to make the purchase for him. In this manner, seller and buyer who do not know each other are "brought together" through the agency of the broker, or commission merchant.

Commission should be thought of only as a particular group of problems in percentage. **The principles of arithmetic required in commission problems are identical with those used previously in the study of percentage.** For example, the *work done* — that is, the amount of sales, or purchases, or collections, etc., is the *base;* the *rate of commission* is the *rate;* and the *commission* is the *percentage.*

Illustration. A real-estate broker sold for a client a city block for $12,500, and received 4% for his services. How much was the commission?

The known facts are:

1. The amount of the sale ($12,500)
2. The rate of commission (4%)

The unknown fact is:

The amount of the commission

The amount of the sale (Base) multiplied by the rate of commission (Rate) gives the commission (Percentage).

$$B \times R = P$$

Therefore, 4% of $12,500 = $500, commission

Illustration. A traveling salesman sold merchandise worth $9480 for his firm in one week. He received a commission of $1\frac{1}{2}$%. How much did he earn that week?

$$B \times R = P$$

$1\frac{1}{2}$% of $9480 = $142.20, commission

Illustration. A commission merchant charged a dairyman $18.93 for selling butter worth $378.60. Find the rate of commission.

$$P \div B = R$$

The fundamental question is:

What per cent of \$378.60 = \$18.93?

Therefore, \$18.93 ÷ \$378.60 = .05 = 5%, rate

Illustration. A collection agency collected for a customer an overdue debt, charging a commission of \$29.14, which was 4% of the amount collected. Find the amount of the debt collected.

$$P \div R = B$$

4% of amount collected = commission

Therefore, \$29.14 ÷ .04 = \$728.50, amount collected

Mental Drill

How much is a commission of

3% of \$1500?	$\frac{1}{2}$% of \$800?	\$.12$\frac{1}{2}$ each on 80 shares?
2% of \$750?	$\frac{1}{4}$% of \$1200?	\$.07$\frac{1}{2}$ each on 100 shares?
4% of \$1250?	$\frac{1}{10}$% of \$2500?	\$.15 each on 250 shares?
8% of \$2000?	$\frac{1}{20}$% of \$3600?	\$.17$\frac{1}{2}$ each on 300 shares?

Problems

---

1. A commission merchant sold for a client 600 bushels of potatoes at \$.74 a bushel. If he charged 5%, find the amount of the commission.

2. A salesman's sales for one month were \$17,985. If he received a commission of 4%, how much did he earn that month?

3. An agent was employed to buy apples for a company in the city. He was to receive 2% commission on all purchases. During the month of October he purchased 13,960 barrels of apples at an average price of \$2.25 per barrel. How much were his commissions?

4. A sales girl's wages were \$15 a week plus a commission of 1$\frac{1}{2}$% of her sales. If her sales were \$1148.50 in one week, how much did she earn that week?

5. An employee received a weekly wage of \$20 plus a commission of $2\frac{1}{2}\%$ of his sales. For four weeks his sales were \$680, \$720, \$640, and \$860, respectively. How much did he earn in the four weeks? What were his average weekly earnings?

6. A young man agreed to act as traveling salesman for a weekly wage of \$27.50 and a commission of 2% of his sales. How much must his weekly sales be in order that his weekly earnings may amount to \$50?

7. Brundage and Tracy, commission merchants, Chicago, Ill., sold for John Weir, Fort Wayne, Ind., a quantity of potatoes, as follows: Dec. 1, 19—, 900 bu. at \$.90; Dec. 2, 700 bu. at \$.90. Their charges were: for freight, \$.06 a bushel; cartage, \$27.50; and commission, 5%. Following is an account sales to show how Brundage and Tracy would report to John Weir the facts of the transaction.

No. 193 **ACCOUNT SALES**

Chicago, Ill., Dec. 3, 19—

BRUNDAGE AND TRACY

Commission Merchants

Sold for account of

John Weir, Fort Wayne, Ind.

Dec.	1	900 bu. Potatoes	@ \$.90	810	00		
	2	700 bu. Potatoes	@ \$.90	630	00	1440	00
		CHARGES					
		Freight 1600 bu.	@ \$.06	96	00		
		Cartage		27	50		
		Commission 5% of \$1440		72	00	195	50
		Net Proceeds				1244	50

Gross Proceeds − Total Charges = Net Proceeds

In the account sales, page 47, name the amount of the gross proceeds. How much are the total charges? How much are the net proceeds?

A little study of the Account Sales shows that it is simply a report made by a commission merchant to a client showing the amount of the sales, and the various charges against the account. The difference between the total sales and the total charges is the net proceeds of the sale.

In an account sales the total amount of the sales is called the **gross proceeds** of the sale. The balance left after paying the charges is called the **net proceeds.**

A quantity of goods sent to a commission merchant to sell on commission is called a **shipment** by the person who sends or ships the goods.

The commission merchant calls the goods received to be sold a **consignment.**

The shipper is often called the **consignor,** and the person to whom the goods are sent is called the **consignee.**

Set up an account sales for each of the following:

8. Wm. B. Ely, Hector, N. Y., shipped to Cartuccio Brothers, New York, N. Y., 1200 baskets of peaches to be sold on commission. On August 21, they sold 475 baskets at $.90; on August 22, they sold 500 baskets at $.88; and on August 23, sold the remainder at $.86 a basket. The charges were: freight, $125.60; storage, $.03 a basket; and commission, 5%.

9. Lazarus and Son, commission merchants, Baltimore, Md., received from A. B. Fritz, Dover, Del., a carload of apples to be sold on commission. On Aug. 1, they sold 135 baskets of apples at $1.15 a basket; on Aug. 3, 95 baskets at $1.16; and on Aug. 4, 70 baskets at $1.10 a basket. Freight was $.08 a basket; cartage, $.05 a basket; storage, $.02 a basket; and commission, 4%.

10. Hardy and Miller, purchasing agents, Minneapolis, Minn., bought for Anthony Petrocini, Nashville, Tenn.,

250 bbl. flour at \$6.50 a barrel, and 125 bbl. at \$6.75 a barrel. The commission was $2\frac{1}{2}\%$; freight prepaid was \$141.25; cartage was \$135; and guaranty, 1%. The account purchase is shown below.

No. 71 **ACCOUNT PURCHASE**

Minneapolis, Minn., Aug. 5, 19__

HARDY AND MILLER

Commission Merchants

Bought for account of

Anthony Petrocini, Nashville, Tenn.

	250 bbl. Flour	@ \$6.50	1625	00		
	125 bbl. Flour	@ \$6.75	843	75	2468	75
	CHARGES					
	Cartage		135	00		
	Freight prepaid		141	25		
	Guaranty 1% of \$2468.75		24	69		
	Commission $2\frac{1}{2}\%$ of \$2468.75		61	72	362	66
	Gross Cost				2831	41

What is done with the charges in an account purchase?

What is done with the charges in an account sales?

Compare the form of an account purchase with the form of an account sales and state in what particular they differ.

Prime Cost + Total Charges = Gross Cost

The chief difference between an **account sales** and an **account purchase** is that in the account purchase the charges are *added* to the prime cost of the goods purchased to show the total cost; in the account sales the charges are *subtracted* from the gross sales to show the net proceeds of the sale.

In an account purchase the cost of the goods purchased, before the charges are added, is called the **prime cost.** The prime cost plus the charges gives the **gross cost.**

Guaranty is a small charge made by the commission merchant, which makes him responsible for the payment for goods sold on credit, or for the quality of goods purchased for his client.

Set up an account purchase for each of the following:

11. Ridley Brothers, Atlanta, Ga., bought for A. S. Benton, Louisville, Ky., 1200 bales of cotton, 500 lb. to the bale, at \$.176 per pound. Freight amounting to \$1275 was paid by Ridley Brothers. Other charges were insurance, $\frac{1}{20}$%; guaranty, $\frac{1}{10}$%; and commission, $\frac{1}{2}$%.

12. R. B. Waterman, commission merchant, New Orleans, La., bought for the Independent Grocers, Little Rock, Ark., 350 bbl. sugar, weighing 300 lb. to the barrel, at \$.04$\frac{1}{4}$ a pound; 72 bbl. molasses, 50 gallons to the barrel, at \$.27 a gallon. He charged 1$\frac{1}{2}$% commission, $\frac{1}{2}$% guaranty, and prepaid the freight amounting to \$275.

13. A glove manufacturer employs salesmen to sell his gloves. The gloves sell for \$4.25 a dozen, net. One salesman receives a commission of 5%, and another one prefers to be paid on the basis of \$.20 a dozen. After a period of three months, the price of gloves drops to \$3.80 a dozen. If the average monthly sales amount to 1150 dozen for each man, find the amount of each man's earnings for six months — three months before the price dropped and three months after the price was lowered.

14. Discuss the effect of the change in price of gloves in problem 13, on the amount of commission received by the two salesmen.

Comprehensive Test

1. An automobile salesman received 12$\frac{1}{2}$% commission for selling new cars, and 8% commission for selling used cars. During one week, he sold 2 new cars at \$650 each, and 3 used cars for $375, $250, and $175 respectively. Find the amount of his commissions for the week.

2. A commission merchant bought for a client 250 bbl. of flour at $6.50 a barrel. The commission for buying was $2\frac{1}{2}\%$. Freight and other expenses were $81.25. Find the total cost of the flour.

3. A broker bought for Mr. Allen 250 shares of railroad stock at $22.50 a share. The commission amounted to $.15 a share. Find the total cost of the stock.

4. A stock broker sold for a client 400 shares of stock at $114.50 a share. The charges against the sale were: commission, $.24 a share; a Federal tax of $2 for each 100 shares; a state tax of $2 for each 100 shares. Find the proceeds of the sale.

5. A salesman's monthly wage was $100. It was increased by commissions to $237.80 a month. If his monthly sales averaged $5512, what rate of commission did he receive?

6. A newsboy sold 120 evening papers at 3¢ each. He received 90¢ for selling them. What rate of commission did he receive?

7. A gardener hired boys and girls to pick berries, paying them $1\frac{1}{2}$¢ a quart. On a given day his force picked 1250 qt. of berries. The berries were sold for $150. Find (*a*) the price per quart at which the berries were sold; (*b*) what per cent of the selling price was paid for picking.

8. A real-estate agent, who receives 5% of the annual rentals on new leases, wrote the following leases in one week:

A store for 3 yr. for $12,000 a year.
A house for 1 yr. for $4000 a year.
An office building for 10 yr. for $75,000 a year.

Find the amount of commission the agent received.

9. Mr. Hunt's agent sold for him 100 tubs of butter of 50 lb. each at 45¢ a pound. His commission was $45. What was the rate of commission?

COMMERCIAL DISCOUNTS

QUANTITY DISCOUNTS

The following, and other similar expressions, are frequently seen in store windows. What do they mean?

"10 cents each, 3 for 25 cents"
"15 cents each, 2 for 25 cents"
"18 cents each, 3 for 50 cents"

Illustration. How much is saved by buying 3 ten-cent cans of corn for \$.25 instead of buying one can at a time at 10 cents a can?

(*a*) What part of the cost of three single cans is saved by buying three cans at one time?

At \$.10 a can, 3 cans would cost \$.30
\$.30 − \$.25 = \$.05, amount saved.

(*b*) What per cent of the cost is saved?

\$.05 is what per cent of \$.30?

$$P \div B = R$$

\$.05 ÷ \$.30 = $.16\frac{2}{3}$ = $16\frac{2}{3}\%$, per cent saved.

(*c*) \$.05 is what part of \$.30?

\$.05 is $\frac{1}{6}$ of \$.30.

These reductions, or savings to the consumer, are not generally spoken of as discounts, though in reality they are quantity discounts. The term **quantity discount** means a discount allowed the purchaser because he buys more than a minimum quantity of a given article at one time.

The term **discount** ordinarily indicates a reduction in the price of an article.

How can a grocer afford to sell two fifteen-cent cans of peaches for \$.25?

Every sale costs something in labor, time, and materials. The sales clerk has to go to the shelf to get the cans and wrap them. It takes time to receive payment and possibly make change. The time required to sell, wrap, and make change for one can of peaches is practically the same as for selling 2 or more cans. As a result, the selling expense per can is reduced by selling more than one can at a time. The profit on the two cans at the reduced price is greater than on one can at the regular price.

Another reason why a grocer can sell two fifteen-cent cans of peaches for \$.25 is that if he can increase his sales sufficiently, he can buy in larger quantities and so obtain a larger discount, or a better price on the goods he buys.

Can you think of other reasons for selling two fifteen-cent cans of peaches for \$.25?

For much the same reasons, *quantity discounts* are allowed in the wholesale trade. A wholesale merchant whose normal net price of men's suits is \$16.50 may offer an additional discount if the purchaser will take 25% to 50% greater quantity of goods.

Illustration. A retail clothier desires to buy 120 suits of clothes at \$16.50. If he will take 150 suits, the wholesaler will allow him an additional discount of 5% on the entire order. How much is the quantity discount?

150 × \$16.50 = \$2475, cost before discount is deducted.
5% of \$2475 = \$123.75, quantity discount.

Mental Drill

State results of the following:

\$.03 is what per cent of \$.15?
\$.04 is what per cent of \$.20?
\$.02 is what per cent of \$.12?
\$.08 is what per cent of \$.56?
\$.07 is what per cent of \$.35?

Problems

Find the quantity discount and the rate of discount on the following purchases:

1. 6 cans of beans at 2 for \$.15; price of 1 can, \$.09

2. 8 cans of peas at 2 for \$.17; price of 1 can, \$.10

3. 12 cans of asparagus at 3 for \$.50; price of 1 can, \$.19

4. 12 cakes of soap at 3 for \$.10; price of 1 cake, \$.04

5. On a weekend sale a woman purchased the following items:

6 bottles ketchup at 3 for \$.20; regular price 3 for \$.25
4 boxes corn flakes at 2 for \$.19; regular price 2 for \$.23
6 cans Old Dutch cleanser at 3 for \$.19; regular price 2 for \$.19
10 lbs. sugar for \$.45; regular price \$.05 a pound

Find the amount she saved, and the rate of discount on the whole order.

6. A plumbing contractor wished to buy 6 dozen bath tubs. They were priced at \$33, less $16\frac{2}{3}\%$. He was told by the manufacturer that if he would increase his order to 10 dozen, he would be allowed an additional discount of 6%. Find the total amount of discount allowed on the increased order.

CASH DISCOUNT

A discount allowed for the early payment of a bill of goods is called a cash discount.

Selling goods and allowing the buyer from 30 to 90 days in which to pay for them is called selling **on account, or on credit.** This plan helps both the seller and the buyer, because if the buyer has to pay "spot" cash for his purchases, he may not be able to buy so freely as he otherwise would. A retailer by having from 30 days to 90 days in which to pay for his purchases, has a chance in the meantime to sell the goods, and so receive money with which to pay for them.

The seller offers a cash discount as an inducement to the purchaser to pay his bills early, and the buyer who has ready cash will find it profitable to accept the offer.

Acceptance of the cash-discount offer helps the seller as well as the buyer. It gives the seller his money early and enables him to use it in his business. It helps the buyer by giving him an additional profit due to the decrease in the cost

Elgin, Ill., May 15, 19__

AUBREY BROTHERS

General Merchants

Sold to Robert Sandstone,
Peoria, Ill.

Terms: 2/10, N/30

2	Wilton Rugs 9 × 12	$42.50	85.00	
1	Wilton Rug 12 × 15		72.50	
			157.50	
	Less 2%		3.15	
				154.35

Received Payment
May 25, 19__
W. Aubrey

of the goods and it also tends to improve his credit standing among businessmen. The invoice shows that Sandstone has paid the bill, and has received a discount of $3.15. The cash discount of $3.15 is a profit to Sandstone.

In the invoice shown above, who is the seller? the buyer?
What is the date of the invoice?
Where is the seller's place of business?
In what city is the buyer's place?
What is the meaning of "Terms: 2/10, N/30"?

Merchants frequently allow their customers a limited time (30, 60, or 90 days) in which to pay for their purchases.

In the terms 2/10, N/30, Aubrey Brothers say to Mr. Sandstone that he may have 30 days from the date of the invoice, May 15, in which to pay for the goods he has bought; or he may pay within 10 days (on or before May 25) and deduct 2% from the amount of the invoice.

The last date on which the buyer may deduct the cash discount is called the date on which the **discount period expires.** The date on which the bill becomes due if the discount offer is not accepted, is called the date on which the **term of credit expires.**

In each of the following, find

a. the date the discount period expires
b. the amount of the cash discount
c. the net cash required to settle the bill
d. the date the term of credit expires

	Date of Invoice	Amount	Terms
1.	April 4	$720	2/10, N/30
2.	May 13	$960	3/10, N/60
3.	Oct. 17	$1140	5/10, N/90
4.	Aug. 16	$1250	3/10, N/60
5.	Sept. 28	$1142.50	2/10, N/30
6.	June 16	$1721.75	3/10, N/60
7.	Dec. 28	$2138.60	3/10, N/60
8.	Jan. 13	$2438.25	3/10 E. O. M.*

* Terms "3/10 E. O. M." mean 3% discount is allowed if bill is paid within 10 days of the end of the month in which the sale is made.

What name is given to each item of discount in the preceding exercises?

9. A retailer purchased a quantity of merchandise valued at $1275; terms 3/10, N/30; date of invoice, May 4. What amount of cash was required to pay for the merchandise, May 14?

10. On April 3, a baseball team ordered

1 catcher's mitt at $4.50
1 catcher's mask at $4.25
18 baseballs at $1
12 bats at $.75

The invoice was dated April 5, and contained this notice: "3% may be deducted from the amount of this bill if paid within 10 days." How much money should the treasurer of the club send in payment on April 13?

11. On February 3, a merchant ordered a bill of goods amounting to $2487.50. The invoice was dated February 6, with terms 5/10, 3/30, N/60. Find the amount of cash required to settle on March 8.

12. Harvey Hadley offered to sell bath tubs, regularly priced at $25, as follows:

In quantities over 1 doz., not over 3 doz., at 5% discount
In quantities over 3 doz., not over 5 doz., at 10% discount
In quantities over 5 doz., not over 8 doz., at 15% discount
In quantities over 8 doz. at 20% discount.

A small dealer may not wish to carry a stock in excess of 2 dozen tubs, while a large dealer may carry a stock of 10 dozen tubs. Find the cost of 2 dozen tubs, purchased by a small dealer. Find the cost of 10 dozen tubs, purchased by a large dealer.

If each dealer sells the tubs at $35 each, how much per tub does each dealer make?

13. L. R. Thurston wished to buy 12 dozen pairs of gloves. The price was $10.75 per dozen. The manufacturer offered a discount of 5% if he would order 20 dozen pairs. Mr. Thurston accepted the offer. Find the amount of discount allowed.

ANTICIPATION

In addition to a cash discount of 2%, 3%, 4%, etc., for early payment for merchandise sold, the seller frequently allows an additional discount, known as "anticipation."

Anticipation is a discount based on the amount of the invoice less the cash discount. It is calculated as simple interest at 6% (or the legal rate, if other than 6%) for the number of days from the date of payment to the expiration of the term of credit. The following invoice will illustrate the method of reckoning *anticipation.*

Indianapolis, Ind., June 10, 19—

T. MITCHELL AND SONS

Office Furniture and Supplies

Sold to Charles Arnold
37 Lake Street
Chicago, Ill.

July 10

Terms: 3/10, E. O. M. Anticipate

6	Flat top desks #FT 32	$30.	180			
8	Roll top desks #RT 37	55.	440			
6	Swivel chairs #SC 34	18.50	111			
12	Filing cases #FC 18	27.50	330			
			1061			
	June 16, 3%		31	83		
			1029	17		
	Anticipation, 24 days		4	12		
					1025	05
	RECEIVED PAYMENT June 16, 19— T. Mitchell and Sons By T. M.					

What is the date of the invoice shown above?

Explain the meaning of 3/10, E. O. M.

How much is the cash discount? How is it reckoned?

On what date was the invoice paid?

On what date did the term of credit expire?

How many days were there from the date of payment to the date the term of discount expired?

What did Arnold gain by anticipation?

Anticipation is reckoned as interest on $1029.17 for 24 days at 6%. It amounts to $4.12.

Deducting $4.12 from $1029.17 gives the net amount to pay on the invoice.

The date from which the term of credit is reckoned may be (*a*) the date of the receipt of the invoice, or (*b*) the date of the receipt of the merchandise. For instance, if the terms are 3/30, anticipate, the period of 30 days may be counted from the date the merchandise is received. If, however, the words "Receipt of Invoice" or the letters "R. O. I.," meaning receipt of invoice, are written on the invoice, the term of credit must be reckoned from the date the invoice is received.

Why should there be a difference in the date of the receipt of invoice and the receipt of the merchandise? Which would normally be received first?

Illustration. A bill of goods valued at $2000 was received May 15; the terms were 5/30 anticipate; and date of payment was May 18. Find amount paid.

5% of $2000 = $100, cash discount
$2000 – $100 = $1900, amount less cash discount
Term of credit expires June 14
From May 18 to June 14 = 27 days
The interest on $1900 at 6% for 27 days = $8.55, anticipation
$1900 – $8.55 = $1891.45, net amount to pay.

Illustration. Mr. Becker received a bill of goods valued at $2500 on April 22. The invoice was received on April 17; the terms were 4/60, anticipate. The letters "R. O. I." were on the heading of the invoice. Becker paid for the goods on April 23. How much did he pay?

4% of $2500 = $100, cash discount
$2500 – $100 = $2400, amount less the cash discount
Credit expires 60 days after April 17, which gives June 16
From April 23 to June 16 = 54 days
The interest on $2400 for 54 days at 6% = $21.60, anticipation
$2400 – $21.60 = $2378.40, net amount to pay.

If anticipation is not to be taken by the buyer, the seller should so indicate in the terms, thus, 3/30, no anticipation, or 4/10, E. O. M. no anticipation.

Problems

Find the net amount of cash required to pay for the following invoices on the dates indicated:

	Amount of Invoice	*Invoice Received*	*Merchandise Received*	*Date of Payment*	*Terms*
1.	$4200	Mar. 14	Mar. 17	Mar. 20	3/30 anticipate
2.	$3600	Sept. 17	Sept. 20	Sept. 21	4/10 E. O. M. anticipate
3.	$4500	Oct. 4	Oct. 9	Oct. 11	5/30 anticipate R. O. I.
4.	$5100	Aug. 10	Aug. 12	Aug. 20	4/10, 2/30, no anticipation
5.	$5500	Nov. 28*	Dec. 2	Dec. 4	3/10 E. O. M. anticipate
6.	$4860	June 26	June 28	July 1	4/10 E. O. M. anticipate
7.	$7500	Apr. 27	Apr. 29	May 1	5/10 E. O. M. anticipate

TRADE DISCOUNT

A wholesale furniture company sent to its customers a discount sheet which contained this information: "Owing to a decreased cost of raw materials we quote discounts as follows, from and after May 1, 19__:

Items	*Former Discount*	*Discount after May 1, 19__*
Mahogany Tables	25%	25% and $16\frac{2}{3}$%
Teakwood Dressers	20% and 10%	20%, 10%, and 5%
Walnut Bedroom Suites	25% and 10%	25%, 10%, and 10%

A **discount sheet** is a written statement issued by a wholesaler, jobber, or manufacturer to customers quoting discounts on merchandise. The discount sheet is used especially when it is desired to notify the trade (see page 62) of a change in the discounts formerly quoted.

How much discount was allowed before May 1 on a table listed at $60? How much additional discount was allowed after May 1?

A number of factors enter into the cost of manufactured goods. Some of these factors are:

1. Cost of raw material
2. Cost of labor (the amount of wages paid)

* Merchandise delivered after the 25th of the month is generally regarded as being delivered as of the following month. The term of credit expires on Jan. 10, not on Dec. 10.

3. Cost of power
4. The use of labor-saving machinery

While varying economic conditions affect these costs, in one sense, however, the cost of labor is the chief factor of manufacturing cost. The raw material used in a furniture factory is the finished product of some other factory. For the parts of furniture made from wood the original raw material was in the form of a tree in the forest; the linen or cotton fabrics in their original form grow in the field; and so on with the other parts. To procure each of these and other raw materials used in the manufacture of furniture, requires much labor. An increase in wages increases the cost, and a decrease in wages decreases the cost.

The invention of labor-saving machinery has done much to reduce the cost of manufactured articles. For instance, it would be impossible today, without the aid of machinery, to make enough automobiles to meet the demand for them.

For these, and other reasons, the furniture manufacturer finds that the cost of manufacturing his product varies.

Manufacturers and wholesalers sell much of their merchandise through salesmen who travel from place to place. It is frequently impossible for salesmen to carry samples of their merchandise. The best substitute for the merchandise is a picture and a printed description made into a book, called a *catalogue.* The catalogue contains the price of each article accompanied with its picture and description. This price is called the "catalogue" or "list" price. The list price is generally higher than the market price. *The seller allows the buyer a discount on the list price to adjust the list price to the market price.*

Illustration. A table listed in the catalogue at $40 may be sold at a discount of 25%. How much, then, would a purchaser pay for it?

25% of $40 = $10, trade discount
$40 − $10 = $30, net price (amount the customer pays).

A trade discount is a reduction on the list price of an article. The term "trade discount" arises from the fact that certain reductions from the list price are allowed to the "trade," that is, to merchants who are in the buying and selling business.

As stated on page 61 *market prices* vary from time to time. Owing to a decrease in manufacturing costs, it may be that the dealer who sold the table at \$40 less 25% (see page 61) could sell it six months later for less money and still make the same rate of profit. If so, he would allow a second discount. The price then might be quoted as \$40, less 25% and 10%. How much would a customer then pay for the table?

25% of \$40 = \$10, first discount
\$40 − \$10 = \$30, price after first discount
10% of \$30 = \$3, second discount
\$30 − \$3 = \$27, net price.

The **net price** is the price resulting after all *trade discounts* have been deducted.

Two or more discounts allowed on a given *list price* are called a **discount series**. The rates may *not* be added in solving a *discount series*. It makes no difference which discount of the series is deducted from the list price first.

Mental Drill

Find the result of:

\$32 less 25%	\$24 less $16\frac{2}{3}$% and 10%
\$40 less $12\frac{1}{2}$%	\$50 less 20% and 10%
\$45 less $33\frac{1}{3}$%	\$60 less $33\frac{1}{3}$% and 25%

Problems

1. Waterman, a furniture manufacturer, lists a table at \$60 in his catalogue. He allows a discount of $33\frac{1}{3}$% to Furness, a retail dealer. How much does Furness pay for the table?

2. Six months later, owing to decreased manufacturing costs, Waterman allows an additional discount of $12\frac{1}{2}$% on the table referred to in ex. 1. That is, he now sells the table at \$60, less $33\frac{1}{3}$% and $12\frac{1}{2}$%. Find the net price.

Find the net price in the following problems.

	List Price	Discounts		List Price	Discounts
3.	$25	20%, 10%	**9.**	$7.20	50%, 20%, 10%
4.	$32	$12\frac{1}{2}$%, 10%	**10.**	$8.40	40%, $33\frac{1}{3}$%, 25%
5.	$27.60	$33\frac{1}{3}$%, 25%	**11.**	$9.60	25%, $12\frac{1}{2}$%
6.	$18.50	10%, 5%	**12.**	$12.50	20%, $12\frac{1}{2}$%, 10%
7.	$36	25%, 20%, $12\frac{1}{2}$%	**13.**	$14.40	$12\frac{1}{2}$%, 10%, 5%
8.	$40	25%, 10%, 5%	**14.**	$16.20	30%, 25%, 15%

15. Which is better for the retailer, and how much better, discounts of 20% and $16\frac{2}{3}$% on a list price of $75 or discounts of 25% and $12\frac{1}{2}$%?

16. One manufacturer offers a steel safe at $450, less 20% and 10%. Another concern offers a similar safe at $475, less 25% and 10%. Which is the better offer? how much better?

17. The Fisk-Orr Company sells lamps at $20 each, less 20% and 5%. The Wadsworth Company sells the same lamps at $24, less $33\frac{1}{3}$%. Which company's offer is better, and how much better?

Finding a Single Discount Equal to a Series of Discounts

Illustration. A young man buying a motor boat listed at $420 was told by one dealer that he would allow a discount of 20% and $16\frac{2}{3}$%, terms net cash. A second dealer offered a similar boat for the same list price less 35%, terms net cash. Which offer was better for the buyer?

Since the list price is the same in each case the real question is, which is better, a discount series of 20% and $16\frac{2}{3}$%, or a single discount of 35%.

One of the simplest methods of finding what *single rate of discount* is equal to a *series of two or more discounts*, is the following:

Subtract each rate from 100%: 100% 100%
20% and $16\frac{2}{3}$%

That leaves 80% and $83\frac{1}{3}$%

Multiply the remainders together: $.80 \times .83\frac{1}{3} = .66\frac{2}{3} = 66\frac{2}{3}\%$

$100\% - 66\frac{2}{3}\% = 33\frac{1}{3}\%$, single discount equal to 20% and $16\frac{2}{3}$%

$35\% - 33\frac{1}{3}\% = 1\frac{2}{3}\%$, extra discount allowed in single discount.

Problems

Find the single rate of discount equal to each of the following discount series:

1. 25% and 20%
2. 25% and 10%
3. $33\frac{1}{3}$% and 25%
4. 20% and $12\frac{1}{2}$%
5. $12\frac{1}{2}$% and 10%
6. 40%, 25%, and 20%
7. $33\frac{1}{3}$%, 25%, and 10%
8. 50%, 20%, and 10%

Discount Table

Business firms which have many discounts to calculate prepare a table showing the net price (per cent) to pay when certain discounts are allowed. In a discount series of 25%, 20%, and $12\frac{1}{2}$%, the net price (per cent) to pay is found as follows:

From	100%	100%	100%
Subtract	25%	20% and	$12\frac{1}{2}$%
Leaving	75%	80% and	$87\frac{1}{2}$%

Multiplying gives $.75 \times .80 \times .87\frac{1}{2} = .52\frac{1}{2} = 52\frac{1}{2}\%$, Net price (per cent)

The net price (per cent) shown here is called the **net-cost-rate factor.**

The following table shows the net-cost-rate factors for a limited number of discount series. A table of Net-Cost-Rate Factors is indispensable to those who reckon their discounts with the aid of a calculating machine.

TABLE OF NET-COST-RATE FACTORS

	10%	$12\frac{1}{2}$%	15%	$16\frac{2}{3}$%	20%	25%	$33\frac{1}{3}$%
$2\frac{1}{2}$%	.87750	.85313	.82875	.81250	.78000	.73125	.65000
5%	.85500	.83125	.80750	.79167	.76000	.71250	.63333
10%	.81000	.78750	.76500	.75000	.72000	.67500	.60000
10%, 5%	.76950	.74813	.72675	.71250	.68400	.64125	.57000
10%, 10%	.72900	.70875	.68850	.67500	.64800	.60750	.54000
$16\frac{2}{3}$%	.75000	.72917	.70833	.69444	.66667	.62500	.55556
20%, 10%	.64800	.63000	.61200	.60000	.57600	.54000	.48000
25%, 10%	.60750	.59063	.57375	.56250	.54000	.50625	.45000

Problems

Using the table, find the net cost of the following:

1. A chair listed at \$36, less $12\frac{1}{2}\%$ and 10%

List Price × Net-Cost-Rate Factor = Net Price

In the column marked $12\frac{1}{2}\%$ find the number opposite 10% in the left-hand column. It is .78750. Hence the net cost of the chair is .7875 × \$36, or \$28.35.

2. A bathtub listed at \$64, less 25% and $16\frac{2}{3}\%$

3. A suite listed at \$190, less 20%, 10%, and 10%

4. A rug listed at \$150, less $33\frac{1}{3}\%$ and 5%

5. A piano listed at \$750, less $33\frac{1}{3}\%$ and $16\frac{2}{3}\%$

6. 3 doz. tires, listed at \$22.50 each, less $16\frac{2}{3}\%$ and 10%

7. 1 doz. electric refrigerators, listed at \$275 each, less 20%, 10%, and 5%

In the column marked 20%, find the number opposite 10%, 5% in the left-hand column. It is .68400. Hence the net cost of the refrigerators is .684 × 12 × \$275, or \$2257.20.

8. 10 office desks, listed at \$75 each, less 15%, 10%, and 5%

9. 10 office chairs, listed at \$35 each, less 25%, 20%, and 10%

10. One wholesale clothing manufacturer offers you 350 suits of clothing at \$25, less 15% and 5%. Another manufacturer offers you clothing of a similar grade and style for \$27.50, less 20% and 5%, and a cash discount of 3% for immediate payment. Which offer is better, and how much better, on 350 suits?

11. A manufacturer of vacuum cleaners lists his cleaners at \$90. He offers discounts of $16\frac{2}{3}\%$ and 10%. To meet competition he is obliged to lower his net price to \$60.75. What additional discount should he offer?

12. Compare a single discount of 40% with a discount series of 25/20/10%, and show how much better for the buyer the better discount is on a quantity of goods listed at \$940.

Denver, Col., Oct. 18, 19__

HUMPHREY AND HUMPHREY

Wholesale Merchants

Sold to Andrew Crowl
Sandusky, Ohio

Terms: 3/10, N/60, Anticipate

75	gal. Oil	@ $ .68	51 00	
45	gal. Turpentine	@ $ .94	42 30	
60	gal. White Paint	@ $2.75	165 00	
			258 30	
	20% and 10%		72 32	
			185 98	
	Less 3%		5 58	
			180 40	
	Anticipation		1 50	
				178 90

RECEIVED PAYMENT
Oct. 28, 19__
Humphrey and Humphrey
By *L. E. S.*

13. State the meaning of the terms 3/10, N/60, anticipate in the invoice shown above.

What name is given to the discount of 20% and 10%? To what single discount are 20% and 10% equal? What is the net-cost-rate factor for a discount of 20% and 10%?

Who deducts the trade discount? When is the trade discount deducted?

What name is given to the 3% discount? Who deducts the 3% discount? When is the deduction made?

Which one of the several amounts shown in the invoice is charged to the buyer?

On the books of the seller, will the cash discount of $5.58 appear as a profit or as a loss? How will the same amount appear on the books of the buyer?

The trade discount does not appear on the books of either the buyer or the seller. Why?

In each of the following, find the cash discount and the net amount of cash required to pay for the purchases:

14. S. E. Selkirk bought from J. D. Burton, terms 2/10, N/30, 2508 ft. of $\frac{1}{2}$ inch galvanized pipe at $.08$\frac{1}{2}$ a foot, and 1372 ft. of $\frac{3}{4}$ inch black pipe at $.11$\frac{1}{2}$ a foot, less 25%, 20%, and 10%.

15. Richard Whitestone sold to Harry Byrd on September 22, terms 3/10, N/60, 150,490 steel screws at $25 per M, and 1350 lb. $\frac{7}{8}$ inch by 4 inch bolts at $5.75 per cwt., less 12$\frac{1}{2}$% and 10%.

A manufacturer quotes prices on golf balls as follows:

On orders up to 50 dozen balls, $9 a dozen, less 25% and 20%
On orders over 50 dozen up to 500 dozen, an additional 10% off
On orders over 500 dozen, a still further discount of 5%

Using the quotations given above, find the net cost of:

16. 25 dozen golf balls

17. 300 dozen golf balls

18. 3210 dozen golf balls

19. 1000 dozen golf balls

20. If the balls were sold at retail for $.75 each, find the profit per ball for each of the purchases indicated in problems 16 to 19.

Comprehensive Test in Discounts

1. A merchant was allowed $17.50 discount for paying for a bill of goods invoiced at $350 within 10 days of date of purchase. What was the rate of discount?

2. To induce a customer to purchase a larger quantity of goods a manufacturer offered an additional discount of 5% over and above his regular discount of 20% and 10%. If the invoice value of the goods purchased was $22,500 (instead of $15,000, originally contemplated by the purchaser) find the *quantity discount* allowed.

3. The terms on an invoice dated May 16 were 3/10, 2/30, N/60. The purchaser paid for the goods on June 15. If the cash discount amounted to $43.75 find the amount of the invoice.

4. A hardware dealer purchased a quantity of hardware listed at $28,960. The trade discount was $33\frac{1}{3}\%$ and 25%. Terms were 3/10, N/60. How much cash was required to pay for the hardware if the cash discount was taken by the purchaser?

5. A manufacturer had been selling an article for $6.40, less 25%. Later he found he could sell the article for $4.00 net. What rate of discount, in addition to the 25% could he then offer?

6. A merchant, by taking advantage of the cash discount offered him, saved $71.20 on an invoice of merchandise valued at $1780. What was the rate per cent of discount?

7. Find the *quantity discount* and the per cent of discount on the following order:

6 cans kidney beans at 3 for $.29; regular price $.11 a can
8 cans tomato soup at 2 for $.17; regular price $.10 a can
12 cans lima beans at 3 for $.22; regular price $.09 a can

8. A radio listed at $127.50 was purchased by a dealer on May 23. The terms were 6/10, N/90 anticipate. A trade discount of $33\frac{1}{3}\%$ and 10% was allowed. Find the net amount of cash required to pay for the radio on June 2, interest 6%.

9. A wholesaler offered washing machines as follows: On orders of not over 12 machines, $175, less 20%; on orders over 12, $175, less 20% and $12\frac{1}{2}\%$. Find the *quantity discount* on an order of 18 washing machines.

10. The Rowe Manufacturing Company offered to sell a dining-room suite to a dealer for $250, less 20%, 10%, and 10%. The Wilson Furniture Company offered to sell a dining-room suite of a similar quality for $260, less 40%. (*a*) Which offer is the better? How much is saved by taking the better offer? (*b*) What single discount is equivalent to the series 20%, 10%, and 10%?

PROFIT AND LOSS

Not all business is profitable at all times. There are periods of time when profits are small, and other periods when losses are sustained. There are many factors and details in the business of any company which obviously cannot be presented in a text of this kind. The purpose here is to present some general principles underlying the subject of profit and loss, and to discuss the interpretation of problems arising therefrom.

A business cannot be run without expense. One of the first things to consider in a business is to make sure that enough profit is made from transactions to cover expenses and have enough left to pay the owners of the business reasonable compensation for running it. A business cannot long exist when expenses continue to exceed income.

How may a company (or an individual) know how much its expenses will be and how much income will be needed to produce a reasonable net profit? Experience is the best guide. For many years records have been kept in many lines of business which show the average expenses, or cost of doing business, and the gross profit necessary to conduct a profitable business. Operating expenses vary considerably with the kind of business and the location of the business. Approximately one half of the cost of running a business is due to wages of employes (the pay roll).

Terms of the Profit and Loss Statement

(1) **Gross Sales** represents the amount of goods sold to customers without considering the return of goods by customers, or allowances made for broken or damaged goods.

(2) **Return Sales** is the term given to merchandise returned by customers. The value of the merchandise returned must be deducted from the gross sales. In case a piece of merchandise is not entirely satisfactory to the buyer, he may

retain it instead of returning it, provided an allowance is made on the price. When this is done the amount of the allowance must also be deducted from the gross sales. In that case the item called *return sales* is called *return sales and allowances*.

(3) **Net Sales** is the value of the goods actually sold and not returned. It is the difference between the gross sales and the returns and allowances.

(4) **Prime Cost** is the cost of goods before the buying expenses are added.

(5) **Buying Expense** is the cost of buying merchandise, such as commission, salary of buyer, and freight.

(6) **Gross Cost** is the total cost. It is the sum of the prime cost and the buying expense.

(7) **Gross Profit** is the difference between the gross cost and the net sales. It is the profit before the selling expenses are paid.

(8) **Selling Expense** is the cost of selling the merchandise. It is not always readily possible to distinguish "selling expense" from other expenses of the business, each of which must be paid out of gross profit. In a small concern the same person may act as salesman, as stock clerk, and as bookkeeper. Office expenses may not be exclusively "selling expense," even though the whole organization exists for the purpose of making sales. Selling expense and other expenses incurred in making sales are frequently referred to as **operating expenses, charges against income,** or **overhead expenses.** These terms are inclusive and cover "selling expense" along with other items of expense.

(9) **Net Profit** is what is left of the gross profit after all expenses are paid. In its relation to sales, net profit indicates whether the volume of sales justifies the expenditures or not.

Finding Profit or Loss

It is a matter of importance to a business concern whether the business has been profitable or not. Every business concern determines periodically how much the profit (or loss) has been.

GROSS PROFIT

To explain the various terms used in discussing profit we shall illustrate largely from the mercantile type of business. **Gross profit,** also called **margin of profit** or **margin,** is found by subtracting the *cost of goods sold* from the *net sales*. It will be necessary to analyze net sales and cost of goods sold to see what those terms comprise.

Net Sales

Illustration 1. Suppose the *gross sales* of goods for the period ending June 30 amounted to \$7475. Of these sales, goods amounting to \$225 were returned and allowances of \$115 were made for damaged goods. Find the net sales.

Gross Sales			\$7475
Less:	Goods Returned	\$225	
	Damaged Goods	115	340
Net Sales			\$7135

Cost of Goods Sold

A **merchandise inventory** is the value of unsold goods. When business statements are being made up at the end of a given fiscal period, it is seldom the case that all merchandise purchased has been sold. A **fiscal period** may be any length of time, one month, three months, six months, or a year, as the management may prefer.

A trading concern cannot find its profit (or loss) without first determining the inventory value of unsold goods. Taking the inventory is, therefore, one of the first steps in finding the profit (or loss) of a business. In the present discussion, however, inventory totals will be stated in the problems.

Illustration 2. **Inventory at the End of a Fiscal Period.** Your purchases, for three months ending March 31, were \$8750. On April 2 you took an inventory and found you had goods on hand worth \$5875. What is the cost of goods sold?

Purchases − Inventory (e. o. p.) = Cost of Goods Sold

Purchases	\$8750
Inventory, March 31	5875
Cost of Goods Sold	\$2875

Assuming that the Inventory is figured at cost price, then the value of the goods on hand at the end of the period (e. o. p.) subtracted from the total purchases will show the cost value of the goods you have sold during a given business period.

Illustration 3. **Inventory at the Beginning of a Fiscal Period.** Your purchases during the succeeding three months, ending June 30, were \$3143. On June 30 your inventory was valued at \$4250. Find the cost of the merchandise you sold during the three months ending June 30.

Inventory (b. o. p.) + Purchases − Inventory (e. o. p.) = Cost of Goods Sold

Inventory, March 31	\$5875
Purchases	3143
Total Cost of Goods for Sale	\$9018
Less Inventory, June 30	4250
Cost of Goods Sold	\$4768

You will note that the inventory taken March 31 is kept in stock and sold along with other goods purchased during the succeeding three months of business. It is, therefore, added to the purchases made during the period. Inventory (b. o. p.) means, as of the *beginning of a period.*

Illustration 4. **Gross Profit.** If your net sales amount to \$7135, and your cost of goods sold is \$4768, find your gross profit.

Net Sales − Cost of Goods Sold = Gross Profit

Net Sales for the Period	\$7135
Cost of Goods Sold	4768
Gross Profit	\$2367

Illustration 5. **Selling Expenses.** Consider your selling expenses for illustration #4 to be \$1427. Find your net profit at the end of the period, June 30.

Gross Profit − Selling Expenses = Net Profit

Gross Profit	\$2367
Selling Expenses	1427
Net Profit	\$940

Problems

Find the *net sales* in each of the following:

1. In a certain store the sales for the month of December before Christmas amounted to $6892.60. In the week following Christmas goods amounting to $575.40 were returned.

2. The sales for a given period in a wholesale store amounted to $28,921.50. Customers returned goods, as unsatisfactory, amounting to $1450.75.

3. The gross sales of Oliver Brothers amounted to $9821.50. Due to faulty packing some of the goods were damaged in delivery, and they allowed their customers $275 for the damaged goods.

Find the *cost of goods sold* in each of the following:

	Inventory (b. o. p.)	*Purchases*	*Inventory (e. o. p.)*
4.	$2191.50	$3284.63	$1876.98
5.	$5678.32	$6387.29	$4724.88
6.	$7287.61	$4159.76	$3948.90
7.	$1928.50	$8439.62	$1729.54

8. On January 1 your stock of goods was valued at $3760. Your purchases for the next 3 months were $14,798. On April 1, your inventory was $4384.

9. For the next 3 months (following dates in problem 5) your purchases were $16,946, on which you paid freight amounting to $570. On July 1, your inventory was $5875.

10. For a period of 6 months beginning July 1, you purchased goods amounting to $38,862.50, and your buying expenses were $637.50. Your inventory at beginning was $5875, and at the end of the period was $6390.

Find the *gross profit on sales* in each of the following:

11. A merchant's sales for 6 months were $23,450. He had $3245 worth of merchandise on hand at the beginning of the period, and he bought $18,750 worth of merchandise during the half year. At the end of the 6 months his inventory was $3825.

12. Bradley's inventory at the beginning of the year was $3600. His purchases were $13,245. His sales amounted to $21,475, and his inventory at the end of the year was $2325.

13. A man's sales for one year amounted to $19,842.50. At the beginning of the year he had on hand merchandise worth $4326.80. During the year he purchased merchandise worth $14,596, and at the close of the year his inventory was $5321.64.

14. Inventory at the beginning of a period was $3642.50, and purchases were $12,367.80 for the period. The sales were $13,210.60. The inventory at closing was $1950.50.

Find the *net profit* in each of the following:

15. If your gross profit is $5675, and your expenses are $1960, how much is your net profit?

16. Your gross profit from sales of goods is $6540. Your selling expenses are rent, $500; salaries $1400; and other expenses are $650. How much is your net profit?

Profit and Loss Statement

A **profit and loss statement** usually is a summary in tabular form of sales, cost of goods sold, gross profit, selling expenses, operating expenses, and net profit, covering a definite period of time. These individual units are best combined in one statement so that all the facts appear in their relation to the whole problem. It shows the merchant not only the facts that have a bearing on the profits of his business, but it enables him to compare each item with all other items in the statement.

Illustration. Henderson and Sons had a small store. Their sales for a year amounted to $27,465. The return sales were $975. At the beginning of the year they had an inventory of $3375, and their purchases for the year amounted to $15,375. At the end of the year their inventory was $2475. Their selling expenses were rent, $1800; salaries, $2100; miscellaneous expenses, $1800. What was the net profit?

HENDERSON AND SONS
Statement of Profit and Loss
For the Year Ending December 31, 19—

Gross Sales		**$27,465**
Less Return Sales		**975**
Net Sales		**$26,490**
Cost of Goods Sold		
Inventory at Beginning of Year	**$3,375**	
Add: Purchases for the Year	**15,375**	
Total Cost of Goods for Sale	**$18,750**	
Less: Inventory at End of Year	**2,475**	
Cost of Goods Sold		**16,275**
Gross Profit on Sales		**$10,215**
Operating Expenses		
Rent	**$1,800**	
Salaries	**2,100**	
Miscellaneous Expenses	**1,800**	
Total Operating Expenses		**5,700**
Net Profit		**$4,515**

Problems

Set up a statement of profit and loss for each of the following:

1. The net sales for a year were $65,000. Inventory at the beginning of the year was $13,960, and purchases were $48,540. The overhead expenses were rent, $3300; wages, $5400; store and office supplies, $1600; fuel and lights, $1140; delivery expense, $1800. At the close of the year the inventory of merchandise was $17,500.

2. A clothier's inventory of merchandise at the beginning of the year was $13,752. Purchases for the year were $51,968. He paid for rent, $2800; light and fuel, $750; wages, $6600; delivery expense, $2400; and miscellaneous expenses, $1250. His inventory of merchandise at the close of the year was $15,720. His sales were $71,300.

3. A man's stock of goods on hand at the beginning of a year was valued at $4500. During the year he purchased merchandise for $6700. His sales amounted to $12,675. Expenses were rent $1400; wages, $2400; delivery expense, $1800; office expense, $900. His inventory of merchandise at the end of the year was $4800.

4. A. H. Ross's inventory of merchandise on Jan. 2, 19—, was $21,297.84. His purchases for the ensuing year were $74,689.16. Gross sales amounted to $103,568.50, and return sales were $4578.90. Overhead expenses were, rent, $4800; salaries, $12,450; heat and light, $2975; delivery expense, $2150; miscellaneous expenses, $753.88. Merchandise inventory Dec. 31, 19— was $28,540.40.

Basing Per Cent Profit (or Loss) on Sales

A merchant is not satisfied with a mere statement of profit and loss. He frequently wants to know what per cent various items are of the net sales. So the bookkeeper, or accountant, when he makes up the statement, indicates what per cent each item is of the net sales. The net sales is the basis and represents 100%.

The primary purpose in showing the following Profit and Loss Statement with various per cents is to depict the relationships (in per cents) between the essential items of a statement. No one business is likely to call for all possible per cents in a given statement, but the student should be readily familiar with the principles of percentage that he may be called upon to use in setting up business statements.

Illustration. A musical instrument dealer's gross sales for a year were $25,692.27. For various reasons, customers returned goods worth $770.77. He paid $15,949.76 for the goods he sold. His buying expenses were $1495.29 and his selling expenses were $4984.30. How much was his net profit? The net profit was what per cent of the net sales? What is the relationship (in per cent) of Gross Cost of Goods sold, Gross Profit on Sales, and Selling Expenses, to Net Sales?

PROFIT AND LOSS STATEMENT
For a Period of One Year

Gross Sales			**$25,692.27**
Less Return Sales			**770.77**
Net Sales			**$24,921.50 = 100%**
Cost of Goods Sold			
Prime Cost of Goods Sold	**(100%)**	**$15,949.76**	
Add Buying Expenses	**($9\frac{3}{8}$%)**	**1,495.29**	
Gross Cost of Goods Sold			**17,445.05 = 70%**
Gross Profit on Sales			**$ 7,476.45 = 30%**
Selling Expenses			**4,984.30 = 20%**
Net Profit			**$ 2,492.15 = 10%**

Analysis of Per Cents

Illustration. In the Profit and Loss Statement the bookkeeper is asked to show what per cent the gross cost of goods sold is of the net sales.

The question, put in equation form, and using the values in the Statement, is

?% of \$24,921.50 = \$17,445.05

Hence, \$17,445.05 ÷ \$24,921.50 = .70 = 70%

This tells the merchant that for every dollar received in net sales, he must use \$.70 of it to pay for the goods he has sold.

Illustration. The bookkeeper is asked to show also what per cent the gross profit on sales is of the net sales.

The equation, ?% of \$24,921.50 = \$7476.45

That is, \$7476.45 ÷ \$24,921.50 = .30 = 30%

This per cent tells him that for every dollar of net sales he has a gross profit of \$.30. Out of this \$.30, he must pay the selling expenses of his business and obtain his net profit (if any).

In the merchandising business there are two kinds of expense — *buying expense* and *selling expense.*

Buying expense is incurred in buying merchandise and transporting it to the buyer's place of business. Such expense may be the salary of the buying agent, or his commission, freight, or other expense connected with the purchase. The effect of buying expense is to increase the cost of the goods purchased.

Buying expense is added to the prime cost of the goods to find the gross cost of goods.

Selling expense is incurred in selling the goods. It covers such items as rent of store, heat and light, wages of salespersons, delivery of goods to buyers, telephone, and insurance.

Selling expense is deducted from the gross profits of the business.

Illustration. Find what per cent the buying expense is of the prime cost of goods.

Refer to the Profit and Loss Statement, page 77.

The equation, ?% of \$15,949.76 = \$1495.29

Thus, \$1495.29 ÷ \$15,949.76 = .09375 = $9\frac{3}{8}$%

This means that for every dollar the proprietor paid for merchandise, he paid \$.09$\frac{3}{8}$ additional as expenses of the purchases.

Illustration. The proprietor may want to know what per cent the selling expenses, or overhead, are of the net sales.

Refer to the Profit and Loss Statement, page 77.

The equation, ?% of \$24,921.50 = \$4984.30

Thus, \$4984.30 ÷ \$24,921.50 = .20 = 20%

This rate per cent tells him that \$.20 out of every dollar of net sales must be used to pay the running expenses of the business.

Illustration. Find what per cent the net profit is of his net sales.

The equation, ?% of \$24,921.50 = \$2492.15

Thus, \$2492.15 ÷ \$24,921.50 ÷ .10 = 10%, rate of net profit

Basing Per Cent Profit (or Loss) on Cost

Some merchants may wish to reckon their expenses and profits on the cost basis. In that case the *gross cost* is the base.

Thus, in the Profit and Loss Statement on page 77, to find the per cent of gross profit divide \$7476.45 by \$17,445.05.

\$7476.45 ÷ \$17,445.05 = .42$\frac{6}{7}$ = 42$\frac{6}{7}$%.

The several per cents may be written on the statement of Profit and Loss, as indicated on page 77. Note that the per cent of buying expense, based on prime cost of goods sold, is written to the left, to distinguish it from the other rates.

It is important that pupils have a clear understanding of the terms used in the preceding statement of profit and loss and the discussion following it.

The amount of net profit does not always tell whether a business is profitable or not. In a small business with an investment of say \$10,000, a net profit of \$2000 would be 20% of the investment, which would be a fine return on the investment. In a larger concern with an investment of \$500,000, a net profit of \$2000 would be considered very poor, since the rate of net profit would be only .4%.

Problems

Answer the following questions:

1. What is meant by gross sales?
2. What is meant by return sales?
3. How are the net sales found?
4. What is meant by prime cost of goods sold?
5. What is meant by buying expenses?
6. Why are the buying expenses added to the prime cost? What is the sum called?
7. Why is the gross cost of goods sold subtracted from the net sales?
8. What is meant by gross profit on sales?
9. What is meant by selling expenses?
10. How is the net profit found?

Check your solutions of the following problems by these formulas:

Prime Cost + Buying Expense = Gross Cost
Net Sales − Gross Cost = Gross Profit
Gross Profit − Selling Expense = Net Profit

11. In a small store the sales for six months were $23,298.70. Customers returned merchandise valued at $347.50. For the goods that were sold (net sales) the merchant paid $15,887.24, and buying expenses amounted to $178.60. The selling expense was $4131.22. Set up a statement of profit and loss to show the net profit. (See model statement, page 77.) Find what per cent each of the following is of the net sales: *a.* gross cost of goods sold; *b.* gross profit on sales; *c.* selling expense; *d.* net profit.

12. A dealer's gross sales were $32,984.75, and the return sales and allowances were $984.75. Prime cost of goods sold was $21,760, and buying expenses were $1280. Overhead expenses were $4160. Prepare a statement of profit and loss. Find the net profit and the per cent of the net sales of: *a.* gross cost of goods sold; *b.* gross profit on sales; *c.* selling expense; *d.* net profit.

13. Using the following facts, make a statement of profit and loss. Gross sales, $27,500; return sales and allowances, $1500; prime cost of goods sold, $18,200; buying expense, $1820; selling expense, $4680. Find the per cents as in the preceding problems.

14. A real-estate broker bought a tract of land for $13,750. Incidental expenses of the purchase were $650. He sold the property for $15,800. Advertising and other expenses were $500. What per cent of the gross cost was his net profit?

15. An automobile dealer allowed $350 on a car, on a "trade in" basis. After spending $50 in time and materials to put the car into good running order, he priced it at $475 and as an inducement he allowed a discount of 5%. He spent $6.25 in advertising the car for sale. How much money did he make (or lose) on the whole transaction? His profit (or loss) was what per cent of the net selling price?

16. A merchant bought fountain pens for $48 a dozen, less $33\frac{1}{3}$% and 25%. If his overhead expenses were 20% of his sales, what per cent of cost did he make if he sold the pens at $3.50 each?

Check your solutions of the following problems by these formulas:

Buying Expense ÷ Prime Cost = Rate of Buying Expense
Prime Cost + Buying Expense = Gross Cost

17. Salary, commission, and freight were $1103.31 on a purchase of goods valued at $23,985. To the nearest tenth per cent, find the buying expense rate.

18. The prime cost of a stock of goods was $17,682.75. Buying expenses were commission, $618.90, freight, $300, and cartage, $229.90. To the nearest tenth per cent, find the buying expense rate and the gross cost of the purchase.

To the nearest tenth per cent, find the buying expense rate and the gross cost of each of the following purchases:

	Prime Cost	Buying Expense		Prime Cost	Buying Expense
19.	$7,192.60	$359.63	**23.**	$19,750.80	$770.28
20.	$11,427.84	$399.97	**24.**	$32,784.77	$2167.73
21.	$13,764.88	$619.42	**25.**	$38,921.50	$3113.72
22.	$24,613.72	$1353.75	**26.**	$48,384.90	$3386.94

Check your solutions of the following problems by this formula:

Selling Expense ÷ Net Sales = Per Cent of Selling Expense

27. A young man and his sister run a lunch stand on the roadside during the summer months. Their sales amount to $4482.50. Their expenses for rent, refrigeration, lights, and cooking gas are $638.54. Find to the nearest tenth per cent their per cent cost of doing business.

28. A druggist's sales for six months are $32,698.75, and his overhead expenses are $9571.75. Find to the nearest tenth per cent his cost of doing business.

29. A fruit dealer's sales for one month are $2197.25. His expenses are $404.29. His expenses were what per cent of his sales?

Find the per cent cost of doing business, to the nearest tenth per cent, for each of the following:

	Sales	Cost of Doing Business		Sales	Cost of Doing Business
30.	$51,750	$9685	**34.**	$158,962.50	$29,982.15
31.	$42,930	$8380	**35.**	$291,684.70	$61,672.30
32.	$17,892.50	$4483.20	**36.**	$198,921.30	$31,684.70
33.	$9,897.25	$2175.60	**37.**	$107,908.25	$18,191.75

Finding Net Profit on Sales When the Rate of Operating Expense Is Given

The following rates of cost of doing business are taken from a United States Department of Commerce Report on Retail Operating Expense. Note the variation in rates depending upon the kind of business.

Kind of Business	Operating Expense* (Based on Sales)
Grocery stores (without meats)	12.8%
Grocery stores (with meats)	14.9%
Department stores	29.2%
Women's specialty shops	28.8%
Motor vehicle dealers (new)	15.4%
Household appliance and radio stores	34.9%
Drug stores	23.7%
Jewelry stores	34.8%

* Average for the country. These rates do not include wages or salary of the owner.

Illustration. The sales in a department store for one year were $194,250 and the total cost of goods sold was $123,543. Using the rate of operating expense shown above, find the net profit.

$194,250 – $123,543 = $70,707, gross profit on sales
29.2% of $194,250 = $56,721, operating expense
$70,707 – $56,721 = $13,986, net profit on sales

Problems

Check your solutions of the following by these formulas:

Net Sales − Gross Cost = Gross Profit on Sales

Gross Selling Profit − Selling Expenses = Net Profit on Sales

Using the rates of operating expense shown on page 82, find the net profit in each of the following cases:

	Kind of Business	Total Sales	Total Cost of Sales
1.	Grocery (without meats) .	$64,250	$49,583
2.	Women's specialty shop . .	$42,795	$22,684
3.	Motor vehicle dealer . . .	$225,700	$156,250
4.	Jewelry store	$110,950	$55,945
5.	Drug store	$71,275	$39,905

A merchant found from past records that his buying expenses averaged 4% of the prime cost of goods and that his overhead expenses were 18% of his net sales. Using those rates, find the net profit (or loss) for each of the following:

	Prime Cost of Sales	*Net Sales*		*Prime Cost of Sales*	*Net Sales*
6.	$25,000	$35,000	9.	$14,580	$17,280
7.	$16,500	$27,500	10.	$47,820	$54,700
8.	$11,250	$12,500			

11. Prince and Ridley, clothing dealers, purchased 625 suits of clothes at a gross cost of $21.75 per suit. They sold 550 suits at $32.50 a suit, and the remainder at $27.50 a suit. Their overhead expenses were 24% of their sales. Find their gross profit and the net profit.

12. A machine was listed by a manufacturer at $360. He allowed a discount of $33\frac{1}{3}$% and 25% from his list price. A retailer who bought the machine sold it for $275 less 10%. Find his per cent of gross profit on the sale price.

13. A stationer's net sales for 6 months were $13,726.84. The cost of goods sold was $9291.87. His net profit was 15% of the sales. How much were the operating expenses?

FINDING THE SELLING PRICE

(When the Rate of Profit Is Based on Sales)

As stated on page 69 it is important that a merchant sell his goods at a price that will not only pay expenses but will leave a reasonable profit. It is essential, therefore, that he shall be able to determine the correct selling price of merchandise for sale. The selling price must be sufficient to cover the following:

(*a*) The cost of the goods sold
(*b*) The expense of running the business
(*c*) The net profit

A merchant who pays \$5 for an article and sells it for \$6 may think he has made a profit of $16\frac{2}{3}\%$ of his selling price, but if he has not made allowance for his selling expenses, his hoped-for profit may turn into a loss when he has paid his expenses.

The problem of determining the selling price is, therefore, an important one.

Determining the Selling Price When the Cost, the Rate of Overhead, and the Rate of Profit Are Known

Illustration. In a certain trading concern experience shows that 18% of the sales must be allowed for overhead expense. The proprietor of this concern wishes to make a net profit of 10% of his sales. At what price should he mark an article that cost him \$10.80?

Selling price = 100% of selling price
Selling expense = 18% of S. P.
Net Profit = 10% of S. P.
Both together = 28% of selling price
The balance is cost, which = 72% of selling price
That is, \$10.80 = 72% of selling price
Therefore, \$10.80 ÷ .72 = \$15, selling price
Check: 18% of \$15 = \$2.70, selling expense
10% of \$15 = \$1.50, net profit
\$10.80 + \$2.70 + \$1.50 = \$15, selling price

Show the foregoing facts in a circle graph.

The whole circle represents the selling price, or 100%.

The circle is measured in degrees. 360 degrees make the complete circle.

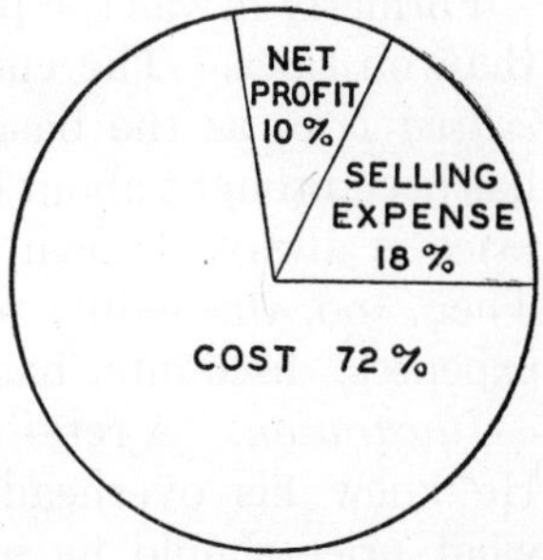

Since the selling expense is 18% of the selling price, the number of degrees to represent the selling expense is 18% of 360°, or 64.8° = 65°, for this purpose.

Using a protractor (see page 246 for explanation of use of the protractor) an angle of 65° is made at the center of the circle.

The net profit of 10% is represented by 10% of 360° = 36°. Then lay off an angle of 36° next to the angle of 65°.

The remaining 72%, which represents cost, is represented by the remainder of the circle.

The circle graph gives a vivid picture of all the facts in the problem; it shows at a glance the relation of each item to all the other items, and to the whole — the selling price.

Problems

1. A merchant's overhead expenses average 19% of his sales. At what price must he sell an article which cost him $21.30, if he expects to make a net profit of 10% on his sales?

2. A wholesale building-supply company sells asphalt slate roofing at $1.62½ a roll, *f. o. b.* factory. A retailer buys 100 rolls and pays freight amounting to $25. The retailer's overhead expenses are 16% of his sales. He wishes to price the roofing to make a net profit of 9% on his sales. Find the selling price per roll.

3. A haberdasher's overhead is 24½% of his sales. He pays $1.33 each for men's shirts, and clears 9% of his sales. At what price should he sell them?

4. A company dealing in farm machinery has overhead expenses equaling 20% of sales and bad debts equaling 6% of sales. They make a net profit of 11½% of sales. At what price should they sell a grain binder which costs them $125?

FINDING THE SELLING PRICE

(When the Rate of Profit Is Based on Cost)

Formerly it was the practice to reckon profits on *cost* rather than on sales. The custom now is quite general to use the *selling price* as the basis for reckoning profits. The change has been brought about largely by reason of the fact the selling price is always known, while cost is not so readily known. Then, too, the selling price is the basis for reckoning selling expenses, discounts, bad debts, etc. Either basis is correct.

Illustration. A retail merchant paid $72 for a 5-tube radio. He knew his overhead expenses were 24.4% of sales. At what price should he sell the radio to make a net profit of 20% of the cost?

In this problem there are two bases — first, the cost is the basis for finding the profit; and second, the selling price is the basis for calculating the overhead expense.

The profit is 20% of the cost.

20% of $72 = $14.40, the net profit

$72 + $14.40 = $86.40, the selling price less the overhead

The known facts are:

1. The rate per cent of overhead
2. The selling price less the overhead

The unknown fact is:

The selling price

The selling price	=	100% of selling price
The overhead expense	=	24.4% of selling price
The selling price less overhead	=	75.6% of selling price

Substituting $86.40 for "selling price less overhead,"

$86.40 = 75.6% of selling price

and $86.40 ÷ .756 = $114.29, selling price.

Illustration. A merchant paid $6.40 for a chair. His average rate of buying expense is 5% of the prime cost of his purchases, and his rate of selling expense is 20% of his sales. If he sells the chair to make a profit of $12\frac{1}{2}$% of the gross cost, for how much does he sell the chair?

In this problem there are two bases — first, the gross cost which is the base for reckoning the profit, and second, the selling price which is the base for reckoning the selling expense.

5% of $\$6.40 = \$.32$, buying expense
$\$6.40 + \$.32 = \$6.72$, gross cost
$12\frac{1}{2}\%$ of $\$6.72 = \$.84$, net profit
$\$6.72 + \$.84 = \$7.56$, selling price less selling expense

The selling price = 100% of itself
The selling expense = 20% of sales
Selling price less selling expense = 80% of the sales
That is, $\$7.56 = 80\%$ of the selling price
$\$7.56 \div .80 = \$9.45$, selling price

Problems

Find the selling price of each of the following:

	Prime Cost	Buying Expense	Rate of Profit	Selling Expense	Selling Price
1.	$12.50	4%	15% of selling price	20%	?
2.	$15.00	5%	8% of selling price	17%	?
3.	$22.50	8%	$16\frac{2}{3}\%$ of cost	30%	?
4.	$32.00	5%	$12\frac{1}{2}\%$ of cost	25%	?
5.	$45.00	8%	6% of selling price	13%	?

6. An article cost $21.60. The selling expenses are 25% of sales. Find the selling price to make a net profit of 20% of cost.

7. A real-estate dealer bought a parcel of land for $9400. He spent $600 for improvements. He then sold it at a gross profit of 20% of his gross cost. The selling expenses amounted to 10% of the sales price. Find his net profit.

8. Hiram Masters bought wash boilers at $2.50, less 20% and 10%. He sold them to clear $16\frac{2}{3}\%$ of cost, after allowing $12\frac{1}{2}\%$ discount to customers. Find his marked price.

9. A young man opened a bicycle shop. Bicycles which cost him $21.60, he sold at an advance of 25% over cost, thinking he was clearing a net profit of 10% of cost after allowing 15% of sales to cover expenses. Did he clear 10% of cost?

If not, what rate of profit did he make on cost? How much was the net profit on one bicycle?

10. A quantity of brass pipe was purchased for \$720, less 25% and 10%. It was priced to sell at a gross profit of $33\frac{1}{3}\%$ of cost. If the selling expenses were 20% of sales, find the net profit.

DEPRECIATION

Depreciation is the name given to the loss of value of property due to use or obsolescence. (What is the meaning of obsolescence?)

There are several methods of reckoning depreciation. Only the **straight line method** will be discussed at this place in the text. For another method, see pages 359–361.

By the *straight line method* of depreciation a fixed amount is allowed for depreciation each year. The fixed amount is determined by three factors, as follows:

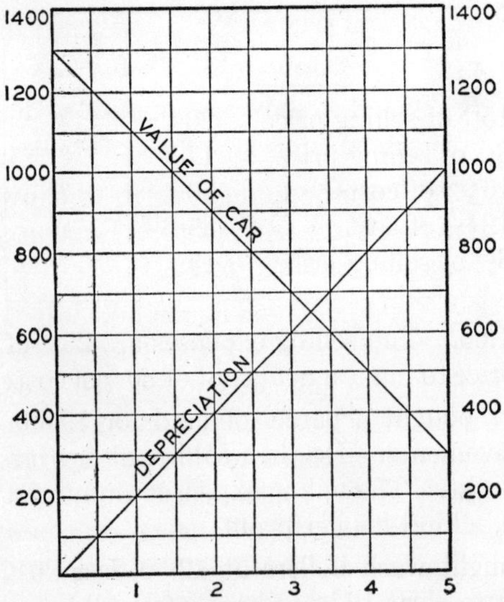

1. The original value, or cost of the article
2. The number of years the article is used
3. The value of the article at the end of the period of use

Illustration. A merchant purchased a truck for \$1300. He estimated he could use it for 5 years and then turn it in for a new truck, receiving \$300 as "trade-in" value of the old truck. Find the average annual depreciation on the truck.

Original cost of the truck,	\$1300
Trade-in value,	300
Total depreciation in 5 years,	\$1000

Average annual depreciation (\$1000 ÷ 5) = \$200.

This method is called the straight line method because, graphically represented, the line showing depreciation is a straight line, as illustrated on the preceding page.

Depreciation is as much an operating expense as is rent or wages. It must, therefore, be included in the list of operating expenses if the correct amount of net profit or loss is to be arrived at.

Problems

Find the annual depreciation and the total depreciation at the end of the year indicated in the following:

	Cost When New	*Expected Years of Use*	*Estimated Value at End of Period of Use*	*Total Depreciation at End of*
1.	$600	4	$60	2 years
2.	$850	6	$100	4 years
3.	$960	8	$200	5 years
4.	$1650	10	$150	6 years

5. Prepare a graph for Probs. 1–4 to show the amount of depreciation and the value of the article for each year of its use.

The following problem is set up in statement form to show more clearly the relation of depreciation to Operating Expenses and also the effect of depreciation on Net Profit.

Illustration. The Fairfax Company had on hand, July 1 (b. o. p.), merchandise inventoried at $34,750. During the next six months their purchases amounted to $98,780, and their buying expenses were $3420. Their sales were $149,690, and return sales and allowances amounted to $5690. Operating expenses were as follows: Rent, $5000; heat and light, $4500; salaries and wages, $24,600; miscellaneous expenses, $6800. Depreciation on furniture and fixtures was $350, and on the delivery equipment, $750. On December 31 (e. o. p.), their merchandise inventory was $58,950. Set up a statement of profit and loss. Indicate, to the nearest tenth per cent, what per cent of the net sales is represented by cost of goods sold, the gross profit on sales, the total operating expenses, and the net profit.

THE FAIRFAX COMPANY
Statement of Profit and Loss
For the Period Ending December 31, 19—

Sales			$149,690
Less: Return Sales and Allowances			5,690
Net Sales			$144,000 = 100%
Cost of Goods Sold			
Inventory July 1, 19—		$34,750	
Purchases for 6 Months	$98,780		
Add: Buying Expenses	3,420	102,200	
Total Cost of Goods for Sale		$136,950	
Less: Inventory Dec. 31, 19—		58,950	
Cost of Goods Sold			78,000 = 54.2%
Gross Profit on Sales			$66,000 = 45.8%
Operating Expenses			
Rent		$5,000	
Heat and Light		4,500	
Salaries and Wages		24,600	
Miscellaneous Expenses		6,800	
Depreciation:			
Furniture and Fixtures		350	
Delivery Equipment		750	
Total Operating Expenses			42,000 = 29.2%
Net Profit			$24,000 = 16.7%

Problems

1. Henry Johnson and Sons do a trading business in a small city. On June 30, 19—, their books showed the following facts: Inventory of merchandise at the beginning of a six months' period, $29,920; purchases for the period, $74,630; buying expenses, $7870; sales, $131,450; return sales and allowances, $6950; salaries of selling force, $18,900; office expenses, $4260; delivery expense, $3280; rent, $5400; heat and light, $3600; depreciation on office furniture, $400; and on delivery equipment, $900. On June 30 the merchandise inventory was $32,500. Set up a statement of profit and loss and show the percentages as indicated in the statement on page 90.

2. Set up a statement of profit and loss for W. W. Wilson, from the following facts: Inventory of merchandise on Jan. 1, 19—, $11,225; purchases for the year, $28,495; buying expense, $1925; sales, $54,850; return sales, $2850; rent, $4000; heat and light, $3000; salaries and wages, $17,500; depreciation on office equipment, $225; depreciation on delivery equipment, $400; insurance cost, $75; inventory of merchandise Dec. 31, $9750. Show the percentages as indicated on page 90.

3. R. L. Ralston runs a small store, employing two clerks, an office assistant who serves as bookkeeper and stenographer, and a young man to deliver goods and perform various duties about the store. Ralston owns his store, which he values at $15,000, and on which he pays taxes averaging $425 annually. To heat and light the store costs $750 a year. On January 1, 19— his inventories other than real estate were merchandise, $16,250; office equipment, $1500; delivery equipment, $900; and unexpired insurance, $125. During the year his merchandise purchases were $31,900, on which he paid $275 freight. His sales were $47,450; his return sales, $1150. Wages of all employees for the year were $5100. Gas, oil, and repairs for the delivery equipment cost $250. At the end of the year Ralston estimated his delivery equipment to be worth $650, and his office equipment, $1300; unexpired insurance was $75. The inventory of merchandise on Dec. 31, 19—, was $23,770. Prepare a statement of profit and loss, and show the percentages as indicated on page 90.

Comprehensive Test

1. An automobile sales company paid $1340 each for cars. They allow an agent a commission of 8% of sales for selling. Overhead is 13% of sales and the desired profit is 12% of sales. At the end of the season, when new models are on the market,

they cut the price of their last car 15%. Find (*a*) an agent's commission for selling the car, and (*b*) the company's net gain or loss on the sale.

2. The buying list price of a chair was $9.60. The trade discount was 25%. The retailer who purchased it sold it so as to make a net profit of 9% of his sales price after allowing 19% of his sales for overhead expenses. Find the selling price.

3. A gas heater listed at $11.40 was sold to a retailer at a trade discount of $16\frac{2}{3}$%. If the retailer sold it to gain 12% of his selling price after allowing 12% of his sales for overhead expenses, for how much did he sell it?

4. A radio manufacturer sold to a retailer a small radio for $16.20 less $16\frac{2}{3}$% and 10%. The retailer sold it at a price to net him 20% of his cost. If his selling expenses were 20% of his sales, find his selling price.

5. An article was purchased by a retailer for $45 less 20% and $16\frac{2}{3}$%. He sold it at a price which would enable him to allow $17\frac{1}{2}$% of his sales for overhead and still make a profit of $7\frac{1}{2}$% of his sales. Find his selling price.

6. A dealer in electric lighting fixtures purchased a chandelier for $76 less 25% and 20%. His cost of doing business was 13% of his sales. At what price should he sell the chandelier to make a net profit of 7% of his selling price? Show the distribution of the sales dollar in a circle graph.

7. Set up a statement of profit and loss, from the following facts: Henry Barker's sales for a year were $76,250, and his return sales were $3750. At the beginning of the year his stock of merchandise was valued at $13,295; his purchases during the year amounted to $68,950, and the buying expenses were $3250. Overhead expenses were: Rent, $3750; salaries and wages, $12,500; heat and light, $1600; depreciation, on furniture, $75; and on delivery equipment, $300; insurance cost $45. Merchandise inventory at the end of the year was $37,250.

8. Show what per cent of the net sales is each of the following items in the statement made in problem 7. (*a*) cost of goods sold; (*b*) gross profit; (*c*) overhead expenses; (*d*) net profit.

INTEREST

Mr. Ray owns and operates a store. He employs a manager at a salary of \$3600 a year. There are 25 other persons employed at an average wage of \$20 a week. For the enlargement of one of the stores, Mr. Ray borrowed \$5000 at 6% from his bank.

(*a*) What name is given to the annual amount paid to the manager of the stores?

(*b*) What name is given to the weekly payments to the other employees?

(*c*) What name is given to the payment to the bank for the loan of \$5000?

Salaries are generally reckoned on a yearly time basis; **wages** are reckoned on an hourly, daily, weekly, or monthly time basis; **interest** is generally reckoned on a yearly time basis. That is, for the use of the money borrowed for one year at 6% the borrower pays 6 cents for every dollar borrowed. Thus, Mr. Ray pays the bank 6% of \$5000, or \$300, for the use of \$5000 for one year.

If the manager of the store should leave at the end of four months in a given year, Mr. Ray would pay him only for the time he worked (4 months), at the rate of \$3600 a year. On that basis the manager would receive $\frac{1}{3}$ of \$3600. The *rate of payment per annum* does not change even though he works only 4 months.

In a similar manner, when Mr. Ray borrows money, he pays on the basis of 6 cents a year for every dollar he borrows. If he borrows money for 4 months, he will pay only $\frac{1}{3}$ of 6 cents, or 2 cents for the use of each dollar. It may be said, then, that **interest** is what one pays for the use of money. The great majority of interest calculations are for short periods of time — less than a year.

The meaning of the following terms should be carefully studied before proceeding further with the subject of interest.

The sum loaned, or borrowed, is called the *principal*.

The sum paid for the use of the principal is called *interest*.

The part of $1 (expressed as hundredths or as a per cent) paid for the use of $1 for 1 year is called the *rate of interest*.

The unit of time in interest calculations is 1 year.

The sum of the principal and the interest is called the *amount*.

Each state establishes a rate of interest known as the legal rate for the state. If a contract does not mention the rate of interest, the *legal rate in the state* governs. Some states allow a rate higher than the legal rate if both parties to the contract agree to the higher rate.

Charging more than the legal rate of interest (except by agreement as noted above) is called usury. Penalties are imposed by the state for usury.

Mental Drill

Illustration. The principal is $575; the rate, 6%; and the time, 1 yr.

$$.06 \times \$575 = \$34.50, \text{ the interest}$$
$$\$575 + \$34.50 = \$609.50, \text{ the amount}$$

1. Find the interest at 6% on a loan of $4500 for 1 year. What is the amount?

2. At 5% what is the interest on $3750 for 1 year? The amount?

3. How much interest is paid semiannually on a mortgage of $2600 at 6%?

4. Mr. Brown borrowed $1800 on April 1, and repaid it with interest at 5% on October 1, the same year. How much should he pay?

SIMPLE INTEREST

Interest is either **simple** or **compound.** For a discussion of compound interest, see pages 273–278.

Simple interest may be either **ordinary interest** or **accurate (exact) interest.**

As to time, the **common or ordinary year** counts 360 days. Each month is considered as having 30 days regardless of whether it has 28 days, 29 days, 30 days, or 31 days.

The **accurate or exact year** counts 365 days. The exact number of days in each month is counted.

Ordinary interest is reckoned on the basis of the common year (360 days to the year).

Accurate (or **exact**) **interest** is interest reckoned on the basis of the accurate year (365 days to the year). (For the method of finding exact interest, see pages 278–280.)

The **60-day method** is the simplest and most practical method of finding *ordinary interest.*

Consider the year as having 12 months of 30 days each, or 360 days.

Interest at 6% means that the interest on $1 for 1 year is $.06.

Interest at 6% means that the interest on $1 for 60 days is $.01.

Since the interest at 6% on $1 for 60 days is $.01,
then the interest at 6% on $5 for 60 days is $.05,
the interest at 6% on $75 for 60 days is $.75,
and the interest at 6% on $950 for 60 days is $9.50.

To find the interest at 6% on any sum of money for 60 days, point off two places from the right in the principal sum.

Mental Drill

State orally the interest at 6% for 60 days on:

	(*a*)	(*b*)	(*c*)	(*d*)	(*e*)	(*f*)	(*g*)
1.	$60	$54	$125	$175	$500	$650	$840
2.	$34	$88	$250	$345	$725	$450	$925
3.	$125	$256	$375	$730	$865	$780	$990
4.	$335	$568	$674	$75.25	$88.50	$954.50	$892.75
5.	$760	$855	$790	$945.80	$576.30	$825.60	$975.90

6. A man borrowed $1500 at 6% for 60 days. How much did it cost him to pay the loan and the interest?

State orally the interest at 6% for 30 days on the following:

	(*a*)	(*b*)	(*c*)	(*d*)	(*e*)
7.	$400	$600	$1600	$2260	$1300
8.	$800	$200	$1680	$900	$1550
9.	$1000	$1400	$1840	$1100	$1790

10. Find the amount of money required to repay a loan of $1750 with interest at 6% for 2 months.

Finding Interest at 6% When the Time Is an Aliquot Part of 60 Days

The simplest form of solution of interest problems is shown in the following illustrations:

Illustration. Find the interest at 6% on $1620 for 20 days.

$16	20	= the interest for 60 days
5	40	= the interest for 20 days

Note. The vertical line takes the place of decimal points. Since the interest for 60 days is $16.20, the interest for 20 days is $\frac{1}{3}$ of $16.20, or $5.40.

Illustration. Find the interest at 6% on $2260 for 21 days.

$22	60	= the interest for 60 days
5	65	= the interest for 15 days
2	26	= the interest for 6 days
$7	91	= the interest for 21 days

The interest for 60 days is $22.60. Think of 21 days as the sum of 15 days and 6 days. 15 days is $\frac{1}{4}$ of 60 days, hence the interest for 15 days is $\frac{1}{4}$ of $22.60, or $5.65. 6 days is $\frac{1}{10}$ of 60 days, hence the interest for 6 days is $\frac{1}{10}$ of $22.60, or $2.26. The interest for 21 days is $7.91 ($5.65 + $2.26).

It is important that the following exact aliquot parts of 60 days be readily recognized.

30 days = $\frac{1}{2}$ of 60 days	6 days = $\frac{1}{10}$ of 60 days
20 days = $\frac{1}{3}$ of 60 days	5 days = $\frac{1}{12}$ of 60 days
15 days = $\frac{1}{4}$ of 60 days	4 days = $\frac{1}{15}$ of 60 days
12 days = $\frac{1}{5}$ of 60 days	3 days = $\frac{1}{20}$ of 60 days
10 days = $\frac{1}{6}$ of 60 days	2 days = $\frac{1}{30}$ of 60 days

1 day = $\frac{1}{60}$ of 60 days

In practice, 1 day, 2 days, and 3 days are usually treated as aliquot parts of 6 days, or some other one of the aliquot parts of 60 days. Practice alone will show the applications.

Mental Drill

21 = 15 + ?	$\frac{1}{4}$ of 60 =	2 is what part of 20?
16 = 10 + ?	$\frac{1}{3}$ of 60 =	3 is what part of 18?
26 = 20 + ?	$\frac{1}{4}$ of 20 =	4 is what part of 20?
33 = 30 + ?	$\frac{1}{3}$ of 18 =	6 is what part of 30?

15 + 6 + 1 =	12 is what part of 60?
20 + 6 + 3 =	15 is what part of 60?
30 + 6 + 2 =	20 is what part of 60?
15 + 3 + 1 =	10 is what part of 60?

Problems

Find the total interest at 6% on each group of items:

1. $1600 for 30 da.	2. $800 for 30 da.	3. $1300 for 15 da.
$1800 for 20 da.	$900 for 20 da.	$1400 for 15 da.
$1500 for 60 da.	$1000 for 15 da.	$1500 for 20 da.
$2400 for 15 da.	$900 for 15 da.	$1700 for 30 da.
$2100 for 20 da.	$1100 for 30 da.	$1900 for 15 da.
4. $4100 for 15 da.	5. $5200 for 15 da.	6. $4260 for 15 da.
$4300 for 30 da.	$5400 for 20 da.	$3150 for 30 da.
$4400 for 15 da.	$5600 for 30 da.	$2970 for 20 da.
$4200 for 20 da.	$5700 for 20 da.	$2772 for 15 da.
$4500 for 20 da.	$5900 for 15 da.	$3168 for 15 da.
7. $750 for 22 da.	8. $650 for 33 da.	9. $657.50 for 13 da.
$732 for 36 da.	$450 for 44 da.	$234.50 for 45 da.
$844 for 55 da.	$738 for 21 da.	$676.90 for 54 da.
$966 for 13 da.	$841 for 19 da.	$454.50 for 32 da.
$135 for 11 da.	$425 for 16 da.	$345.75 for 17 da.

10. Arthur Jamieson bought an automobile from the Auto Sales Company for $1750. He was allowed $250 for his old car and he paid $500 in cash at the time of purchase. For the balance of the payment he gave four promissory notes of equal

face value. The first note was payable in 30 days, the second in 60 days, the third in 90 days, and the fourth in 120 days. Each note bore interest at 6%. Write the four notes and find the amount of money required to settle each when due.

11. A cattle dealer bought 32 head of cattle at $43.75 each, giving in payment a 60-day note with interest at 6%. At the expiration of the 60 days the cattle had all been sold at an average of $56.25 a head. Feed, shelter, and labor had cost the dealer $125. After paying the note and interest, how much did the dealer have left?

12. (*a*) An order of merchandise was invoiced, April 5, at $900, terms: 3/10, N/30. How much discount would the buyer be entitled to if he paid the bill on April 15? How much money would it take to settle the bill on April 15?

(*b*) As the buyer did not have sufficient money on April 15 to pay for the merchandise, he borrowed the amount required to settle the bill and gave his note for 20 days with interest at 6%. How does the interest on the note compare with the cash discount? Did he gain or lose by borrowing the money instead of waiting till the 30 days were up to pay for the merchandise?

Interest Charged after Due Date

If the buyer of merchandise does not pay for the goods he buys the day the bill is due, the seller has a right to charge interest for the number of days the bill is overdue.

Bills of goods were bought as follows and payment was due as indicated, but payment was not made till the dates shown. Find how much it took to settle each bill with interest at 6%.

	Amount of Bill	*Date Due*	*Date Paid*		*Amount of Bill*	*Date Due*	*Date Paid*
13.	$975	Apr. 4	Apr. 24	**16.**	$2500	May 1	May 31
14.	$1260	Mar. 5	Mar. 20	**17.**	$2760	June 20	June 30
15.	$1890	Feb. 2	Feb. 14	**18.**	$5500	Aug. 15	Aug. 30

Finding Interest for Short Periods of Time

In finding interest for short periods of time, it is often advisable to begin with the interest for 6 days instead of the interest for 60 days, as follows:

To find interest at 6% on any sum of money for 6 da., point off three places in the principal.

Illustration. Find the interest at 6% on $3180 for 37 da.

$3	180	= interest for 6 da.
$19	08	= interest for 36 da. (6 × 6 da.)
	53	= interest for 1 da. ($\frac{1}{6}$ of 6 da.)
$19	61	= interest for 37 da.

First find the interest for 6 da. by pointing off three places in $3180. Multiply by 6 to get interest for 36 da. Divide $3.18, the interest for 6 da., by 6 to get the interest for 1 da. The total interest is $19.61.

Problems

Find the interest at 6% on:

1. $1460 for 7 da.
2. $9180 for 5 da.
3. $1320 for 8 da.
4. $1560 for 9 da.
5. $1440 for 13 da.
6. $1260 for 14 da.
7. $1620 for 19 da.
8. $1430 for 3 da.
9. $1650 for 2 da.
10. $7500 for 1 da.
11. $6000 for 1 da.
12. $3000 for 3 da.
13. $4500 for 2 da.
14. $1890 for 20 da.
15. $1960 for 24 da.
16. $1870 for 25 da.
17. $1390 for 27 da.
18. $1470 for 31 da.
19. $1680 for 37 da.
20. $4880 for 7 da.
21. $4320 for 8 da.
22. $5760 for 11 da.

To Find the Interest at:

$1\frac{1}{2}$% divide interest at 6% by 4.
2% divide interest at 6% by 3.
$2\frac{1}{4}$% divide interest at 6% by 3 and add $\frac{1}{8}$ of the result.
$2\frac{1}{2}$% divide interest at 6% by 3 and add $\frac{1}{4}$ of the result.

$2\frac{3}{4}\%$ divide interest at 6% by 2 and deduct $\frac{1}{12}$ of the result.
3% divide interest at 6% by 2.
$3\frac{1}{4}\%$ divide interest at 6% by 2 and add $\frac{1}{12}$ of the result.
$3\frac{1}{2}\%$ divide interest at 6% by 2 and add $\frac{1}{6}$ of the result.
$3\frac{3}{4}\%$ divide interest at 6% by 2 and add $\frac{1}{4}$ of the result.
4% deduct $\frac{1}{3}$ of the interest at 6%.
$4\frac{1}{4}\%$ add $\frac{1}{16}$ of interest at 4%.
$4\frac{1}{2}\%$ deduct $\frac{1}{4}$ of interest at 6%.
$4\frac{3}{4}\%$ deduct $\frac{1}{6}$ of interest at 6% and then deduct $\frac{1}{20}$ of that result.
5% deduct $\frac{1}{6}$ of interest at 6%.

To Find Interest for Any Number of Days at Any Rate Per Cent

Illustration. Find the interest at $3\frac{1}{2}\%$ on $4500 for 33 days.

$45	00	= int. at 6% for 60 da.
22	50	= int. at 6% for 30 da.
2	25	= int. at 6% for 3 da.
$24	75	= int. at 6% for 33 da.
12	375	= int. at 3% for 33 da.
2	0625	= int. at $\frac{1}{2}\%$ for 33 da. ($\frac{1}{6}$ of 3%)
$14	4375	= int. at $3\frac{1}{2}\%$ for 33 da.
$14	44	

First, find the interest at 6%, which is $24.75. $\frac{1}{2}$ of $24.75 = $12.375, interest at 3%. $\frac{1}{6}$ of $12.375 = $2.0625, the interest at $\frac{1}{2}\%$. $12.375 + $2.0625 = $14.4375, or $14.44, the interest at $3\frac{1}{2}\%$.

Illustration. Find the interest at $3\frac{3}{4}\%$ on $4800 for 28 days.

$48	00	= int. at 6% for 60 da.
16	00	= int. at 6% for 20 da.
4	80	= int. at 6% for 6 da.
1	60	= int. at 6% for 2 da.
$22	40	= int. at 6% for 28 da.
11	20	= int. at 3% for 28 da.
2	80	= int. at $\frac{3}{4}\%$ for 28 da. ($\frac{1}{4}$ of 3%)
$14	00	= int. at $3\frac{3}{4}\%$ for 28 da.

First, find the interest at 6%, which is $22.40. Next, find the interest at 3% by taking $\frac{1}{2}$ of $22.40, which gives $11.20. The remaining $\frac{3}{4}\%$ is $\frac{1}{4}$ of 3%, hence find $\frac{1}{4}$ of the interest at 3% — that is, find $\frac{1}{4}$ of $11.20, which gives $2.80. $11.20 + $2.80 = $14, the interest at $3\frac{3}{4}\%$.

Problems

Find the interest on each of the following:

1. On \$3300 at $3\frac{1}{2}\%$ for 36 da.
2. On \$4500 at $2\frac{1}{2}\%$ for 43 da.
3. On \$2400 at $3\frac{1}{4}\%$ for 37 da.
4. On \$3200 at $2\frac{3}{4}\%$ for 51 da.
5. On \$1875 at $4\frac{1}{2}\%$ for 67 da.
6. On \$928 at $4\frac{1}{2}\%$ for 50 da.
7. On \$1140 at $2\frac{1}{2}\%$ for 48 da.
8. On \$1460 at $2\frac{1}{4}\%$ for 36 da.
9. On \$2750 at $2\frac{5}{8}\%$ for 33 da.
10. On \$3150 at $3\frac{1}{4}\%$ for 27 da.
11. On \$472.50 at $3\frac{3}{4}\%$ for 45 da.
12. On \$984.90 at $3\frac{3}{8}\%$ for 72 da.
13. On \$15,428.65 at $4\frac{1}{4}\%$ for 39 da.
14. On \$27,546.80 at $1\frac{3}{4}\%$ for 18 da.

Problems

1. A note of \$1360 with interest at 5% was paid 38 days after its date. Find the amount paid.

2. Find the interest at $4\frac{1}{2}\%$ on a note of \$947.50 if it was paid 75 days after its date.

3. To meet a bill on its due date, a man borrowed \$5400 at 6% and paid it back 90 days later. Find the amount of the payment.

4. Mr. Atwater loaned \$1400 at 6% with the understanding that it would be paid back on demand. Mr. Atwater demanded the return of the money 53 days later. How much money was required to meet the loan?

5. On Oct. 1, Mr. Hood gave a 3-months note of \$2500 to Mr. Steel. The note bore interest at 6%. Find the due date of the note, and the amount required to pay it.

6. A loan of \$543.50 at 5% was made on May 13. It was repaid on Aug. 28. Find the amount paid.

Finding Interest for the Exact Number of Days

There are two ways of indicating the time a note has to run.

1. The time may be expressed as 30 days, 40 days, or 60 days, etc., in which case the exact number of days must be counted to find the due date. Interest is then reckoned in the usual way.

2. The time may be expressed in months, as one, two, or three months, etc., in which case calendar months must be counted to fix the due date.

A calendar month is the time from a given date in one month to the same date in the following month, except in those cases in which there is no corresponding date in the second month. Thus a month from July 16 is August 16, but a month from August 31 is September 30, because there is no 31st day in September. So also, one month from January 29, 30, or 31 is February 28 (29 in leap year).

Illustration. Find the interest on $3500 at 6% from Oct. 4 to Dec. 18.

The exact number of days from Oct. 4 to Dec. 18 is 75.

$35	00	= interest for 60 days
8	75	= interest for 15 days
$43	75	= interest for 75 days

Problems

Count the exact number of days in these problems.

1. A demand note of $987.50 dated March 18 was paid May 13, with interest at 6%. Find the amount paid.

2. Mr. Bonner owed $1198.75, which was due April 20. He was unable to pay before July 8, and was therefore charged interest at 5%. Find the amount paid.

3. On May 16, the Best Hardware Company purchased a bill of hardware amounting to $1872.60, terms, 3/10, N/60. To take advantage of the cash discount, they borrowed for 50 days, at 6%, enough money to pay the net amount of the bill. How much less than the cash discount was the interest paid?

4. Snell Brothers bought merchandise Sept. 15 for $2891.80, terms 5/10, N/90. To pay for the goods on Sept. 25, they borrowed on their 80-day note at 5% enough money to make payment. When was the note due? How much did they save by borrowing and taking advantage of the cash discount?

SHORT METHODS OF RECKONING INTEREST

Finding Interest by Interchanging Principal and Days

Illustration. Find the interest on $60 for 77 da. at 6%.

Interchange dollars and days and find the interest on $77 for 60 da. instead of on $60 for 77 da. The result is the same, $.77.

This is called the interchanging principle and permits of interchanging days for dollars and dollars for days whenever it is advantageous to do so.

To find interest at 6%

for 6 da., point off three places in the principal.
for 60 da., point off two places in the principal.
for 600 da., point off one place in the principal.
for 6000 da., point off no place.

Problems

Interchanging principal and time, find the interest at 6% on:

1. $1800 for 38 da.	**13.** $3600 for 19 da.
2. $2400 for 31 da.	**14.** $6000 for 117 da.
3. $3600 for 73 da.	**15.** $7200 for 85 da.
4. $4800 for 29 da.	**16.** $6600 for 96 da.
5. $1200 for 35 da.	**17.** $5400 for 40 da.
6. $1500 for 44 da.	**18.** $3000 for 74 da.
7. $2000 for 45 da.	**19.** $420 for 14 da.
8. $3000 for 28 da.	**20.** $360 for 13 da.
9. $150 for 38 da.	**21.** $480 for 19 da.
10. $300 for 46 da.	**22.** $200 for 39 da.
11. $1500 for 52 da.	**23.** $180 for 23 da.
12. $2400 for 13 da.	**24.** $4200 for 13 da.

BORROWING MONEY FROM A BANK

Discounting a Personal Note

Banks perform many services for a community, one of the most common and important of which is the lending of money.

Illustration. Arthur B. Condon wished to borrow $1000 for 60 days. He went to his bank and wrote the note shown below, promising to repay the money at the expiration of 60 days.

$1000 00/100 **St. Louis, Mo.,** Aug. 10, **19 —**

Sixty days **after date** I **promise to pay**

to the order of The Traders Bank

One thousand 00/100 **Dollars**

at THE TRADERS BANK

Value received Arthur B. Condon

Due Oct. 9, **19 —**

A NOTE PAYABLE

Each bank generally has a special form of note for those wishing to borrow, especially if the borrower deposits stocks or bonds with the bank as security for the loan.

This note is a **note payable** to Arthur B. Condon because he is the *maker* and is liable for it to the amount of $1000.

When money is borrowed at a bank on a note like the one shown above, *the bank collects interest in advance.* This prepayment of interest is called **bank discount.** In other words, the bank **discounts** the note.

In the note on this page, if the bank charges 6% discount, Condon receives $1000 less the interest on $1000 for 60 da. at 6%. Hence he receives $1000 − $10, or $990.

For the note on page 104:

August 10 is the *date of the note.*
October 9 is the *date of maturity.*
60 days is the *term of discount.*
$1000 is the *face of the note.*
$10 is the *bank discount.*
$990 is the *proceeds of the note.*

The **bank discount** is the interest charged by the bank on the face of the note for the term of discount. It is deducted from the amount of the note when the note is discounted. The $10 deducted by the bank when Mr. Condon discounted the note is the bank discount.

The **proceeds** of a note is the amount paid for the note when the note is discounted. It equals the face of the note less the bank discount. The proceeds of Mr. Condon's note was $990.

Discounting Another Person's Note

If a dealer receives a note from one of his customers, he may take the note to the bank and have it discounted at once, instead of waiting for his money until the note is due.

$2800 00/100 **St. Louis, Mo.,** April 10, **19** —

Three months **after date** I **promise to pay**

to the order of Arthur B. Condon

Twenty-eight hundred 00/100 **Dollars**

at THE TRADERS BANK
Value received
Due July 10, **19** — John R. Kent

A Note Receivable

This note is a **note receivable** to Arthur B. Condon because the note is made in his favor this time and he is to receive payment for it. Condon is the *payee* and Kent is the *maker.*

Condon has Kent's note for $2800, due July 10. Condon cannot require Kent to pay the $2800 before July 10; but if

Condon needs the money immediately, he may take the note to his bank and ask the bank to discount it. In effect, this is asking the bank to lend him the money on Kent's promise to pay on July 10. If both Kent and Condon are responsible persons, the bank will probably advance the money to Condon.

The bank requires Condon to sign his name on the back of the note. This is called endorsing the note. By endorsing the note, Condon promises the bank that, if Kent does not pay the note at maturity, he, Condon, will pay it. The bank charges interest for the *exact number of days* from the date the note is discounted to the date it is due.

Illustration. Condon discounts Kent's note on May 11.

Date of maturity	= July 10
Date of discount	= May 11
Term of discount	= May 11 to July 10 = 60 da.
Bank discount	= interest on \$2800 for 60 da. at 6% = \$28.00
Proceeds	= \$2800 − \$28.00 = \$2772.00

Study the several steps in finding bank discount and proceeds in the preceding solution.

a. Find *the date of maturity of the note.*

b. Find *the term of discount* — the exact number of days from the date of discount to the date of maturity.

c. Find *the bank discount* — the interest on the maturity value of the note for the term of discount.

If a note does not bear interest, the face of the note and the maturity value are the same.

d. Find *the proceeds* — the maturity value of the note minus the bank discount.

Mental Drill

How many days are there from

1. May 15 to May 31?
2. Apr. 20 to May 5?
3. June 30 to July 19?
4. Aug. 24 to Sept. 11?
5. Oct. 19 to Nov. 11?
6. Feb. 14 to March 12?
7. Jan. 3 to Feb. 15?
8. Nov. 8 to Dec. 23?

Problems

Find the due dates of the following:

	Date	*Time to Run*		*Date*	*Time to Run*
1.	May 10	90 da.	**4.**	Aug. 15	30 da.
2.	June 5	60 da.	**5.**	July 22	4 mo.
3.	Apr. 4	3 mo.	**6.**	Sept. 11	90 da.

Find the term of discount of the following:

	Date	*Time*	*Disc. Date*		*Date*	*Time*	*Disc. Date*
1.	May 4	3 mo.	June 7	**4.**	May 31	4 mo.	Aug. 15
2.	Apr. 23	2 mo.	Apr. 30	**5.**	Jan. 28	60 da.	Feb. 1
3.	June 10	90 da.	July 7	**6.**	Feb. 15	3 mo.	Feb. 25

Find the bank discount and the proceeds for each of the following notes:

Illustration. A note for $1740, to run 3 mo. from Aug. 1, was discounted Sept. 10 at 6%. Find the bank discount and the proceeds.

Date of maturity = 3 mo. from Aug. 1 = Nov. 1.
Term of discount = Sept. 10 to Nov. 1 = 52 da.

$17	40	= interest for 60 da.
$8	70	= interest for 30 da.
5	80	= interest for 20 da.
	58	= interest for 2 da.
$15	08	= interest for 52 da.

Proceeds = $1740 − $15.08 = $1724.92

	Face	*Date*	*Time*	*Date of Discount*	*Rate of Discount*
1.	$1560	Jan. 15	3 mo.	Feb. 15	6%
2.	$2400	Mar. 1	90 da.	Apr. 10	5%
3.	$3000	May 10	2 mo.	June 1	8%
4.	$4500	July 15	60 da.	July 25	6%
5.	$2000	Sept. 20	4 mo.	Nov. 12	7%
6.	$1800	Nov. 11	100 da.	Dec. 18	5%
7.	$5000	Feb. 18	2 mo.	Mar. 1	6%

DISCOUNTING INTEREST-BEARING NOTES

A note draws interest only in case it contains a promise to pay interest. However, if a note is past due, it draws interest after maturity at the legal rate.

In discounting an *interest-bearing note,* one step must be added to what has been shown in the preceding solutions —it is necessary to find the *amount due at maturity.*

> $1500 00/100 **Minneapolis, Minn.** March 13, **19 —**
>
> Four months **after date** I **promise to pay**
>
> **to the order of** Milton Mason
>
> Fifteen hundred 00/100 **Dollars**
>
> **at THE SECOND NATIONAL BANK**
>
> **Value received, interest at** 6%
>
> **Due** July 13, **19 —** *Henry Ballentine*

AN INTEREST-BEARING NOTE

Illustration. Find the proceeds of the note above if it is discounted April 4, at 6%.

Due date = March 13 + 4 mo. = July 13

Term of discount = from April 4 to July 13 = 100 days

$15	00	= int. for 2 mo.
$30	00	= int. for 4 mo.

Amount due at maturity = $1500 + $30 = $1530

$153	00	= int. for 600 da.
$25	50	= int. for 100 da.

Bank discount = $25.50

Proceeds = $1530 − $25.50 = $1504.50

In this solution it should be noted that:

a. Interest on the face of the note is found for the full time of the note (4 mo.) and added to the face of the note to find the amount due at maturity (maturity value).

b. **The bank discount is reckoned on the maturity value (face + interest) of the note.**

Problems

Find the proceeds of the following interest-bearing notes:

	Face	*Date*	*Time*	*Rate of Interest*	*Date Discounted*	*Rate of Discount*
1.	$750	Aug. 3	3 mo.	6%	Aug. 20	6%
2.	$960	Oct. 11	4 mo.	5%	Oct. 31	6%
3.	$1250	Nov. 24	90 da.	6%	Dec. 1	7%
4.	$1680	Dec. 1	60 da.	6%	Dec. 1	5%
5.	$2500	Feb. 28	3 mo.	6%	Mar. 1	6%

6. Mr. Brooks had on hand a 3-months note of $1500, with interest at 6%. The note was dated May 23. June 4, Brooks discounted the note at 6%. Find the proceeds.

7. To settle a debt of $750 due April 5, Mr. Hudson gave Mr. Hart a 4-months note with interest at 6%. Hart discounted the note at 6% on April 10. How much did he receive for the note?

Collection Charges

Illustration. On June 14 John Andrews of Chicago sent a 90-day note of $1140 with interest at 5% to William Castle in Philadelphia. On June 18, Castle discounted the note at 6%. His bank charged a collection fee of $\frac{1}{10}$%. How much did Castle receive for the note?

June 14 + 90 days = Sept. 12, due date
From June 18 to Sept. 12 = 86 days, term of discount

$11	40	= interest at 6% for 60 days
5	70	= interest at 6% for 30 days
$17	10	= interest at 6% for 90 days
2	85	= interest at 1% for 90 days
$14	25	= interest at 5% for 90 days

$1140 + $14.25 = $1154.25, maturity value of note

$11	5425	= interest at 6% for 60 days
3	8475	= interest at 6% for 20 days
1	1542	= interest at 6% for 6 days
$16	5442	= interest at 6% for 86 days

$\frac{1}{10}$% of \$1154.25 = \$1.15, collection fee
\$16.54 + \$1.15 = \$17.69, bank's total charge
\$1154.25 − \$17.69 = \$1136.56, proceeds, received by Castle

Observe

1. Collection fee is based on maturity value of the note.
2. Collection fee plus bank discount equals total charge by the bank.
3. Bank's total charge is deducted from maturity value of the note.

Problems

Find the proceeds of each of the following:

	Face	*Date*	*Time*	*Rate of Interest*	*Date of Discount*	*Rate of Dis-count*	*Collec-tion Charge*
1.	\$3000	Oct. 9	2 mo.	5%	Oct. 15	6%	$\frac{1}{20}$%
2.	\$1440	Jan. 10	60 da.	5%	Feb. 11	6%	$\frac{1}{10}$%
3.	\$1860	Nov. 30	3 mo.	6%	Dec. 10	$7\frac{1}{2}$%	\$1.50
4.	\$4320	Mar. 31	90 da.	5%	Apr. 20	6%	$\frac{1}{20}$%
5.	\$6300	Feb. 20	60 da.	6%	Mar. 12	5%	\$1.25

Comprehensive Test

1. Express each rate as a decimal: $4\frac{1}{2}$%; $2\frac{3}{4}$%; $6\frac{1}{2}$%; $2\frac{1}{4}$%; $3\frac{3}{8}$%.

2. What part of 6% is 5%? $4\frac{1}{2}$%? 4%? 3%?

3. What fractional part of 6% must be subtracted from 6% to give 5%? 4%? $4\frac{1}{2}$%? $5\frac{1}{4}$%?

4. What part of 60 days is each of the following: 30 da.? 20 da.? 15 da.? 12 da.? 10 da.? 6 da.?

5. If the interest for 60 days is \$13.20, illustrate how you would find the interest for 45 da.; 40 da.; 44 da.; 50 da.; 35 da.

6. If the interest at 6% is \$18.60, illustrate how you would find the interest at 5%; $4\frac{1}{2}$%; $3\frac{1}{2}$%; $2\frac{3}{4}$%; $3\frac{1}{4}$%.

7. A debt of \$1428.75 was paid with interest at $3\frac{3}{4}$% for 72 days. How much was paid?

8. A merchant purchased a bill of goods valued at $12,600, terms 3/10 E. O. M., anticipate. He received the goods on June 3, and paid for them on June 4. Find the amount he paid, interest at 6%.

9. Elmer Hood's bank balance on August 13 was $928.64. He wished to pay on that day for a bill of goods amounting to $1475.60, less 4% for cash. To provide himself with the necessary funds he discounted at his bank at 6%, a 3-months note of $1850, dated July 18. How much was his bank balance after depositing the proceeds of the note and paying for the merchandise?

10. Find the proceeds of a 60-day note of $2475, dated June 17, with interest at 6%, if it was discounted at 5% on July 1.

11. On Sept. 15, James Wood's bank account was overdrawn by $275.50. On that date he discounted at 6% the following notes: a 60-day non-interest-bearing note for $325.50, dated August 22, and a 90-day 6% interest-bearing note for $242.50, dated August 16.

(*a*) Find the proceeds of each note.

(*b*) What was Wood's bank balance after depositing the proceeds of both notes?

12. On October 14, you issued a 3-months note for $727.50, favor of Harry Brooks. The note bore interest at 5%. Brooks had the note discounted at his bank on October 26 at 6%. If the bank charged a collection fee of $\frac{1}{10}$%, how much were the proceeds of the note? How much will you have to pay the bank when the note is due?

13. You have received an invoice of merchandise valued at $3450, terms, 3/10, n/60. The invoice is dated May 17. On May 27 your bank balance is $1345.64. To provide funds to meet the invoice and secure the cash discount, you discount at the bank George Knox's note for $2850 due July 16. If the rate of discount is 6%, find your bank balance after the proceeds have been deposited and you have paid for the merchandise.

TAXES

The Purpose of Taxes. Just as a family must have an income in order to pay for rent, food, clothing, and all the other expenses of a home, so the city, the state, or the nation must have an income to pay its running expenses.

The expenses of the government — city, state, or national — are for the welfare and protection of its citizens.

Here is a partial list of items of expense in a small city:

Police Fund	$21,426.57
Fire Fund	15,245.42
Board of Health Fund	7,010.41
Street and Sewer Fund	29,000.03
Board of Education Fund	81,580.79
Library Fund	5,001.00
Old Age Relief Fund	3,464.99
Street Lighting Fund	17,695.25
Bond and Interest Fund	37,113.18

These and other items not mentioned in this list constitute the city's budget, amounting to $362,361.99 for a year. These are all services which the residents of the city require and without which they would suffer. They are services which the citizens demand.

The Bond and Interest Fund is to repay money borrowed and to pay interest on borrowed money. A city, a state, or a nation often has to borrow money, just as an individual does, to meet large emergency payments.

Sources of Taxes. The source of the money required to pay the public expenses of a city or a state is the taxes paid by the citizens. Special taxes, called **license fees, permits, rents,** etc., are paid by special kinds of businesses. Every driver of an automobile must pay for a license to drive and every automobile must be registered and license plates must be issued to the owner. Water rents are another source of income to a city. The tax on gasoline and many other special forms of tax also help to provide money for public expenses.

From the total budget there is deducted the sum of all the special fees, permits, etc., and the balance is charged against the citizens in proportion to the amount of real estate they own. Real estate consists of immovable property such as land, houses, stores, etc.

Illustration. From a city's total budget of $362,361.99 there is to be deducted $35,482.70, which it is estimated will be received from special forms of taxes. The value of all taxable real estate in the city is $5,304,200. What rate of tax must be charged?

$362,361.99 − $35,482.70 = $326,879.29, amount to be raised
The question is
$326,879.29 = ? % of $5,304,200
$326,879.29 ÷ $5,304,200 = .0616265, the rate of tax

The tax rate is expressed in various ways in different communities. In some places the rate is expressed as a per cent of the assessed valuation of the property to be taxed, as 2.25%, or as 3.657%; in some localities, the rate is stated as a number of mills per dollar of assessed valuation, thus 32.5 mills per dollar, or 27 mills per dollar. In other places the tax rate is given as dollars and cents per $100 or $1000, thus $3.274 per $100, or as $27.345 per $1000.

The method of expressing the tax rate is immaterial, so long as the rate is understood. The tax rate stated in any of the foregoing methods may be expressed in any of the other ways. Thus, a rate of 32.5 mills is equivalent to 3.25%, or as $3.25 per $100, or $32.50 per $1000.

A group of men called *assessors*, whose duty it is to examine property, place a value on each piece of real estate in their city or town for taxation purposes. That value is called the assessed valuation. The tax to be paid is reckoned on the assessed valuation.

Problems

1. Copy the following, and fill in the missing rates as indicated:

	Tax Rate in Mills per Dollar	Tax Rate as a Per Cent	Tax Rate on $100	Tax Rate on $1000
1.	?	2.25%	?	?
2.	?	?	$1.75	?
3.	17.75	?	?	?
4.	?	?	?	$27.75
5.	$26\frac{1}{4}$	?	?	?
6.	?	$3\frac{1}{2}$%	?	?
7.	?	?	$1.875	?
8.	?	?	?	$30.56

2. Find results to the nearest fifth decimal place:

$15.75 ÷ $18,492.50 $1348.75 ÷ $115,847.50
$32.84 ÷ $49,764.80 $9487.60 ÷ $298,764.40

Find results to the nearest cent:

.01235 × $175 .048216 × $15,250 .019835 × $45,650
.03426 × $8750 .022567 × $18,900 .0203762 × $23,500

3. The total assessed valuation in a city is $314,895,650. The amount of the tax levy is $10,768,121.47. Find the tax rate per $100 correct to 4 decimal places.

4. Using the tax rate found in Problem 3, find the tax paid on property assessed at $14,800.

5. A man has 3 vacant lots assessed at $240 each. The tax rate is $12\frac{1}{4}$ mills per dollar. Find the amount of tax paid.

6. Find the tax paid by a man if his property is assessed at $2500, and the rate is $6.16265 per $100.

7. In a certain city, the total tax levied against real estate was $12,595,302.53. The assessed valuation of all real property was $331,922,256. Express the tax rate as a per cent to the nearest ten-thousandth of one per cent.

8. Mr. Long's house and lot was assessed at $14,100. Using the tax rate found in Problem 7, find the amount of tax Mr. Long paid.

9. A business block is assessed at $35,000. If the tax rate is $4.2425 per $100, find the amount of the tax.

Taxes are often payable in two equal installments. In one city the first installment is due April 2 and may be paid any time up to and including May 1 without penalty. The second installment is due Aug. 1 and may be paid any time in August. A penalty of 1% is charged on payments for the first half made after May 1 and on payments for the second half made after Aug. 31.

10. If the first half of the tax in Problem 9 was paid May 20 and the second half Aug. 30, find the amount of each payment.

11. Mr. Anderson's house and lot is assessed at $9600. The tax rate is $33\frac{1}{4}$ mills per dollar. If the tax is paid in four equal installments, find the amount of each installment.

12. In some communities the tax collector is allowed as his compensation a small percentage of the taxes he collects. Find the total amount paid by a man whose property is assessed at $4800, if the tax rate is $2.75 per $100 and the collector charges 2% for collecting.

13. Property valued at $48,000 is assessed at $37\frac{1}{2}$% of its value. Find the tax to be paid at the rate of 27 mills on the dollar.

14. Mr. Ames has three pieces of real property, assessed at $6400, $5800, and $9500, respectively. The tax rate is $2\frac{1}{4}$%. The collector's fee is $1\frac{1}{2}$% of the amount of the tax he collects. Find the total amount paid by Mr. Ames.

15. In a town where the assessed value of all real estate is $1,450,000, the total amount to be raised by tax is $27,187.50. Find the tax rate in mills per dollar.

16. Find the amount of the tax paid by Mr. Graham if his property is assessed at $3600 at the rate found in Problem 15.

17. Mr. Smith bought a house for $8000. He paid $3000 in cash and gave a mortgage on the property for $5000. Interest on the mortgage was 6%. Taxes were $2.625 per $100 on an assessed value of $\frac{3}{5}$ of the cost of the house. Insurance,

6400
58
95
217

5000
300.00

5000

repairs, and other expenses amounted to $150 for the year. After paying all the expenses, how much money did Mr. Smith have left at the end of the year if he received $65 a month rent for the house?

18. A piece of property having a 50-foot frontage is assessed at $14,000. The tax rate is $27.85 per $1000. In addition to the regular tax there is a county sewer tax amounting to $.58 per $1000, a water-frontage tax of $.05 a foot, and a water tax of $3.75 per quarter. Find the total tax.

SALES TAX

In some places a tax is imposed on practically all sales except sales of food. The proceeds of the tax may be used for the relief of those unfortunate persons who are out of work, or for other municipal or state needs. The rates and regulations differ in different places. In one city the rates of sales tax are as follows:

On sales not exceeding $.12	no tax
On sales from $.13 to $.62	$.01 tax
On sales from $.63 to $1.12	$.02 tax
On sales from $1.13 to $1.62	$.03 tax
On sales from $1.63 to $2.12	$.04 tax, etc.

To each of the above scales $.01 is added to the tax for each $.50 increase, or fraction thereof, in the amount of the sale.

The sales tax is a *visible tax;* that is, it is a tax that people know about when they pay it. It does not become a part of the selling price, but is added to the sale price at the time of the sale. Another visible tax is the tax on gasoline. The tax on gasoline differs from the sales tax on other items in that it is a fixed number of cents per gallon of gasoline without regard to the price of the gasoline.

Some taxes are included in the sales price. Such a tax is a *hidden tax,* because the purchaser often does not realize he is paying it.

A responsible official of the United States Chamber of Commerce recently made the statement that in the price of a fence bought by a farmer, there were no less than 191 taxes; that in a suit of clothes, there are 105 taxes; and in the price of a cotton work dress for a woman, there are 125 taxes — all of which have become a part of the price of the article sold.

Illustration. Find the total tax paid by a woman who made the following purchases: A hat for $3.25; a pair of shoes for $4.50; a pencil for $.10; and a coat for $17.50.

Tax on the hat	= $.07
Tax on the shoes	= $.09
Tax on the coat	= $.35
Total tax	= $.51

The tax rates given on the preceding page are generally referred to as a "2% sales tax." The change in the amount of tax from $.01 to $.02, and from $.02 to $.03, etc., is as indicated.

Problems

Using the rates of sales tax given on page 116, find the tax on each of the following, and the total tax: (Assume that the tax is paid separately on each kind of item purchased.)

1. 3 tubes of tooth paste at $.19 each
2 tubes of shaving cream at $.29 each
2 mirrors at $.49 each

2. 4 pictures at $1.75 each
3 reams of paper at $.85 a ream

3. An auto robe for $7.50
An electric battery for $13.75

4. Find the total sales tax on the following purchases:
3 pairs of hose at $.65
2 pairs of shoes at $5.25
1 pair of rubbers at $.90

5. A girl purchased the following items for school. Each item was a separate purchase. For any single purchase under $.13 there was no tax. 2 pencils at $.05; 3 pads of paper at $.10 (a single purchase); an eraser for $.05; 2 loose-leaf binders and fillers at $.25 each; and a bottle of ink for $.10. Find the total cost, including tax, of her purchases.

6. A young married couple purchased the following items of furniture for their home: An electric refrigerator, $175; a bedroom suite for $125; a day bed for $45; 3 chairs at $55 each; kitchen utensils for $57.50; and rugs for $150. Reckoning the sales tax as 2% of the total purchases, find the total cost of their purchases.

7. A merchant's sales on which he collected a sales tax of 2%, amounted to $85,575.50. How much tax did he collect?

8. Find the total cost, including a sales tax of $2\frac{1}{2}$%, of an overcoat at $35.50, and a half-dozen shirts at $1.95 each.

9. A man bought a new automobile for $1335, and paid a sales tax of $1\frac{1}{2}$%. By how much did the sales tax increase the cost of the automobile?

10. Mrs. Harrington bought for her children 2 pairs of mittens at $.75 each, 4 rompers at $.95 each, and 2 coats at $5.60 each. If she paid a sales tax of 2%, how much did she pay for her purchases?

FEDERAL INCOME TAX

The expenses of the United States Government are very great. To meet these expenses the government depends in part on taxes of various kinds, some of which are income taxes, alcohol and tobacco taxes, customs duties, social security taxes, etc.

The *income-tax law* as we know it became effective in 1913. Its plan of operation is to distribute the burden of taxation equitably among the people. To this end it requires those with larger incomes to pay a proportionally larger share of the cost of government and to relieve those with very small incomes from paying any income tax.

Income taxes are levied not only on individuals but also on corporations and fiduciaries. In this text only the tax on individual incomes is considered.

The Return of Income. A return of income must be made (*a*) By a single person (or a married person not living with husband or wife for any part of the taxable year) if the gross income is $800 or over. (*b*) By a married person living with husband or wife for the entire taxable year, if the combined gross income of husband and wife (or of either alone) is $2000 or over. (*c*) By a married person living with husband or wife for only *part* of the taxable year, if their total gross income is $2000, or over, or is equal to, or in excess of, their total personal exemption.

The Net Income. The *net income* is arrived at by deducting from the gross income certain items, some of which are, real estate taxes, state income tax, and the state tax on gasoline, bad debts, losses by fire, storm, or other casualty not covered by insurance, and contributions to charitable or religious purposes.

Exemptions. From the *net income,* derived by deducting the items listed in the preceding paragraph, there is deducted the taxpayer's *personal exemption* and *credit for dependents,* as follows: A single person (or a married person not living with husband or wife) is entitled to an exemption of $800 plus $400 for each person dependent on him for support; a married person living with husband or wife is entitled to an exemption of $2000 plus $400 for each person dependent on him for support. (Children under 18 years of age are regarded as dependent.) The balance of income thus found is known as **surtax net income.**

Other Deductions. From the *surtax net income* the taxpayer is entitled to deduct interest on certain types of government obligations, and 10% of his *earned income.*

Earned income is salary or fees received as compensation for services rendered.

When net income regardless of source does not exceed $3000, the entire net income is regarded as earned net income. No amount over $14,000 may be regarded as earned income.

The balance left after these deductions are made is the amount on which the **normal tax** of 4% is to be paid.

The **surtax** is computed at the graduated rates shown in the table on page 122.

Illustration. Charles Hooker and his wife, Mary, residing at 144 Houston Street, Cleveland, Ohio, have together salary and wages of $5000, and other income as follows: Dividends on corporation stock, $1000, interest on a mortgage, $3475, and interest on government obligations, $500. They own their home on which there is a mortgage of $3000 bearing

FORM 1040
Treasury Department
Internal Revenue Service

UNITED STATES
INDIVIDUAL INCOME AND DEFENSE TAX RETURN 1940

Page 1

(Auditor's Stamp)

FOR GROSS INCOMES OF MORE THAN $5,000 FROM SALARIES, WAGES, DIVIDENDS, INTEREST, ANNUITIES, AND FOR INCOMES FROM OTHER SOURCES REGARDLESS OF AMOUNTS

For Calendar Year 1940

or fiscal year beginning ...., 1940, and ended ...., 1941

To be filed with the Collector of Internal Revenue for your district not later than the 15th day of the third month following the close of your taxable year

PRINT NAME AND ADDRESS PLAINLY. (See Instruction C)

Charles and Mary Hooker.
(Name) (Use given names of both husband and wife, if this is a joint return)

144 Houston Street.
(Street and number, or rural route)

Cleveland, ... Ohio
(Post office) (County) (State)

(Do not use these spaces)
File Code
Serial No.
District
(Cashier's Stamp)
Cash—Check—M. O.
First Payment
$..................

Item and Instruction No.

INCOME

Item			
1. Salaries and other compensation for personal services. (From Schedule A)	$5000 –		
2. Dividends	1000 –		
3. Interest on bank deposits, notes, mortgages, etc.	3475 –		
4. Interest on corporation bonds			
5. Taxable interest on Government obligations, etc. (From Schedule B)	500 –		
6. Income (or loss) from partnerships, syndicates, pools, etc. (other than capital gains or losses). (Furnish names and addresses):			
7. Income from fiduciaries. (Furnish names and addresses):			
8. Rents and royalties. (From Schedule C)			
9. Income (or loss) from business or profession. (From Schedule D)			
10. (a) Net short-term gain from sale or exchange of capital assets. (From Schedule F)			
(b) Net long-term gain (or loss) from sale or exchange of capital assets. (From Schedule F)			
(c) Net gain (or loss) from sale or exchange of property other than capital assets. (From Schedule G)			
11. Other income (including income from annuities). (State nature)			
12. Total income in items 1 to 11. (Enter nontaxable income in Schedule I)			$9975 –

DEDUCTIONS

13. Contributions paid. (Explain in Schedule H)	$725 –	
14. Interest. (Explain in Schedule H)	150 –	
15. Taxes. (Explain in Schedule H)	127 40	
16. Losses from fire, storm, shipwreck, or other casualty, or theft. (Explain in Schedule H)		
17. Bad debts. (Explain in Schedule H)		
18. Other deductions authorized by law. (Explain in Schedule H)		
19. Total deductions in items 13 to 18		1002 40
20. Net income (item 12 minus item 19)		$8972 60

COMPUTATION OF TAX

21. Net income (item 20 above)		$8972 60	28. Normal tax (4% of item 27)	$206 90
			29. Surtax on item 24. (See Instruction 29)	90 36
22. Less: Personal exemption. (From Schedule J-1)	$2000		30. Total (item 28 plus item 29)	$291 26
23. Credit for dependents. (From Schedule J-2)	800	2800 –	31. Total income tax (item 30, or if you had a net long-term capital gain or loss, enter line 16, Schedule F)	$291 26
			32. Less: Income tax paid at source	$
24. Balance (surtax net income)		$6172 60	33. Income tax paid to a foreign country or U. S. possession. (Attach Form 1116)	
25. Less: Interest on Government obligations, etc. (See Instruction 25)	$500		34. Balance of income tax (item 31 minus items 32 and 33)	$291 26
26. Earned income credit. (From Schedule K-1 or K-2)	500	1000 –	35. Defense tax (10% of item 31). (See Instruction 35)	29 73
27. Balance subject to normal tax		$5172 60	36. Total income and defense taxes due (item 34 plus item 35)	$326 99

NOTE.—In order that this return may be accepted as meeting the requirements of the Internal Revenue Code, the data called for herein must be set forth FULLY and CLEARLY.

interest at 5%. Their taxes for the year amount to $127.40. They have two children under 18 years of age. They contribute $600 a year to the Presbyterian Church, and give $125 to the American Red Cross. Find the amount of their income tax. Study the solution as shown in the Income Tax Return on pages 120 and 121.

Schedule H.—EXPLANATION OF DEDUCTIONS CLAIMED IN ITEMS 13, 14, 15, 16, 17, AND 18 — Page 4

1. Item No.	2. Explanation	3. Amount	1. Item No. (Continued)	2. Explanation (Continued)	3. Amount (Continued)
13	Presbyterian Church	$ 600 -	15	Real Estate tax	$
	American Red Cross	125 -		on residence	127 40
		725 -			
14	Interest on mortgage on residence	150 -			

Schedule I.—NONTAXABLE INCOME OTHER THAN INTEREST REPORTED IN SCHEDULE B. (See Instruction G)

1. Source of income	2. Nature of income	3. Amount
		$

Schedule J.—EXPLANATION OF CREDITS CLAIMED IN ITEMS 22 AND 23. (See Instructions 22 and 23)

(1) Personal Exemption

Status	Number of months during the year in each status	Credit claimed
Single, or married and not living with husband or wife		$
Married and living with husband or wife	12	2000 -
Head of family (explain below)		

(2) Credit for Dependents

Name of dependent and relationship	Number of months during the year: Under 18 years old	Over 18 years old	Credit claimed
Harry H. (Son)	12		$ 400 -
Ethel R. (Daughter)	12		400 -
			800 -

Reason for support if over 18 years old ....

Schedule K.—COMPUTATION OF EARNED INCOME CREDIT. (See Instruction 26)

(1) If your net income is $3,000 or less, use only this part of schedule

Net income (item 20, page 1)	$
Earned income credit (10% of net income, above)	

(2) If your net income is more than $3,000, use only this part of schedule

Earned net income (not more than $14,000)	$ 5000 -
Net income (item 20, page 1)	8972 60
Earned income credit (10% of earned net income or 10% of net income, above, whichever amount is smaller, but do not enter less than $300)	500 -

QUESTIONS

1. State your principal occupation or profession *Cashier*
2. Check whether you are a citizen ☑ or a resident alien ☐.
3. Did you file a return for any prior year? *yes* If so, what was the latest year? *1939* To which Collector's office was it sent? *Cleveland, Ohio*
4. Are items of income or deductions of both husband and wife included in this return? *yes*
5. State (*a*) Name of husband or wife if separate return was made ....
   (*b*) Personal exemption, if any, claimed thereon..........
   (*c*) Collector's office to which it was sent..........
6. Check whether this return was prepared on the cash ☑ or accrual ☐ basis.
7. Did you at any time during your taxable year own directly or indirectly any stock of a foreign corporation or a personal holding company as defined by section 501 of the Internal Revenue Code? (Answer "yes" or "no") *no* (If answer is "yes," attach statement required by Instruction J.)

AFFIDAVIT. (See Instruction E)

I/we swear (or affirm) that this return (including any accompanying schedules and statements) has been examined by me/us, and to the best of my/our knowledge and belief is a true, correct, and complete return, made in good faith, for the taxable year stated, pursuant to the Internal Revenue Code and the regulations issued under authority thereof.

Subscribed and sworn to by ....
before me this .... day of ...., 194...

....
(Signature and title of officer administering oath)

A return made by an agent must be accompanied by power of attorney. (See Instruction E.)

....
(Signature) (See Instruction E)

....
(Signature)

(If this is a joint return (not made by agent), it must be signed by both husband and wife. It must be sworn to before a proper officer by the spouse preparing the return. If neither or both prepare the return, it must be sworn to by both spouses.)

AFFIDAVIT. (See Instruction E)

(If this return was prepared for you by some other person, the following affidavit must be executed)

I/we swear (or affirm) that I/we prepared this return for the person or persons named herein and that the return (including any accompanying schedules and statements) is a true, correct, and complete statement of all the information respecting the tax liability of the person or persons for whom this return has been prepared of which I/we have any knowledge.

Subscribed and sworn to before me this .... day of ...., 194...

....
(Signature and title of officer administering oath)

....
(Signature of person preparing the return)

....
(Signature of person preparing the return)

....
(Name of firm or employer, if any)

U. S. GOVERNMENT PRINTING OFFICE 10—17104

Schedule A provides space for the taxpayer to state the name and address of his employer, and the amount of his wages or salary.

Schedule B provides space for the taxpayer to state the kind or kinds of Government obligations from which he receives interest, and the amount of interest he receives from each.

The schedules are a part of the Income Tax Return and must be filled out by the taxpayer as a part of his Return.

SURTAX RATES

AMOUNT OF SURTAX INCOME	RATE	AMOUNT OF SURTAX INCOME	RATE
$0 to $4,000	No Tax	$18,000 to $20,000	21%
4,000 to 6,000	4%	20,000 to 22,000	24%
6,000 to 8,000	6%	22,000 to 26,000	27%
8,000 to 10,000	8%	26,000 to 32,000	30%
10,000 to 12,000	10%	32,000 to 38,000	33%
12,000 to 14,000	12%	38,000 to 44,000	36%
14,000 to 16,000	15%	44,000 to 50,000	40%
16,000 to 18,000	18%	50,000 to 60,000	44%

The surtax rates continue to increase till on incomes of over $5,000,000 the rate is 75%.

In addition to the normal tax of 4% plus the surtax at the rates stated above, there is a defense tax of 10% of the sum of the normal tax and surtax. See form on pages 120 and 121.

Problems

From the following data determine the surtax net income:

1. Total income is $13,500; total deductions are $4200; personal exemption is $800.

2. Total income is $8500; deductions are $2100; personal exemption is $800.

3. The total income is $14,250; deductions are $3750; personal exemption is $2000; and credit for dependents is $1200.

4. The total income is $14,225; deductions are: contributions, $550; taxes, $622.50; interest on indebtedness, $450; bad debts, $960. Personal exemption is $2000; and credit for dependents is $1600.

From the following data find the net income subject to normal tax:

5. Salary, $3750; interest income, $500; deductions, $625; personal exemption, $2000; credit for dependents, $400.

6. Salary, $4350; interest on government obligations, $100; dividends from corporations, $250. Deductions are $685; personal exemption is $2000; and credit for dependents is $800.

7. Salary is $7800; income from partnership is $900, and from dividends, $640. Deductions are $1640. The personal exemption is $2000, and credit for dependents is $1200.

8. The income is: salary, $8500; from interest on bank deposits, $275; from royalties, $4515. Deductions are: contributions, $650; taxes, $722.50; interest paid, $300; fire loss not compensated for by insurance, $1500. The personal exemption is $2000, and credit for dependents is $2400.

9. A young unmarried man has a salary of $2100, and receives interest on a mortgage amounting to $800. If he gives $200 a year to charity, how much income tax does he pay?

10. A private secretary has a salary of $2800 a year. She also receives $200 a year interest on a first mortgage on real estate. For her automobile she bought 750 gallons of gasoline on which there was a state tax of $.04 a gallon. She paid a state income tax of $44.60, and gave $250 to charity. If she is unmarried, find the amount of her Federal income tax.

11. A married man with four children under 18 years of age has a salary of $6500. His other income is a royalty on an invention, $3425. His taxes are, on real estate, $528.50, and a state income tax of $157.48. Interest paid was $251.50, and his contributions for religious and charitable purposes are $325. How much should his Federal income tax be?

12. James Boswell has an income of $13,282, of which $10,000 is salary. He is married and has two children under 18 years of age. His taxes are $620 a year, and he pays interest at 5% on a $6000 mortgage on his residence. During the year he purchased 840 gallons of gasoline on which there was a state tax of $.04 a gallon. He contributed $1575 to religious and charitable institutions. Find the amount of his income tax.

INSURANCE

The owner of property should have it insured in the event of fire or other events causing loss. He should also know the meaning of all the stipulations in the policy contract. What kind of losses are covered in a fire-insurance policy? Does a fire-insurance policy cover "loss by fire," regardless of its cause? Is it better to study the policy before or after the fire occurs?

Suppose that one hundred people agreed among themselves that they would each contribute \$1 a month to provide a fund on which any one of the hundred people might draw to pay for a loss caused by accident. Each month \$100 would be paid into the fund. In a year \$1200 would be paid into the fund. If during the year one of the persons had a motor accident which caused a loss of \$350, that person could draw on the general fund for \$350 to pay his loss.

In principle, a plan like the one outlined above is at the foundation of all insurance, whether it is fire insurance, life insurance, health insurance, accident insurance, or any one of the dozens of kinds of insurance.

Insurance companies are formed to receive the money paid by the persons insured, to invest the money received so that it will increase through accumulations of interest, and to pay the losses when they occur. The insurance business is so vast (most of the people of the United States carry some kind of insurance) that it requires many people to perform the necessary work of the companies.

Every person who is insured receives from the insurance company a contract, called a **policy**, in which the person insured agrees to make a certain payment or payments, called **premiums**, and the company agrees to pay for certain losses, if they occur, up to an agreed amount.

Insurance is for the protection of the one insured. Only the amount of loss is paid, if this amount is not greater than the face of the policy. If the loss is greater than the amount of the policy, only the face of the policy is paid, not the total loss.

Insurance companies know from long experience the approximate number of people who will die each year, the number of accidents that will occur during the year, the number of fires and the amount of loss that will be sustained in a year's time, etc. Knowing these things, the companies are able to reckon the cost of insurance to each person insured. A small payment from each of a large number of people provides the funds needed to pay the losses of the few.

Of the many kinds of insurance only fire insurance, life insurance, and workmen's compensation insurance will be considered in this text.

FIRE INSURANCE

Fire insurance is protection against loss caused directly or indirectly by fire. A loss caused by water used in fighting a fire is an example of an indirect loss.

Fire-insurance policies are generally written for 1 yr. or more, 3-year and 5-year policies being common.

The rates charged for fire insurance are based on 1 yr. of insurance. The cost of a 3-year policy is usually $2\frac{1}{2}$ times the 1-year rate and the cost of a 5-year policy is 4 times the annual rate. The rate charged for less than 1 yr. is higher proportionally than the rate for 1 yr.

There are many factors that enter into the problem of determining the annual rate.

(1) The material of which the building is constructed is important. A stone or a brick building with a slate roof or a tile roof

will carry a lower rate of insurance than a frame building with wood shingles, other things being equal.

(2) The location of a building is an important factor. A higher rate is charged on buildings located near other buildings in which the fire hazard is greater.

(3) The rate is higher on a building in which inflammable materials are used or made.

(4) The rate is lower if the property is within easy reach of an efficient fire department.

Rates are based on $100. Thus, a rate of $.40 means that $.40 is charged for each $100 of insurance.

To Find the Cost of Insurance

Illustration. A house is insured for $12,000. Find the yearly premium at $.20 per $100.

$12,000 ÷ $100 = 120; 120 × $.20 = $24, the premium

Problems

Find the premium on each of the following:

1. A $9600 policy at $.30 per $100

2. A $7500 policy at $.32 per $100

3. A $15,000 policy at $.40 per $100

4. A policy for $12,500 for 3 yr. at $.50 per $100

5. A policy for $22,500 for 5 yr. at $.80 per $100

6. A store was insured for $35,000 on a 5-year policy. The rate was $1.10 per $100. Find the premium. How much was this a year?

A fire-insurance policy may be canceled at any time either by the company or by the person insured.

If the company cancels the policy, a notice of five days is generally given to the insured. This enables him to procure other insurance before the date of cancellation.

If the company cancels the policy, the pro-rata, unearned premium is returned to the insured. Thus, if a premium of $40 has been paid for a policy to run 1 yr. and the company cancels the policy at the expiration of 3 mo., $\frac{3}{4}$ of the premium will be returned to the insured.

No advance notice is required to be given by the insured if he wishes to cancel the policy. The company will return a portion of the premium, the amount returned being the difference between the total premium paid and the higher charge made by the company for the short period the insurance has been in force.

Short-rate Scale. For periods of time less than 1 yr. the company charges a rate determined by what is known as the *short-rate scale.*

The following are the short rates charged for some periods less than 1 yr.:

For 1 mo., 20% of the annual premium
For 2 mo., 30% of the annual premium
For 4 mo., 50% of the annual premium
For 6 mo., 70% of the annual premium
For 8 mo., 80% of the annual premium
For 9 mo., 85% of the annual premium
For 10 mo., 90% of the annual premium
For 11 mo., 95% of the annual premium

Illustration. The Harwood Insurance Company insured a residence for $18,000 at $.40 per $100 on a 1-year policy. At the expiration of 4 mo. the insured canceled the policy. How much did the company return to him?

$$\$18{,}000 \div \$100 = 180$$
$$180 \times \$.40 = \$72, \text{ premium}$$

The short rate for 4 mo. is 50% of the annual premium. 100% − 50% = 50%. Therefore the company returned 50% of $72, or $36.

If the company cancels the policy, the amount returned is proportional to the unexpired time of the policy.

Illustration. If the Harwood Insurance Company had canceled the foregoing policy at the expiration of 4 mo., how much would have been returned?

4 mo. is $\frac{1}{3}$ of a year.
Therefore $\frac{2}{3}$ of the premium would have been returned.
$\frac{2}{3}$ of $72 = $48, amount returned.

Problems

Find the annual premium and the premium returned for the following canceled policies:

	Date of Policy	Face of Policy	Rate per $100	Date Canceled	By Whom Canceled
1.	Apr. 1	$9,000	$.45	Oct. 1	Insured
2.	Mar. 10	$7,500	$.50	Sept. 10	Insured
3.	Jan. 20	$11,500	$.40	Oct. 20	Insured
4.	Feb. 15	$3,000	$.35	Nov. 15	Company
5.	July 1	$2,500	$.44	Dec. 1	Company
6.	Aug. 25	$6,000	$.55	Nov. 25	Company

The Amount of Loss Paid by the Insurance Company

The Co-insurance Clause. The co-insurance clause reads as follows:

"This Company shall not be liable for a greater proportion of any loss or damage to the property described herein than the sum hereby insured bears to . . . per cent (. . .%) of the actual cash value of the property at the time such loss shall happen."

The insured, in accepting a policy containing a co-insurance clause, agrees to carry insurance on his property equal to the stated per cent of its value or to be personally responsible for a share of the losses that may occur.

The percentage of insurance required varies; but 80% is a very common rate. The following problem illustrates the application of the 80% co-insurance clause.

Illustration. An office building, valued at $50,000, was insured for $25,000 in a policy containing an 80% co-insurance clause. Fire caused a loss of $12,000. How much of this loss did the company pay?

80% of $50,000 = $40,000, insurance required

$\frac{25000}{40000} = \frac{5}{8}$, part of loss to be paid by the company

$\frac{5}{8}$ of $12,000 = $7500, amount of loss paid by the company

Problems

Find the amount of loss paid in each of the following cases:

If the policy does not contain a "co-insurance clause," the company will pay any loss up to the amount of the policy. This is called an ordinary policy.

	Value of Property	Face of Policy	Kind of Policy	Amount of Loss
1.	$35,000	$20,000	Ordinary	$8,000
2.	$15,000	$10,000	80% co-insurance	$4,000
3.	$7,500	$6,000	80% co-insurance	$3,000
4.	$5,000	$3,500	Ordinary	$5,000
5.	$10,000	$7,000	80% co-insurance	$10,000
6.	$8,000	$5,000	80% co-insurance	$4,000
7.	$20,000	$12,000	Ordinary	$14,000
8.	$25,000	$20,000	80% co-insurance	$8,000
9.	$40,000	$25,000	90% co-insurance	$18,000

10. A store valued at $35,000 was insured for 3 yr. as follows: in Company A for $8000 at $.70 per $100; in Company B for $6000 at $.70 per $100; and in Company C for $10,000 at $.70 per $100. Fire caused a loss of $14,000.

(*a*) Find the premium paid to each company.

(*b*) Find the amount of loss paid by each company. (Each company pays the proportion of the loss that its insurance bears to the total insurance.)

11. A house valued at $12,500 was insured for $8000. Its contents, valued at $5000, were insured for $4000. Both policies contained the 80% co-insurance clause. Fire caused damage of $5000 to the house and of $3000 to the contents. Find the amount of insurance payable by the company.

LIFE INSURANCE

Among the several forms of personal insurance (that is, insurance of persons), such as accident insurance, health insurance, liability insurance, and life insurance, only *life insurance* will be considered in this text.

Life insurance is an agreement whereby an insurance company agrees to pay at a stated time, or at the death of the insured person, a specified sum of money to the person insured, to his estate, or to a person named in the contract, provided certain payments are paid to the company by or for the person insured.

The agreement between the company and the insured person is called a **policy.**

The payments made to the insurance company by the insured are called **premiums.**

The person to whom the policy is made payable is the **beneficiary.**

Premiums are payable in advance. They may be paid annually, semiannually, quarterly, or in such manner as is agreed upon.

Life insurance furnishes protection to those dependent on the person insured. A man with a family, who puts part of his savings into life insurance, makes some provision for the care of his wife and children in case he should die before they are otherwise provided for.

In addition to protection for dependents, life insurance is an excellent way of saving money.

Policies are of various kinds, the most common and important of which for the average run of people are:

1. Ordinary or whole life policy
2. Limited payment life policy
3. Endowment policy
4. Endowment income policy
5. Term policy

In the **ordinary life policy,** premiums are payable as long as the insured person lives or, in some companies, to the age of 85. The amount of the insurance is payable only at death or at age 85. The ordinary policy is an excellent policy for those who desire protection for dependents rather than for savings.

The **limited payment life policy** is similar to the ordinary policy in that it continues in force during the life of the insured, but instead of premiums being payable as long as the insured lives, the policy provides that premiums will be paid for a stated number of years, as 20, 25, or 30, and when these premiums have been paid the policy becomes "paid-up" for life. The premiums for this form of policy are somewhat greater than for the ordinary life policy.

The **endowment policy** provides both protection and savings. This policy runs for 10 yr., 15 yr., 20 yr., or longer, according to agreement. Premiums are paid during the term of the policy. If the insured should die before the policy matures, the amount of the policy is payable to the beneficiary, as in the ordinary policy; but if the person insured lives until the agreed number of years has elapsed, the amount of the policy is payable to himself or to a designated beneficiary. The endowment policy is an excellent policy for those who wish not only protection, but means of support in later life when earning capacity is less or has ceased altogether.

The **endowment income policy,** maturing at age 60 or 65, provides that premiums shall be paid by the insured during his lifetime up to age 60 or 65 and that at that age the insured will receive an annuity of a stated amount per month or per year for life. If the insured dies before reaching age 60 or 65, as the case may be, the amount becomes payable to the designated beneficiary, either for the life of the beneficiary or for a definite number of years, according to the agreement in the policy. This is an excellent policy for one who wishes to provide a definite income for his own old age or to leave a fixed income for dependents.

The **term policy** provides protection for a limited time only. Partners in a business may each insure the other for a period of 5 yr., 10 yr., or longer, so that if one of the partners dies, the other partner or partners will be somewhat compensated for the loss sustained by the death of one of their number. Premiums are much less for term policies than for others. No payment is made by the company unless the insured person dies before the policy matures.

The table on page 132 shows the premiums payable per $1000 on policies for persons 20 yr., 25 yr., 30 yr., and 35 yr. old.

ANNUAL PREMIUMS FOR $1000

AGE	ORDINARY LIFE POLICY (Payable at Age 85)	LIMITED PAYMENT LIFE POLICY (Premiums Payable for 20 yr.)	20-YEAR ENDOWMENT POLICY	ENDOWMENT INCOME POLICY, AGE 60	10-YEAR TERM POLICY
20	$16.22	$24.14	$44.14	$28.28	$9.70
25	$18.19	$26.29	$44.56	$33.60	$10.13
30	$20.72	$28.90	$45.18	$40.93	$10.74
35	$24.00	$32.13	$46.12	$31.43	$11.70

Most life-insurance policies contain a schedule of *cash surrender values*. This schedule states the amount the company will return to the insured, after the policy has been in force 2 yr. or 3 yr. or more, if the insured person is unable to continue paying the premiums and offers to surrender the policy for its surrender value. The insured person may, if he wishes, accept a "paid-up" policy for the full amount of his policy for a limited time or for a smaller amount for a longer period. These various provisions make it possible for the insured to choose whether he will surrender his policy for a cash payment or let the policy continue in force with modified conditions as to time and amount. The tables covering these provisions are too long for inclusion in this book.

Illustration. At 20 yr. of age, a young man took out an ordinary life policy for $5000. How much must he save each month for a year to pay the annual premium when it is due?

Premium on $1000 at age 20 is $16.22 for an ordinary life policy. (See the table above.)

Premium on $5000 is $5 \times \$16.22 = \$81.10$

Amount to be saved monthly $= \$81.10 \div 12 = \$6.76$

Problems

Use the table on this page for the following problems:

1. How many years will it take the young man (in the above illustration) to pay the company an amount equal to the face of the policy?

2. Find the annual cost of a 20-year endowment policy for $15,000, taken out when the insured is 25 yr. old.

3. At age 30 a school teacher took out an endowment income policy for $10,000, payable at age 60. What annual premium did she pay?

4. The policy in Problem 3 contained an agreement to pay the teacher, if she lived to be 60 yr. of age, $10 a month for each $1000 in the face of the policy for as long as she lived or for 20 yr. certain to a designated beneficiary, if she died before reaching age 60. If the teacher lived to be 80 yr. of age, how much did she receive in all from the company?

5. Two men, 30 yr. and 35 yr. old, respectively, form a co-partnership for 15 yr. It is agreed that each shall be insured for $15,000 under a 10-year term policy, the premiums being taken from the profits of the business, and that the firm shall be the beneficiary in each policy.

(*a*) Find the total annual premium.

(*b*) If one of the partners dies at the end of 8 yr., how much will the firm receive from the insurance company?

(*c*) If neither partner dies during the 10 yr., but one of them dies 12 yr. after the policies are taken out, how much will the firm receive from the insurance company?

In many cases investments made by an insurance company pay a higher rate of interest than the company originally estimated. In such cases, the additional income thus received by the company is divided among the policy holders in accordance with the terms of the policies. Such distribution of profits is called a **dividend**. This dividend may be used either to reduce the amount of the annual premium or to increase the amount of insurance payable at the maturity of the policy.

√**6.** A young man 25 yr. old took out an ordinary life policy for $12,000.

(*a*) Find the amount of the annual premium.

(*b*) How much will he have paid the company in 20 yr.?

(*c*) If during the first 20 yr. the company paid the young man dividends amounting to $1303.08, find the average net annual cost per $1000 for these years.

7. At age 35 a man took out an endowment income policy of $20,000, payable at age 65. The annual premium was $39.41 per $1000. Find the amount of the annual premium.

8. The policy in Problem 7 provides for payment, to the person taking out the policy, of $200 a month for 20 yr. certain after age 65. If he dies prior to age 65, the company will pay $200 a month to the beneficiary for 20 yr. from the date of the man's death. If the man dies at age 60, find (*a*) the amount he has paid the company and (*b*) the amount by which the premium payments are more or less than the total payment made by the insurance company.

9. Find the cost per year of a $3000 20-year endowment policy taken out at age 25.

10. If the dividends paid by the company in Problem 9 during the 20-year period amount to $658.02, find the net average annual cost of the insurance.

11. At 21 yr. of age Mr. Taylor was insured for $2000 under an ordinary policy at an annual cost of $16.58 per $1000. At 30 yr. of age he took out an endowment income policy for $5000, payable at age 60, at an annual cost of $40.93 per $1000. At 35 yr. of age he secured a 25-year endowment policy for $5000, at $36.64 per $1000 per year.

(*a*) Find the annual cost of each policy.

(*b*) Find the total amount of the premiums that Mr. Taylor will pay annually after age 35.

12. A young man 30 years of age applied for a $7500 20-year limited payment life policy of insurance. How much will he have paid to the insurance company in 20 years?

13. At age 25 a man takes out a 20-year endowment policy of $5000 and a 20-year limited life payment policy for $5000. Find his annual cost of insurance on both policies.

14. On a $7500 20-year limited payment life policy taken out at age 25, the insured received in dividends an amount equal to $236.40 per $1000, during the time he was paying premiums. Find the net annual cost of his insurance.

FORMS OF CREDIT

Walter Anderson of New York purchased from The General Supply Company of Louisville, Ky., a quantity of merchandise worth $98.60; terms, net 30 days. At the expiration of 30 days, Anderson must make payment. He can send currency (money), but that is not a safe method of making payment; or he can send his personal check. If Anderson does not have a checking account, he can make payment in any of the following ways:

1. By express money order.
2. By postal money order.
3. By telegraph money order.
4. By a bank draft, or cashier's check.

By each of the foregoing methods Anderson can pay his bills without the actual transfer of money. The whole matter is chiefly a matter of bookkeeping. In general, the several methods of making payment are based on the same plan. Before a check can be drawn on a bank, the drawer must have funds on deposit in the bank sufficient to pay the check when it is presented for payment. To obtain a postal or express money order, a telegraph money order, or a bank draft, one must pay the amount of the money order or draft, plus a small fee for the service of the person or company issuing the order. In each case, except the telegraph money order, the purchaser is handed the money order or draft, which he sends to the person or company to whom payment is to be made. The one to whom the money order or bank draft is sent has it cashed at his express office, post office, or bank; or he may deposit it to his account in his bank.

In the case of a telegraph money order, the "order" is sent by telegraph to pay a certain sum of money to a certain person named in the telegram. When would a telegraph money order be used? Why?

636,500

MONEY ORDERS

Postal and Express Money Orders

The fees charged for postal or express money orders are the same. They are as follows:

For	$2.50 or less	6¢	$20.01 to $40.00	15¢
	$2.51 to $5.00	8¢	$40.01 to $60.00	18¢
	$5.01 to $10.00	11¢	$60.01 to $80.00	20¢
	$10.01 to $20.00	13¢	$80.01 to $100.00	22¢

The largest amount for which a single *postal money order* may be issued is $100. For amounts over $100 more than one money order is required. More than one endorsement on a postal money order is prohibited by law, except the endorsement of banks.

Express money orders may be endorsed any number of times in the same manner as checks. The largest amount for which a single express money order may be issued is $50. If one wishes to purchase an express money order for more than $50, he must buy more than one order. Thus, for an express money order for $70, one would buy a $50 money order and a $20 money order and not two money orders for $35 each. The combined price of the two money orders (if made payable to the same person) would be the same as the price for a single postal money order for $70. How much would that be?

Problems

Find the cost of money orders as follows:

Express Money Orders	*Postal Money Orders*
1. $14.25	**6.** $19.72
2. $27.50	**7.** $34.60
3. $38.90	**8.** $72.40
4. $65.80	**9.** $88.75
5. $79.70	**10.** $98.90

Telegraph Money Orders

The cost of a *telegraph money order* consists of three parts, as follows:

1. A toll charge, which is the regular charge for a fifteen word telegram.
2. A transfer charge as follows:

For $25 or less	$.25
Over $25 and not over $50	$.35
Over $50 and not over $75	$.60
Over $75 and not over $100	$.85

After the first $100, up to and including $3000, add $.25 for each $100 or fraction thereof. For amounts above $3000, add $.20 for each $100 or fraction thereof.

3. A Federal tax as follows:

$.01 on a toll charge not exceeding $.29
$.02 on a toll charge from $.30 to $.49 inclusive.
$.03 on a toll charge from $.50 to $.69 inclusive.
$.04 on a toll charge from $.70 to $.89 inclusive.
$.05 on a toll charge from $.90 to $1.09 inclusive.

And so on, adding $.01 to the tax for each additional $.20, or fraction thereof, in the toll charge. The tax is equivalent to 5% of the toll charge.

The toll charges for sending telegrams vary according to distance and the number of words in the telegram. There is a fixed charge for 10 words or less for each of the several zones or districts into which the country is divided. For each word in excess of 10 words there is an additional charge. In the following schedule of rates, the first number is the toll charge for 10 words or less, and the second number is the charge in cents for each additional word.

Toll Charges * on Telegrams

30–2.5	36–2.5	42–2.5	48–3.5	60–3.5	72–5	90–6	120–8.5

* In addition to the rates mentioned above, there is a local rate applicable to New York City only. For telegrams within a single borough, except Manhattan and the Bronx, which are treated like a single borough for the purpose of the toll charge, the rate is 20–1. Telegrams from one borough to another (except Manhattan and the Bronx, where the rate is 20–1) are charged for at the rate of 30–2.5.

Illustration. H. M. Manion, Pittsburgh, Pa., sends a telegraph money order to Lester Behrens, Louisville, Ky. The amount of the order is $150, with the following message, "Received in good condition your shipment of the twentieth." The check word is "Success." Find the cost of sending the order with the message.

a. How does the telegraph agent in Louisville know he is paying the money to the right person?

b. What word must Lester Behrens give to identify himself?

c. If the toll charge is 42–2.5, how much did it cost to send the telegraph money order?

Note. The charge for the "Message to be delivered with the money" is calculated at the extra word rate ($.02½ per word in this case).

The cost of sending the telegraph money order with message is reckoned as follows:

1. Toll charge for 15 words at 42–2.5	$ .55
2. Toll charge for 9-word message at $.02½	.23
3. Transfer charge for $125	1.10
4. Tax on the toll charge	.04
Total charge	$1.92

Problems

Find the cost of sending telegraph money orders as follows:

1. $250 to a zone where the charge for a 10-word message is $.30.

2. $750 and a 12-word message to a zone where the charge for a 10-word message is $.60.

3. $1000 to a zone where the charge for a 10-word message is $.90.

4. $2500 and a 16-word message to a zone where the 10-word message costs $1.20.

5. $5000 to a zone where the charge for a 10-word message is $.48.

DRAFTS

Bank Drafts

A *bank draft* is essentially a check. The only difference is that a bank draft is drawn on a bank by *another bank* instead of by an individual. It is used in all respects like a check. A *bank draft* is purchased in the same way that an express money order is purchased. The purchaser pays to the bank the amount of the draft plus a small fee for the service.

It is advisable to have a bank draft made payable to the person purchasing it. The purchaser, who then becomes the payee, may endorse the draft to the person or firm to whom payment is to be made. This plan carries the evidence as to the person making payment. To make the draft payable to the person who is to receive it as payment of any bill might lead to difficulty, because the name of the payer is not on the draft. It opens the door to errors in making the records on the books of the person receiving the draft.

NATIONAL BANK 88-124
Houston, Texas

Sept. 8, 19— NO. 4875

PAY TO THE ORDER OF George Hamlin $180.00

One Hundred Eighty $\frac{00}{100}$ DOLLARS

TO COMMERCIAL BANK 1-76
New York, N.Y.

John Doe
CASHIER

BANK DRAFT

In the form of a bank draft shown above, which bank is the drawer bank? The drawee bank?

To whom is the draft made payable?

If the payee is the person who bought the draft why should he have the draft made payable to himself? What must he do to use the draft to pay some other person the amount stated in the draft?

A cashier's check is a check drawn by the cashier of a bank on his own bank. For all practical purposes it is a bank draft except that it is drawn on the cashier's own bank instead of on some other bank.

The suggestions with respect to making the check payable to the purchaser of the check, which were made regarding the bank draft apply to the cashier's check.

Commercial Drafts

A commercial draft is an order by one person or firm directing another person or firm to pay a certain sum of money to a designated payee, either at sight or at some determinable future date. It may be used to request payment of a debt that is due, or to collect a debt that is past due.

$150.00 **Denver, Colo.,** July 8, **19—**

~~~~At sight~~~~ **Pay to the order of**

~~~~Myself~~~~

One hundred fifty $\frac{00}{100}$ ~~~~ **Dollars**

Value received, and charge to the account of

To L. O. McIntyre,
Des Moines, Ia. A. E. Bader

SIGHT DRAFT

1. In the sight draft illustrated above, who is the drawer? the payee? the drawee?

2. In what city does the drawer live? the drawee?

3. When is the draft payable?

4. What is the meaning of "At sight"?

5. How does Bader collect the amount of the draft from McIntyre?

The usual procedure followed in collecting the amount due by means of a commercial draft, is as follows: The payee endorses the draft to his bank for collection. The payee's bank will then send the draft to a bank in the drawee's home city or town, who will, in turn, collect the amount from the drawee, and return the amount of the draft, less a small fee for collecting it, to the payee's bank. The payee's bank then notifies the payee that his account has been credited with the proceeds of the draft.

When a draft is made payable "at sight" as in the illustration, it means that the draft is to be paid as soon as it is presented to the drawee. The draft drawn "at sight" is called **a sight draft.**

The commercial draft may be made payable at some future date in which case it is called a **time draft.**

$450.00 **Little Rock, Ark.,** November 5, **19—**

At sixty days sight **Pay to the order of**

Myself

Four hundred fifty $\frac{00}{100}$ **Dollars**

Value received, and charge to the account of

To Henry Bates
Dallas, Texas

G. F. Hempstead

Accepted Nov. 10, 19— Henry Bates

TIME DRAFT (days after sight)

$1200.00 **Knoxville, Tenn.,** November 5, **19—**

Sixty days after date **Pay to the order of**

Myself

Twelve hundred $\frac{00}{100}$ **Dollars**

Value received, and charge to the account of

To D. B. Carson
Joliet, Ill.

S. B. Karpen

Accepted Nov. 11, 19— D. B. Carson

TIME DRAFT (days after date)

Study the two drafts on page 141 and note how they differ.

1. What is the date of each draft?

2. How is the time expressed on the first draft? on the second one?

3. When is the first draft due?

4. When is the second draft due?

5. At what date do the sixty days begin to run in the first draft? in the second one?

The draft drawn "Sixty days after date" does not require acceptance as the date of payment is fixed. It is advisable, however, to have it accepted so the payee may know if it will be paid at maturity. The draft drawn "At sixty days sight" requires acceptance to fix the date of maturity. The acceptance must be dated because the *acceptance date* is the date from which the sixty days begin to run.

The drawee of a draft is under no obligation to accept a draft if he chooses not to do so. But once he has accepted a draft, he is obligated to pay it just the same as if he had written a promissory note.

Acceptance consists in the drawee writing across the face of the draft the word "Accepted" and signing his name. The acceptance of a draft drawn a given number of days after sight must be dated.

The **trade acceptance** is a two party draft used exclusively by the seller of merchandise to draw on the buyer for the

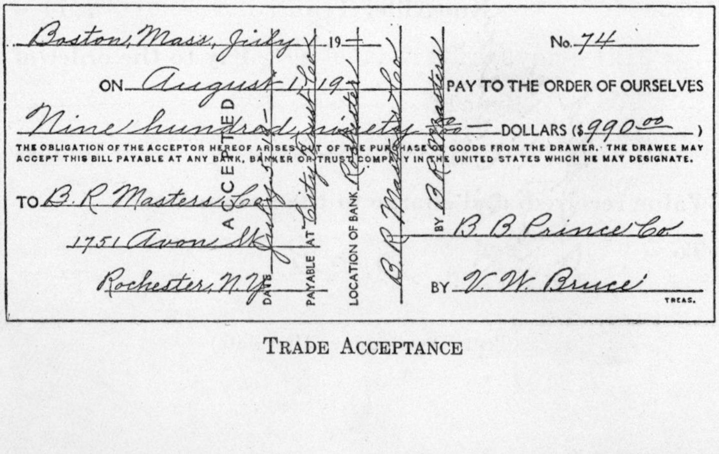

Boston, Mass., July 1 19— No. 74

ON August 1, 19— PAY TO THE ORDER OF OURSELVES

Nine hundred ninety 00/100 DOLLARS ($990.00)

THE OBLIGATION OF THE ACCEPTOR HEREOF ARISES OUT OF THE PURCHASE OF GOODS FROM THE DRAWER. THE DRAWEE MAY ACCEPT THIS BILL PAYABLE AT ANY BANK, BANKER OR TRUST COMPANY IN THE UNITED STATES WHICH HE MAY DESIGNATE.

TO B. R. Masters Co.
1751 Avon St.
Rochester, N.Y.

ACCEPTED
DATE July 1, 19—
PAYABLE AT City Trust Co.
LOCATION OF BANK Rochester
B. R. Masters Co.
BY B. R. Masters

BY B. B. Prince Co.
BY V. W. Bruce TREAS.

TRADE ACCEPTANCE

amount of a sale. In many kinds of business it is customary to allow 30, 60, or 90 days credit to the buyer. The *trade acceptance* serves both buyer and seller in the following ways:

1. The buyer may have 30, 60, or 90 days in which to pay for the goods he has purchased.

2. The seller may discount the accepted trade acceptance at his bank and thus have the money for the goods he has sold, without waiting till the term of credit has expired.

One point of difference between the trade acceptance and the commercial draft is, that the *trade acceptance* is usually sent to the buyer for his acceptance at the time of the sale, while the *commercial draft* is sent later, or at the time payment is due.

In the trade acceptance, note that the date of payment is written on the face of the acceptance, rather than indicating the number of days after the date of the paper to fix the date of maturity.

Problems

Find the total cost of paying each of the following bills by postal money orders:

1. $25.75	**3.** $52.40	**5.** $78.90
2. $38.50	**4.** $61.50	**6.** $125

State the number of express money orders required, and the total cost of the money orders for paying each of the following bills:

7. $59.80	**9.** $52.34	**11.** $111.54
8. $63.70	**10.** $68.72	**12.** $175.60

13. A traveling salesman telegraphed his firm asking for immediate transfer to him of $275. His firm sent him a telegraph money order for the amount. If the regular charge of a 10-word telegram was $.72, find the cost of the money order.

14. A buying agent, to take advantage of a cash offer for a quantity of desired merchandise, asked his firm for $2750, which was sent to him by telegraph money order. How much was the transfer charge?

Using the charges (page 137) made for sending telegraph money orders, find the total cost of sending each of the orders in Problems 15–20.

	Amount of M. O.	Toll Charge 10 Words		Amount of M. O.	Toll Charge 10 Words
15.	$325	36	**18.**	$1500	60
16.	$50	48	**19.**	$3200	120
17.	$75	72	**20.**	$5000	90

21. A. M. Postman of Buffalo, Minn., owes P. R. Rogers of Cleveland, Ohio, $750 due May 14. P. R. Rogers draws a thirty-day draft, dated April 14, on A. M. Postman, in favor of himself, for the amount of his debt to him.

(*a*) Write the draft.

(*b*) Name the parties to the draft.

(*c*) State the steps followed in making collection of the draft.

Traveler's Checks

Another way in which people may make use of the principles underlying the subject of exchange is in the use of **traveler's checks.**

Comparatively few people are well enough known by the public at large to make it safe for banks or business men to accept their checks when they are traveling in parts of the country far distant from home.

A person traveling in different parts of the country does not wish to carry large sums of money with him. Since he may not readily have his personal checks cashed when he needs money, he buys from his home bank, or from the American Express Company, traveler's checks.

Traveler's checks may be bought from a bank or the American Express Company in amounts of $10, $25, $50, or $100, by paying to the bank or Express Company, the amount of the orders desired, plus a small fee for the service (generally $\frac{3}{4}$% of the face value of the checks issued). The purchaser writes

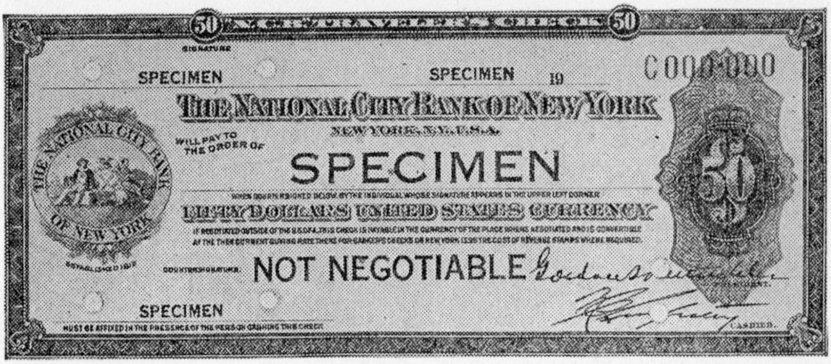

A TRAVELER'S CHECK

his name on the traveler's check at the time he buys it. When wishing to receive cash for it, he is required to sign his name again on the check. If the two signatures are alike, the traveler's check is readily accepted and cashed.

Certified Check

The drawer or the holder of a personal check may request an officer of the bank on which the check is drawn to *certify* that the bank will be liable for payment when the check is properly endorsed. The officer writes *Certified* or *Good* across the face of the check and signs his name thereto. A certified check has better credit status, therefore, than an ordinary personal check, because the certification assures the holder that the bank is retaining sufficient of the drawer's money to cover the amount of the check.

Problems

Find the cost of traveler's checks as follows, if $\frac{3}{4}\%$ is charged for issuing them.

1. Five \$50 checks. **2.** Twenty \$25 checks.

3. Twelve \$50 checks. **4.** Four \$100 checks.

5. Three \$25 checks and six \$50 checks.

6. Five \$25 checks, four \$50 checks, and three \$100 checks.

7. Four \$100 checks, five \$50 checks, and eight \$25 checks.

8. Eight \$25 checks, ten \$50 checks, and ten \$100 checks.

RECONCILING BANK BALANCES

In business most cash payments are made by check. Individuals also frequently pay their bills by checks. Some of these checks are sent to distant cities, and often a week or a longer period of time elapses before the checks are returned to the depositor's bank and charged to his account. As a result, the balance of cash in the bank rarely agrees with the balance shown in the depositor's checkbook or cashbook. For the sake of detecting possible errors, it is important that the depositor's record, kept on the stub of his checkbook or in his cashbook be compared frequently with the record kept by the bank.

The bank furnishes a *statement* of the depositor's account monthly or on request. The statement shows the balance at the last report, the deposits made, the checks drawn and presented to the bank for payment, and the balance of the account at the time the statement is made. It includes also a record of charges and credits made by the bank for interest and services rendered by the bank.

If certain checks sent by mail to customers have not been returned to the bank when the statement is prepared, the balance reported by the bank will be greater than the balance shown in the depositor's checkbook or cashbook. The bank returns all canceled checks with the statement. Hence the depositor can tell which checks have not been cashed.

Comparing the bank statement with the checkbook record, making allowances for checks not yet returned to the bank and for other items, is called **reconciling the bank balance.**

Illustration. Your bank statement shows a balance of $1728.92 to your credit. By comparing the returned checks with the stubs in your checkbook, you find that three checks have not been returned. They are #596 for $128.70, #598 for

$72.60, and #599 for $250. The checkbook balance is $1277.62. Reconcile the account.

Bank's balance			**$1728.92**
Outstanding checks:	**#596**	**$128.70**	
	#598	**72.60**	
	#599	**250.00**	**451.30**
Checkbook balance			**$1277.62**

Bank's Balance − Outstanding Checks = Checkbook Balance
Checkbook Balance + Outstanding Checks = Bank's Balance

Interest and Service Charges

Illustration. On April 15, Fred Blakely's checkbook balance was $1367.49. His bank statement dated the same day showed a balance of $1150.45. The following checks had not been returned to the bank: $8.25, $28.50, $16.17. The bank statement contained the following items which had not been recorded in the checkbook: a check of $6.40, an item of $1 for a service performed by the bank, and an interest charge of $3.56 on a demand note held against Mr. Blakely. One check of $250 which had been deposited was returned marked "no funds," and was charged against the account. Another check for $165 had been entered on the check stub as $156. Reconcile the balances.

Bank balance is				**$1150.45**
Outstanding checks:	**$8.25**			
	28.50			
	16.17			**52.92**
Adjusted bank balance				**$1097.53**
The checkbook shows			**$1367.49**	
Deduct:	**Check omitted**	**$6.40**		
	Service charge	**1.00**		
	Interest charge	**3.56**		
	Error on stub	**9.00**		
	Returned check	**250.00**	**269.96**	
Adjusted checkbook balance				**$1097.53**

Problems

Set up reconciliation statements for each of the following:

1. The bank statement shows a balance of $2391.64. Checks not returned: #401 for $75, #403 for $101.60, #404 for $4.80, #405 for $1.25, and #406 for $17.66. The checkbook shows a balance of $2191.33.

2. Your checkbook shows a balance of $328.72. Your bank reports a balance of $417.95. Three checks have not yet been returned: #76 for $42.31, #78 for $22.85, and #79 for $28.75. In the bank statement you find that an interest item of $4.68 charged on a demand loan has not been entered in the checkbook.

3. Your balance at the beginning of the month was $476.34. During the month you deposited $634.56, $421.30, and $117.80 and drew checks amounting to $978.76. When you receive your bank statement, you find that four of your checks have not been returned. They are #212 for $75.60, #213 for $25.50, #214 for $102.69, and #216 for $15.20. The bank has given you a credit of $224.44 for cash received on a note you asked them to collect for you. This item has not been entered in the checkbook. The bank reports your balance as $1114.67.

4. On January 2, William Clark received from the bank his monthly bank statement, showing the bank's balance to be $3961.70. On comparing the report with the checks issued, it was found that the following checks had not been returned: $207.06, $58.23, and $437.10. The following items had not been recorded in the checkbook, but had been paid at the bank: $25, $30, and a note for $125.50. What balance should Clark's checkbook show?

5. On June 1, M. E. Delmar received his bank statement. His checkbook balance is $1242.09. The following checks had not been returned to the bank: $40.20, $125.68, $75.50, and $286.90. Mr. Delmar had neglected to enter on the checkbook stub the amount of one check for $50.60. He had also made an error by writing on the stub of one check $78.90 when it should have been entered at $87.90. What is the bank's balance? Prepare a reconciliation statement.

6. According to the monthly bank statement C. M. Rader's bank balance on October 31 was $2176.15. His checkbook balance

was $1838.14 on the same date. By checking off the returned checks he found the following checks still outstanding: $215.20, $186.06, and $62.25. One check which Mr. Rader had deposited had been returned marked "no funds," and had been charged to his account, but no record of this charge had been made on his checkbook. What was the amount of the bad check? Reconcile the accounts.

7. Brady and Company's Daily Cash Report for June 14 was as follows:

DAILY CASH REPORT. JUNE 14, 19—

	PETTY CASH	CASH DRAWER	BANK	BALANCE ON HAND
Balances, June 13	$23.71	$317.86	$4468.90	$4810.47
Receipts		1482.74		1482.74
	23.71	1800.60		6293.21
Deposits		1560.97	1560.97	
		239.63	6029.87	
Payments	10.00		1742.27	1752.27
Balances, June 14	$13.71	$239.63	$4287.60	$4540.94

On June 15 receipts and payments were as follows: Receipts, $1194.87; payments by check, $919.38; petty cash payments, $4.75; deposited in the bank, $1208.50. Prepare the daily cash report.

On June 16 Brady and Company's cashbook showed the following: *Receipts:* $1697.90; proceeds of a note collected by the bank, $575; fee for collecting, $1.50. *Payments:* By check, $767.50; by petty cash, $11.80. A deposit of $1650 was made and a check of $25 was drawn and cashed to replenish the petty cash fund. Prepare the daily cash report.

8. At the close of business on May 1, Adams and Company's daily cash report showed the following balances: Petty cash $17.92; cash drawer, $196.13; bank, $3984.72; balance, $4198.77. On May 2, the following cash transactions were recorded: Receipts at the office, $1721.43, and at the bank, $239.40. A deposit of $1750 was made in the bank. Checks were drawn as follows: For the payment of bills, $2264.80, and for the petty cash fund, $30. Payments from the petty cash fund were $37.98. Prepare a daily cash report, using the form shown above.

FUNDAMENTAL PROCESSES

The exercises in this section consist of additional drills in the fundamental processes of arithmetic — *addition, subtraction, multiplication,* and *division.* These processes are also called "fundamental operations" because one or more of these processes are used in solving every arithmetical problem. These processes, therefore, should be readily performed. Thus, in the solution of a problem in interest, the pupil should devote his attention almost wholly to the principles of interest and use the processes of addition, subtraction, multiplication, or division automatically with precision and speed. He should not hesitate or "fumble" over the fundamental operations. He should likewise be facile in counting time and in employing aliquot parts in solving a great variety of problems.

Some pupils may not need these drills, but most pupils are deficient in the skillful use of the fundamentals and need constant drill in them. The exercises are provided for those who need them.

ADDITION

Addition is the most commonly used and, therefore, the most important fundamental operation. Much practice is required in being able to read sums without hesitation.

A. Read at sight the sums of the following pairs of single digits. Time yourself and keep a record of the time required to give the sums.

	a	*b*	*c*	*d*	*e*	*f*	*g*	*h*	*i*	*j*	*k*	*l*
1.	4	8	6	9	4	7	6	8	9	7	5	8
	7	7	3	2	8	8	9	6	8	6	5	5
2.	9	9	6	8	5	5	8	6	9	8	7	5
	9	7	7	4	7	8	3	8	6	2	9	6
3.	1	5	3	7	6	7	8	9	8	4	7	2
	6	4	9	3	6	7	9	5	8	6	5	8

B. The digits in *A* are repeated in this exercise with the digit **1** in tens' place in the upper addend.

Read at sight the sums of the following, comparing the time required with the time taken on exercise *A*:

	a	*b*	*c*	*d*	*e*	*f*	*g*	*h*	*i*	*j*	*k*	*l*
4.	14	18	16	19	14	17	16	18	19	17	15	18
	7	7	3	2	8	8	9	6	8	6	5	5
5.	19	19	16	18	15	15	18	16	19	18	17	15
	9	7	7	4	7	8	3	8	6	2	9	6
6.	11	15	13	17	16	17	18	19	18	14	17	12
	6	4	9	3	6	7	9	5	8	6	5	8

C. In *C* the digits found in *A* and *B* are arranged in a different order with the digit **2** in tens' place in the upper addend.

Read without hesitation the sums of the following pairs of numbers, comparing the time required with the time taken on exercises *A* and *B*:

	a	*b*	*c*	*d*	*e*	*f*	*g*	*h*	*i*	*j*	*k*	*l*
7.	28	29	27	28	27	28	24	28	26	29	25	26
	7	2	8	6	6	5	7	4	6	5	8	3
8.	29	26	25	28	29	27	25	27	27	24	22	29
	9	7	7	3	6	9	4	3	7	6	8	8
9.	29	24	25	26	28	25	21	23	26	28	28	27
	7	8	5	9	2	6	6	9	8	9	8	5

D. The digits in *D* are arranged in miscellaneous order.

State the sums of the following, noting the time required:

10.	9	28	36	44	37	29	23	34	41	48	47	56
	7	6	9	8	6	8	7	7	9	5	8	9

11.	54	62	57	53	27	32	64	56	43	72	86	67
	7	8	8	9	8	9	9	7	8	8	9	8

12.	39	43	69	18	9	8	29	31	18	29	26	57
	7	8	7	7	9	7	8	8	9	9	5	9

E. Adding groups of digits.

To acquire ability to add by groups of digits, practice on exercises like the following. Begin by adding the sum of two digits to one digit and later add the sum of two digits to the sum of two or more digits.

6	7
4	5
8	9
18	21

In the first group at the left, adding from the top, think, "10, 18," *not* "6, 10, 18." The sum of 6 and 4 should be recognized instantly and the 8 added to it.

In the second group, think "12, 21," *not* "7, 12, 21."

Practice is the road to success.

Read without hesitation the sums of the following:

	a	*b*	*c*	*d*	*e*	*f*	*g*	*h*	*i*	*j*	*k*	*l*
13.	7	6	2	4	9	5	6	8	9	8	7	9
	3	4	8	6	1	5	6	7	4	8	8	9
	4	5	9	7	9	8	4	3	5	6	5	2

	a	*b*	*c*	*d*	*e*	*f*	*g*	*h*	*i*	*j*	*k*	*l*
14.	4	6	9	8	9	7	6	5	6	8	9	8
	5	7	6	5	3	7	8	6	9	7	4	9
	6	8	4	4	7	4	7	9	4	6	7	2

	a	*b*	*c*	*d*	*e*	*f*	*g*	*h*	*i*	*j*	*k*	*l*
15.	6	3	7	8	6	7	8	9	1	6	8	8
	9	7	8	4	6	1	2	1	9	7	8	7
	7	8	5	7	7	7	8	8	9	1	1	1

	a	*b*	*c*	*d*	*e*	*f*	*g*	*h*	*i*	*j*	*k*
16.	32	46	28	32	23	37	43	28	56	70	65
	5	7	6	5	6	4	7	7	8	9	7
	1	1	3	4	2	3	3	2	4	6	4

	a	*b*	*c*	*d*	*e*	*f*	*g*	*h*	*i*	*j*	*k*
17.	37	47	21	33	41	39	62	74	19	22	92
	9	8	8	9	8	8	5	6	8	3	7
	3	3	7	6	6	3	7	6	4	8	6

Apply the grouping idea in adding the following columns:

18.	**19.**	**20.**	**21.**	**22.**
$12.75	$17.21	$5.38	$7.26	$1.47
6.84	5.94	12.96	8.34	.53
9.31	32.67	13.27	54.58	12.93
.86	15.82	1.51	22.64	17.27
11.54	8.37	.88	83.26	8.68
7.08	.68	12.84	1.84	2.42

23.	**24.**	**25.**	**26.**	**27.**
$31.45	$36.78	$56.01	$53.75	$1.56
45.60	15.45	9.08	4.59	34.57
7.52	9.58	134.63	347.54	99.89
958.02	87.64	78.61	96.59	101.03
70.13	9.06	78.57	157.04	34.58

CHECKING ADDITION

The following are two very important habits if you wish to do good work in arithmetic:

1. *Be neat.* Make neat figures, placing them in straight vertical columns.

2. *Be accurate.* A correct result obtained in two and one half minutes is better than a wrong result obtained in one and one half minutes. An incorrect calculation is worthless. Checking the work is as much a part of the work in arithmetic as the actual working of the exercise.

Method #1. The best check for addition is to add the columns in the reverse direction. If you first add from the bottom up, check by adding from the top down.

Method #2. Another good check is to add the several columns of digits separately, without carrying, and writing the totals as illustrated. Then add the several totals.

Illustration

```
 476
 834
 957
 682
 ---
  19
 23
27
----
2949
```

Method #3. The accuracy of the work in addition may be checked by **casting out nines.**

Illustration

147	= 12	= 3		
229	= 13	= 4		
331	= 7	= 7		
707	= 14	= 14		
		5	= 5	

The sum of the digits 1, 4, and 7 is 12, equal to one 9 and 3 over. The sum of the digits in the second addend is 13, equal to one 9 and 4 over; and the sum in the third addend is 7, equal to no 9's and 7 over. The sum of the several remainders, 3, 4, and 7, is 14, equal to one 9 and 5 over. The sum of the digits in the sum, 707, is 14, equal to one 9 and 5 over. Hence the addition is probably correct.

NOTES. (1) The digits of 147 are the numbers 1, 4, and 7.

(2) The remainders 3, 4, 7, and 5 are the sums of the digits in 12, 13, 7, and 14, respectively. 12 is equal to one 9 with a remainder of 3. The division is unnecessary, however, as the excess (remainder) can always be found by adding the digits.

(3) The remainders 3, 4, and 7 are generally called the "excess of nines," and the principle is stated thus: "The excess of nines in a sum is equal to the excess in the sum of the excesses."

(4) Casting out nines is not an absolute test of accuracy. Transposition of figures cannot be detected by this check, nor can the omission or addition of 9's or ciphers be discovered.

Method #4. Casting out elevens will detect errors not located by the *nine check.*

Illustration

475	= 2
382	= 8
479	= 6
1336	= 5

Find the sum of the digits in the odd places (beginning at units) and from it deduct the sum of the digits in the even places. If the sum of the digits in the even places exceeds the sum of those in the odd places, add 11, or some multiple of 11, to the sum of the digits in the odd places.

Thus,

$$\left.\begin{array}{l} 5 + 4 - 7 = 2 \\ 2 + 3 + 11 - 8 = 8 \\ 9 + 4 - 7 = 6 \\ \hline 6 + 3 - 3 - 1 = 5 \end{array}\right\} \begin{array}{l} 6 + 8 + 2 = 16; \\ 16 = \text{one 11 and 5 over.} \end{array}$$

2, 8, and 6 are called the "excess of elevens" of the several addends. The sum of the excesses is 16, equal to one 11 and 5 over. The excess of elevens in the sum, 1336, is 5, as shown in the illustration. Since the excess of elevens in the sum of the excesses equals the excess of elevens in the sum of the numbers, the addition is considered correct.

CUMULATIVE DRILLS

Experience has shown that the following drill is one of the very best devices for developing skill in addition. It is excellent for encouraging competition among the members of the class.

1. Write any two numbers, as (1) and (2) in the column at the right.
2. Below (2) write (3), the sum of (1) and (2).
3. Below (3) write (4), the sum of (2) and (3).
4. Continue in this way, adding only the last two numbers each time, until you have a column of ten numbers.
5. Draw a line and find the sum of the entire column.

(1)	47865
(2)	93276
(3)	141141
(4)	234417
(5)	375558
(6)	609975
(7)	985533
(8)	1595508
(9)	2581041
(10)	4176549
	10840863

In adding the entire column, put into practice the suggestion made about adding groups of figures, naming only the results. For example, in adding the first column of digits from the bottom up, the sum of the first three digits, 9, 1, and 8, should be recognized at once as 18; the sum of the next two digits, 5 and 3, should be thought of as 8 and added to 18, giving 26, and so on.

That is, in adding the first column, think "18, 26, 41, 53."

The carrying figure, 5, should be combined with the first two digits of the next column, 4 and 4, and the result, 13, should be the first number thought of in adding this column.

This plan provides the necessary drill on two-figure combinations and also furnishes practice in adding columns of numbers. With practice, the entire column should be written and added in one and one half minutes.

By writing the first two numbers of one or more drills on the blackboard, before the pupils enter the room, this exercise may be worked while the attendance is being recorded, or while other class duties are performed.

Problems

Using each of these groups as the first two numbers of your column, write and add according to the instructions on page 155. Check results by Method #1.

1. 59286	**2.** 67843	**3.** 59476	**4.** 94872
37452	82179	87218	99765
5. 89109	**6.** 45179	**7.** 31497	**8.** 74198
92458	97876	79503	98236

Check results by Method #2.

9. 63024	**10.** 24681	**11.** 76543	**12.** 38476
96357	35792	87654	91384

Check results of 13 to 20 by Method #3.

13. 47296	**14.** 54862	**15.** 48627	**16.** 52864
38249	76459	67439	91897
17. 48916	**18.** 59764	**19.** 76947	**20.** 98765
69841	39295	73829	56789

Check results of 21 to 28 by Method #4.

21. 51419	**22.** 42824	**23.** 82478	**24.** 98724
16171	63842	67129	99638
25. 52417	**26.** 32865	**27.** 14.25	**28.** 141
82689	4791	1.256	3.82

HORIZONTAL ADDITION

Many financial and statistical reports are set up in tabular form. For instance, a firm having six traveling salesmen desires to keep a record of their weekly sales not only for the purpose of knowing the amount of sales made each week by each man and by all the men, but also for the purpose of comparing the sales of one man with the sales of each of the other men. Having such a record the employer is able to tell which are his best salesmen and which of the men are not making good.

Problems

1. Assume the following weekly sales are reported by the six salesmen:

Salesmen	*1st Week*	*2d Week*	*3d Week*	*4th Week*	*Totals*
A	$725.50	$694.90	$850.75	$915.60	$???? ??
B	843.30	716.25	634.80	832.70	???? ??
C	541.65	413.20	516.35	272.80	???? ??
D	913.55	1142.68	928.64	1082.96	???? ??
E	839.95	784.67	848.75	916.34	???? ??
F	1124.63	734.98	916.88	879.85	???? ??
Totals	???? ??	???? ??	???? ??	???? ??	????? ??

By adding the columns vertically, the total weekly sales are shown, and one week's sales for all salesmen may readily be compared with the sales for any other week. By adding horizontally, the total of each man's sales for the four weeks is obtained.

Check the results by adding both sets of totals to get the grand total. If you are right, the two sets of totals will add to the same amount. Which salesman would you let go if one man is to be dismissed?

2. In the following exercises, add both vertically and horizontally, and then add the two sets of totals to get the grand total. Don't hurry, but try to be accurate. Speed will come with practice.

a	*b*	*c*
54 + 78 + 72 =	38 + 28 + 54 =	74 + 37 + 45 =
36 + 29 + 83 =	27 + 36 + 38 =	56 + 78 + 58 =
85 + 34 + 96 =	54 + 79 + 29 =	89 + 56 + 79 =
92 + 56 + 87 =	93 + 87 + 98 =	79 + 33 + 46 =
+ + =	+ + =	+ + =

d	*e*	*f*
382+592+848=	568+827+584=	382+916+538=
961+796+796=	729+968+763=	976+693+872=
729+816+382=	384+817+972=	438+821+279=
384+723+794=	754+927+475=	728+572+186=
+ + =	+ + =	+ + =

3. One week's sales in three departments of a large store. Give the horizontal, vertical and grand totals of the following:

Sales	Uniforms	Leggings	Caps	Totals
Monday	$1249.96	$28.75	$368.42	???? ??
Tuesday	1585.98	392.52	793.65	???? ??
Wednesday	1896.47	87.50	715.26	???? ??
Thursday	807.96	92.75	156.91	???? ??
Friday	1193.53	136.50	653.65	???? ??
Saturday	3168.49	148.25	876.52	???? ??
Totals	???? ??	??? ??	???? ??	????? ??

4. Find the total sales for each day, the total sales in each department for the week, and the grand total.

Sales	Dress Goods	Shoes	Notions	Totals
Monday	$87.68	$18.75	$16.83	??? ??
Tuesday	125.76	26.82	9.76	??? ??
Wednesday	235.67	76.85	23.82	??? ??
Thursday	89.62	89.75	48.98	??? ??
Friday	123.98	110.60	75.67	??? ??
Saturday	982.76	234.50	163.97	??? ??
Totals	???? ??	??? ??	??? ??	???? ??

5. Find the total monthly sales, the total departmental sales, and the grand total of sales for the six months.

Months	Books	Shoes	Millinery	Dry Goods	Totals
July . . .	$4653.90	$6543.87	$5346.75	$8235.53	????? ??
August . .	3253.76	4324.80	7636.65	9845.75	????? ??
September .	4324.45	7342.98	4898.90	7342.89	????? ??
October . .	8780.19	8756.65	3756.98	6547.87	????? ??
November .	3738.98	3655.45	8765.89	8453.00	????? ??
December .	7544.45	7298.90	9755.35	9879.00	????? ??
Totals . .	????? ??	????? ??	????? ??	????? ??	?????? ??

6. Find the total postal revenue for each day, the total weekly revenue for each class of service, and the total revenue for the week.

POSTAL REVENUE AT ONE POST OFFICE

DAYS	FIRST CLASS	SECOND CLASS	THIRD CLASS	PARCEL POST	SPECIAL DELIVERY	REGISTRY	INSURANCE	TOTALS
M.	$106.22	$23.15	$13.24	$43.41	$3.60	$4.50	$6.80	??? ??
T.	145.61	33.43	21.13	57.57	4.50	5.30	7.75	??? ??
W.	131.99	19.22	14.56	49.92	3.10	1.30	4.80	??? ??
Th.	201.13	31.52	22.10	28.88	4.70	3.90	1.50	??? ??
F.	187.67	20.78	31.57	65.72	7.70	7.50	2.50	??? ??
S.	149.78	31.56	43.44	38.48	4.80	6.50	3.45	??? ??
Totals	???? ??	??? ??	??? ??	??? ??	?? ??	?? ??	?? ??	???? ??

MAKING CHANGE

If a person buys an article for 57 cents and pays for it with a dollar, the clerk hands back change in the following order: **3** pennies, **1** nickel, **1** dime, and **1** quarter. As the coins are given in change, the cashier or the clerk says, "57, 60, 65, 75, $1."

Problems

Assume that you are a cashier making change for the following purchases. Name the amounts as you hand back the change.

	Amount Purchased	*Amount Paid*		*Amount Purchased*	*Amount Paid*
1.	$.37	$1.00	**6.**	$1.94	$5.00
2.	$.63	$1.00	**7.**	$2.09	$3.00
3.	$1.04	$1.25	**8.**	$3.16	$4.00
4.	$1.28	$2.00	**9.**	$4.81	$10.00
5.	$1.59	$2.00	**10.**	$11.13	$20.00

The ability to add numbers like 79 and 384 mentally is well worth acquiring. Skill in this type of exercise may be readily developed by practicing as follows: Think of 79 as 80 − 1. Now add 80 and 384, obtaining 464, and then subtract 1, which gives 463.

Problems

Practice on the following:

1. 59 + 276	**9.** 19 + 247	**17.** 28 + 576	**25.** 622 + 53
2. 39 + 152	**10.** 29 + 764	**18.** 38 + 317	**26.** 149 + 87
3. 89 + 384	**11.** 49 + 637	**19.** 88 + 432	**27.** 213 + 73
4. 79 + 564	**12.** 39 + 574	**20.** 58 + 149	**28.** 347 + 88
5. 69 + 922	**13.** 89 + 639	**21.** 334 + 101	**29.** 219 + 105
6. 29 + 394	**14.** 78 + 647	**22.** 375 + 105	**30.** 324 + 98
7. 39 + 476	**15.** 68 + 536	**23.** 413 + 97	**31.** 427 + 78
8. 99 + 247	**16.** 98 + 639	**24.** 521 + 37	**32.** 738 + 106

In adding any two numbers, as 147 and 324, it is advisable to add from left to right. Thus, think of 324 as 300 + 20 + 4. Then add 147 + 300 = 447; 447 + 20 = 467, and 467 + 4 = 471.

Practice will readily give proficiency in this type of mental addition. Using the illustration just shown, add mentally:

33. 123 + 234	**41.** 325 + 517	**49.** 314 + 145	**57.** 423 + 154
34. 216 + 372	**42.** 313 + 428	**50.** 178 + 781	**58.** 324 + 451
35. 321 + 134	**43.** 274 + 676	**51.** 219 + 227	**59.** 243 + 541
36. 516 + 276	**44.** 341 + 634	**52.** 347 + 264	**60.** 432 + 145
37. 721 + 234	**45.** 196 + 413	**53.** 816 + 129	**61.** 617 + 277
38. 543 + 684	**46.** 238 + 776	**54.** 547 + 324	**62.** 428 + 597
39. 117 + 276	**47.** 372 + 191	**55.** 638 + 176	**63.** 436 + 718
40. 196 + 243	**48.** 167 + 542	**56.** 572 + 321	**64.** 372 + 167

SUBTRACTION

The difference between any single-digit number and any two-digit number should be recognized instantly.

Problems

Subtract, reading the answers at sight:

	a	*b*	*c*	*d*	*e*	*f*	*g*	*h*	*i*	*j*	*k*
1.	27	36	47	46	29	33	42	64	56	32	46
	8	9	8	7	6	8	9	8	9	5	7
2.	28	32	23	37	43	29	56	37	46	33	47
	7	8	7	6	9	7	5	9	7	8	6
3.	52	44	53	67	72	52	43	87	67	35	43
	9	8	9	8	8	7	9	8	8	7	7
4.	43	63	47	38	28	70	65	37	76	81	75
	8	7	8	9	8	8	9	9	9	9	7

CHECKING SUBTRACTION

In subtraction the best check is to **add the remainder to the subtrahend**; the result should be the minuend. It is not necessary to rewrite the numbers, but add mentally the remainder to the subtrahend to see whether the sum equals the minuend.

Illustration. Add mentally 32,967 and 14,857. The sum should be 47,824 if the remainder 14,857 is correct.

47824	(minuend)
32967	(subtrahend)
14857	(remainder)

Problems

Subtract and check each result:

1. 98764	**2.** 76543	**3.** 74059	**4.** 67258
39725	64219	23568	47869
5. 32805	**6.** 48597	**7.** $432.75	**8.** $29.81
18796	37948	96.84	9.98
9. $109.16	**10.** $200.50	**11.** $5.87	**12.** $101.62
87.28	47.85	4.93	9.08

13. 98764 49787	**14.** 70596 38298	**15.** 83207 45708	**16.** 59005 39508
17. 62090 43799	**18.** 74876 32986	**19.** 50906 31927	**20.** 54078 32969
21. 52678 21985	**22.** 95484 48459	**23.** 72090 45689	**24.** 26300 17624
25. $592.60 17.88	**26.** $47.85 9.37	**27.** $859.65 721.08	**28.** $932.81 78.64

MULTIPLICATION

Multiplication is a short method of adding numbers.

Illustration. If a man receives $175 a month, how much does he get in a year?

Instead of writing $175 twelve times in a column and adding, you can get the result in a much shorter way by multiplying $175 by 12.

Problems

Give the products orally:

	a	*b*	*c*	*d*	*e*	*f*	*g*	*h*	*i*	*j*	*k*	*l*
1.	5 8	6 7	9 4	7 6	8 7	6 9	4 7	6 8	3 9	9 5	7 4	8 9
2.	9 9	6 3	5 7	4 4	5 4	2 9	3 7	6 5	8 6	8 8	9 8	7 7
3.	4 8	8 4	5 5	7 5	2 8	4 9	5 9	9 7	6 6	7 8	5 3	7 9

Write the products on a separate sheet of paper:

4. 72864 5	**5.** 38297 6	**6.** 40782 8	**7.** 57976 7

8. 84297	9. 62785	10. 52547	11. 38926
4	9	8	3
12. 45176	13. 78219	14. 85109	15. 72469
7	2	9	6

MULTIPLYING BY 10, 100, AND 1000

To multiply an integer (a whole number) by 10, 100, 1000, etc., annex as many zeros as there are zeros in the multiplier.

To multiply a decimal by 10, 100, 1000, etc., move the decimal point in the number as many places to the right as there are zeros in the multiplier. Thus:

$10 \times 572 = 5720$	$10 \times 57.2 = 572$
$100 \times .026 = 2.6$	$100 \times 2.6 = 260$
$1000 \times 38.75 = 38{,}750$	$1000 \times .3875 = 387.5$

Observe the following:

a. The decimal point is not shown when writing an integer.

b. The position of the decimal point is at the right of units' place.

c. To "move" the decimal point to the right of an integer, zeros must be used to indicate the number of places the point is moved.

Multiply:

1. 100×54.3	**6.** 10×4285
2. 10×3.76	**7.** 100×9.4786
3. 1000×52.47	**8.** 1000×7.5625
4. $10000 \times .4275$	**9.** $100000 \times .0275$
5. $100 \times .003$	**10.** $1000 \times .03$

Multiplying by a Number Beginning or Ending with 1

When multiplying by a number beginning or ending with 1, as 17, 19, 41, 61, etc., place the multiplier to one side, instead of under the multiplicand.

Illustration. (*a*) Multiply 3978 by 61.

Write the work as shown at the right.
This plan saves multiplying through by 1.

3978	*61*
23868	
242658	

Illustration. (*b*) Multiply 5843 by 17.

Write the work as shown at the right.
Place the figures of the partial product obtained by multiplying by 7 one place to the right.

5843	*17*
40901	
99331	

Problems

Apply the plan in (*a*) and (*b*) to the following examples:

1. 13 × 3894	**7.** 16 × 5417	**13.** 16 × 4726
2. 14 × 7472	**8.** 61 × 8321	**14.** 19 × 3817
3. 18 × 9683	**9.** 41 × 7285	**15.** 17 × 8426
4. 31 × 9847	**10.** 71 × 3286	**16.** 41 × 3821
5. 51 × 5768	**11.** 91 × 5409	**17.** 51 × 4197
6. 71 × 8432	**12.** 21 × 9296	**18.** 61 × 8627

DIVISION

The purpose of the fundamental process called division is: (1) to find how many times one number will contain another number of the same kind; (2) to divide a number into equal parts.

The mechanical operation of division is not difficult to perform, but failure to make the *process* of division function correctly in solving problems is frequently the cause of wrong answers or conclusions. It is important that the quotient be labeled correctly as well as made mathematically correct.

There are four terms that must be considered in dealing with division — *dividend, divisor, quotient,* and *remainder.*

The dividend is the number to be divided.

a. The *dividend* may be either an *abstract* or a *concrete number.* That is, 2 (abstract) or $2 (concrete).

The **divisor** is the number by which the dividend is divided.

a. The *divisor* must be an *abstract number* if the *dividend is abstract.* That is, 10 ÷ 5 = 2. Since the dividend **10** is abstract, the divisor **5** must be abstract.

b. The *divisor* may be either *abstract* or *concrete* if the *dividend* is *concrete;* but, if the *divisor* is *concrete,* it must be the same kind as the *dividend.* That is, $10 ÷ $5 = 2.

The **quotient** is the result obtained by dividing the dividend by the divisor.

a. The *quotient* is *abstract* when the *dividend* and *divisor* are alike. That is, 18 ft. ÷ 3 ft. = 6.

In this case the quotient **6** shows how many times 18 feet contain 3 feet.

b. The *quotient* is like the *dividend* if the *divisor* is *abstract.* That is, 18 ft. ÷ 6 = 3 ft.

The **remainder** is the part of the dividend remaining after dividing the dividend into an integral number of equal parts.

a. The *remainder* is like the *dividend.*

Problems

State the quotients in full:

	a	*b*	*c*
1.	$56 ÷ $8	$72 ÷ $8	48 ÷ 12
2.	$64 ÷ 8	$63 ÷ 9	72 ÷ 9
3.	$63 ÷ $7	$42 ÷ $7	$72 ÷ 12
4.	$42 ÷ $6	$36 ÷ $9	$84 ÷ 7
5.	$48 ÷ $8	$36 ÷ 6	$88 ÷ 11
6.	$54 ÷ 9	$35 ÷ $7	96 ÷ 12
7.	$49 ÷ $7	$32 ÷ $8	$120 ÷ 10
8.	$45 ÷ $9	$40 ÷ 12	$144 ÷ 12
9.	$42 ÷ 3	$44 ÷ $4	$75 ÷ 5
10.	$35 ÷ $5	$52 ÷ $4	$86 ÷ 12
11.	$55 ÷ $11	$62 ÷ $2	$76 ÷ 4

CHECKING DIVISION

Long Division involves three distinct operations — *division, multiplication,* and *subtraction.* This is one reason for its seeming difficulty. All operations in *division* should be checked.

To check division multiply the divisor by the quotient and add the remainder, if there is any. The result should be the dividend.

Illustration. Divide 784 by 64, and check the answer.

```
      12                 Check
  64)784                   64
     64                    12
     144                  768
     128                   16
      16, remainder       784
```

Problems

Divide and check:

1. 694 ÷ 27	**8.** 3925 ÷ 287	**15.** 54987 ÷ 948
2. 876 ÷ 33	**9.** 5487 ÷ 425	**16.** 83726 ÷ 767
3. 985 ÷ 46	**10.** 997 ÷ 38	**17.** 93827 ÷ 679
4. 17853 ÷ 426	**11.** 1276 ÷ 76	**18.** 3064 ÷ 214
5. 27493 ÷ 516	**12.** 1487 ÷ 62	**19.** 9475 ÷ 324
6. 12807 ÷ 484	**13.** 1588 ÷ 69	**20.** 12775 ÷ 256
7. 4286 ÷ 185	**14.** 17963 ÷ 389	**21.** 9738 ÷ 478

AVERAGE

1. A grocer mixed a pound of 20-cent coffee with a pound of 30-cent coffee. What was the total value of the mixture? If the two pounds of mixed coffee are worth 50¢, how much is 1 lb. worth? 25¢ is said to be the *average price* of the coffee.

To find the average of two or more numbers, divide the sum of the numbers by the number of numbers.

2. Find the average cost of 5 sheep for which a man paid out \$4, \$5, \$3.50, \$6, and \$7.50.

3. The temperature on a given day was read every 3 hr. from 6 A.M. to 9 P.M. The readings were 9°, 12°, 22°, 24°, 20°, and 15°. What was the average temperature for the day?

4. John's marks in arithmetic for four months were 89, 93, 90, and 96. Henry's were 93, 91, 90, and 94. Alfred's were 90, 98, 95, and 86. Which boy had the highest average? What was his average?

5. In a 4-acre field a man raised 110 bu. of oats. In a 5-acre field he raised 115 bu. of oats. How much did his oat crop average per acre (*a*) in each field? (*b*) in both fields?

6. What is the average of all the numbers from 1 to 12 inclusive?

7. A man worked 15 days for 1¢ the first day, 2¢ the second day, 4¢ the third day, and so on, his wages being doubled daily. What was his average daily wage? How much did he receive for the last day's work?

8. Make up and bring to class, with their solutions, three problems on average.

DIVIDING BY 10, 100, AND 1000

To divide an integer by 10, 100, 1000, etc., point off as many places in the integer as there are zeros in the divisor.

To divide a decimal by 10, 100, 1000, etc., move the decimal point in the decimal as many places to the left as there are zeros in the divisor.

Illustrations.

a. $325 \div 10 = 32.5$
b. $.64 \div 100 = .0064$
c. $47862 \div 1000 = 47.862$
d. $3.25 \div 10 = .325$
e. $6.4 \div 100 = .064$
f. $478.62 \div 1000 = .47862$

Problems

Divide, writing the results at sight:

	a	*b*	*c*
1.	428 by 100	287 by 10	42786 by 100
2.	1728 by 1000	5 by 100	32945 by 1000
3.	75 by 10000	16 by 1000	89450 by 100
4.	128 by 1000	.01 by 100	625.5 by 10
5.	5.6 by 100	100 by 1000	7.485 by 100

C, Cwt., M, and T

In handling commodities by the hundred, the hundredweight, or the thousand, it is customary to use **C** for *hundred*, cwt. for *hundredweight*, and **M** for *thousand*, and **T** for *ton*.

Illustrations.

a. "500 sheets" may be written "5 C sheets,"
b. "8475 lb." may be written "84.75 cwt." and
c. "21,580 ft." may be written "21.58 M ft."

Problems

Express each of the following in terms of C, cwt., or M:

1. 12,000 bricks as M
2. 565 posts as C
3. 1680 lb. as cwt.
4. 1560 lb. as M
5. 21,485 posts as M
6. 16,890 bricks as M
7. 15,862 lb. as cwt.
8. 42,764 lb. as M
9. 28,472 lb. as cwt.
10. 36,750 lb. as cwt.

To find the charge or cost by the "hundredweight" (cwt.), point off two places in the number of pounds and multiply the number of cwt. by the rate per cwt.

Illustration. Find the amount charged for shipping by freight merchandise that weighs 375 lb., at $.41 per cwt.

375 lb. = 3.75 cwt.
3.75 × $.41 = $1.54, freight charge

$$\begin{array}{r} 3.75\ .41 \\ \underline{1500} \\ 1.5375 \end{array}$$

Problems

Find the charge for shipping each of the following by freight:

1. 425 lb. at 61¢ per cwt.
2. 770 lb. at 66¢ per cwt.
3. 1148 lb. at 18¢ per cwt.
4. 1765 lb. at 47¢ per cwt.
5. 2782 lb. at $1.24 per cwt.
6. 3470 lb. at 81¢ per cwt.
7. 4784 lb. at $1.10 per cwt.
8. 3967 lb. at 71¢ per cwt.
9. 6485 lb. at $2.21 per cwt.
10. 4786 lb. at $1.61 per cwt.

11. The freight rate on a carload of wrapping paper weighing 38,000 lb. was $.21 per cwt. Find the freight charge.

12. A carload of livestock weighing 22,500 lb. was shipped from Des Moines, Iowa to Chicago, Ill. The rate was $.34 per cwt. What was the freight charge?

Some commodities, such as brick, shingles, and lumber, are bought and sold by the **Thousand (M)**. Others, such as hay, coal, and iron, are sold by the **Ton (T)**. Some are sold by the **net ton of 2000 lb.** and others, by the **gross ton of 2240 lb.**

To find the cost of commodities sold by the thousand, point off three places in the quantity and multiply the result by the price per thousand (M).

Illustration. Find the cost of 4750 ft. of lumber at $38 per M.

$$4750 \text{ ft.} = 4.75 \text{ M ft.}$$
$$4.75 \times \$38 = \$180.50, \text{ cost}$$

To find the cost of commodities sold by the Ton (T), divide the total number of pounds by the number of pounds in a ton and multiply the result by the price per Ton.

Illustration. Find the cost of 17,860 lb. of hay at $17 a ton.

$$17{,}860 \text{ lb.} \div 2000 \text{ lb.} = 8.93, \text{ number of tons}$$
$$8.93 \times \$17 = \$151.81, \text{ cost}$$

Illustration. Find the cost of a carload of coal weighing 93,072 lb. at $6.75 a gross ton.

$$93{,}072 \text{ lb.} \div 2240 \text{ lb.} = 41.55, \text{ number of tons}$$
$$41.55 \times \$6.75 = \$280.46, \text{ cost}$$

To find costs by the net ton, if the price is an even number of dollars, as $12, $14, etc., point off three places in the number of pounds and multiply the result by one half the price.

Illustration. Find the cost of 15750 lb. of coal at $12 a ton.

15.750 × $6 = $94.50, cost

Problems

Find the cost of each of the following:

1. 13,750 ft. of lumber at $22.50 per M
2. 28,490 ft. of lumber at $33 per M
3. 16,250 brick at $14.50 per M
4. 27,980 lb. of hay at $17.50 per ton
5. 18,500 shingles at $7.75 per M
6. 38,750 ft. of lumber at $37.50 per M
7. 43,232 lb. of coal at $6.25 per gross ton
8. 43,750 shingles at $8.75 per M
9. For the erection of a garage a man ordered 13,750 bricks at $11.25 per M, 3450 ft. of lumber at $33.75 per M, and 3250 shingles at $7.50 per M. How much did these materials cost?
10. A farmer sold 27,480 lb. of hay at $18 a ton. He purchased 16,750 lb. of coal at $12 a ton and 4250 shingles at $8.50 per M. How much money did he have left?

COMMON FRACTIONS

The Unit of the Fraction. Into how many parts has the line below been divided? What is 1 part of the line called? What are 3 parts called? 5 parts? 4 parts?

When anything is divided or "broken" into equal parts, one or more of the parts is a *fraction* of the whole thing.

The thing that is divided into equal parts represents **the unit of a fraction,** that is, it is thought of as a single object or **1.** It may be a line, a yard of ribbon, a quart of milk, or a sum of money, etc. Thus, we speak of $\frac{1}{2}$ of a yard, $\frac{2}{3}$ of a foot, $\frac{3}{4}$ of an acre of land, $\frac{2}{5}$ of a sum of money, and so on. Each of these statements represents a fraction of the *whole unit* or **1.**

A Fractional Unit. A *single part* of a **unit** is called a **fractional unit.** Thus, $\frac{1}{8}$, $\frac{1}{3}$, $\frac{1}{5}$ are *fractional units,* because each fraction represents only one part of the *whole unit.*

A fraction is any number of fractional units.

The Terms of a Fraction. The part of the fraction that stands above the dividing line is called the **numerator.** The *numerator* denotes the number of parts taken of the **unit.**

The part of the fraction that stands below the dividing line is called the **denominator.**

Thus, in the fraction $\frac{3}{8}$, the *numerator* **3** indicates that 3 parts of the unit are taken; the *denominator* **8** indicates that the unit is divided into 8 equal sections or parts called **eighths.** *The numerator tells the number of parts taken* and the *denominator tells the number* (or name) *of parts into which the unit is divided.*

REDUCING FRACTIONS

Reduction of fractions is used frequently in solving problems.

Changing the form of a fraction without changing its value is called **reducing** the fraction.

Thus, when we change $\frac{1}{2}$ dollar to $\frac{2}{4}$ dollar, we *reduce* $\frac{1}{2}$ to $\frac{2}{4}$.

Reducing Fractions to Higher or Lower Terms

A proper fraction is a fraction whose numerator is smaller than its denominator.

Thus $\frac{9}{12}$ and $\frac{3}{4}$ are *proper fractions.*

Reduction to lower terms is called **reduction descending.**

A proper fraction may be reduced to lower terms by dividing its numerator and denominator by the same number.

Illustration. A proper fraction may be expressed in smaller or *lower terms* and still be of the same value. If both terms of the fraction $\frac{9}{12}$ are divided by 3, for example, the result is $\frac{3}{4}$, which has the same value as $\frac{9}{12}$.

Dividing both terms of a fraction by the same number does not change the value of the fraction.

Reduction to higher terms, as from $\frac{1}{2}$ to $\frac{6}{12}$, is called **reduction ascending.**

A proper fraction may be reduced to higher terms by multiplying its numerator and denominator by the same number.

Illustration. A fraction may also be expressed in larger or *higher terms.* If both terms of the fraction $\frac{3}{4}$ are multiplied by 3, the result is $\frac{9}{12}$, which has the same value as $\frac{3}{4}$.

Multiplying both terms of a fraction by the same number does not change the value of the fraction.

Problems

Reduce each of the following fractions to its lowest terms:

	a	*b*	*c*	*d*	*e*
1.	$\frac{12}{15}$	$\frac{24}{36}$	$\frac{35}{50}$	$\frac{48}{56}$	$\frac{25}{35}$
2.	$\frac{15}{21}$	$\frac{27}{36}$	$\frac{36}{48}$	$\frac{49}{63}$	$\frac{25}{45}$
3.	$\frac{14}{28}$	$\frac{32}{40}$	$\frac{42}{49}$	$\frac{48}{64}$	$\frac{45}{63}$
4.	$\frac{18}{24}$	$\frac{33}{44}$	$\frac{44}{55}$	$\frac{45}{72}$	$\frac{64}{72}$
5.	$\frac{21}{28}$	$\frac{33}{48}$	$\frac{45}{54}$	$\frac{56}{64}$	$\frac{72}{84}$

Reduce each of the following fractions to a fraction having the denominator or the numerator indicated:

	a	*b*	*c*	*d*
1.	$\frac{3}{4} = \frac{\quad}{16}$	$\frac{27}{36} = \frac{\quad}{12}$	$\frac{1}{3} = \frac{15}{\quad}$	$\frac{3}{5} = \frac{9}{\quad}$
2.	$\frac{5}{6} = \frac{\quad}{18}$	$\frac{15}{16} = \frac{30}{\quad}$	$\frac{1}{4} = \frac{\quad}{48}$	$\frac{3}{8} = \frac{\quad}{56}$
3.	$\frac{2}{3} = \frac{16}{\quad}$	$\frac{21}{24} = \frac{\quad}{8}$	$\frac{27}{54} = \frac{\quad}{18}$	$\frac{3}{5} = \frac{\quad}{35}$
4.	$\frac{5}{9} = \frac{\quad}{18}$	$\frac{5}{8} = \frac{45}{\quad}$	$\frac{32}{72} = \frac{\quad}{9}$	$\frac{3}{10} = \frac{\quad}{30}$
5.	$\frac{5}{7} = \frac{\quad}{21}$	$\frac{5}{7} = \frac{\quad}{35}$	$\frac{28}{56} = \frac{1}{\quad}$	$\frac{3}{4} = \frac{\quad}{60}$

6. Reduce $\frac{1}{3}$, $\frac{2}{5}$, $\frac{3}{4}$, and $\frac{4}{15}$ to sixtieths.

7. Reduce $\frac{3}{4}$, $\frac{5}{8}$, and $\frac{9}{4}$ to sixteenths.

8. Reduce $\frac{2}{3}$, $\frac{5}{8}$, $\frac{1}{6}$, and $\frac{5}{12}$ to twenty-fourths.

9. Reduce $\frac{1}{2}$, $\frac{3}{5}$, $\frac{5}{6}$, $\frac{7}{10}$, and $\frac{4}{15}$ to thirtieths.

To reduce an improper fraction to a whole number or to a mixed number, divide the numerator by the denominator.

An improper fraction is one whose numerator is equal to or greater than its denominator. $\frac{8}{8}$ and $\frac{3}{2}$ are *improper fractions.*

Illustration. Reduce $\frac{8}{8}$ and $\frac{16}{4}$, respectively, to whole numbers.

Thus, $8 \div 8 = 1$; $16 \div 4 = 4$.

A mixed number is a number expressed by an integer and a fraction combined. $1\frac{1}{2}$ is a *mixed number.*

Illustration. Reduce $\frac{3}{2}$ to a mixed number.

Thus, $3 \div 2 = 1\frac{1}{2}$.

Conversely, to reduce a mixed number to an improper fraction, multiply the integer by the denominator of the fraction and to the result add the numerator of the fraction. Write the sum over the denominator of the fraction.

Illustration. How many half dollars are there in $\$7\frac{1}{2}$?

$2 \times 7 = 14$; $14 + 1 = 15$. Therefore $\$7\frac{1}{2} = \$\frac{15}{2}$.

Problems

Reduce each of the following to a whole, or mixed, number:

	a	*b*	*c*	*d*	*e*
1.	$\frac{13}{3}$	$\frac{31}{4}$	$\frac{47}{5}$	$\frac{72}{4}$	$\frac{12}{7}$
2.	$\frac{15}{8}$	$\frac{28}{3}$	$\frac{54}{6}$	$\frac{66}{3}$	$\frac{49}{8}$
3.	$\frac{16}{4}$	$\frac{19}{6}$	$\frac{63}{7}$	$\frac{59}{8}$	$\frac{75}{4}$

Change each of the following to an improper fraction:

4.	$3\frac{2}{3}$	$12\frac{1}{2}$	$6\frac{7}{8}$	$47\frac{3}{4}$	$9\frac{1}{2}$
5.	$8\frac{1}{4}$	$13\frac{2}{3}$	$16\frac{1}{4}$	$53\frac{5}{8}$	$5\frac{3}{8}$
6.	$7\frac{1}{3}$	$17\frac{3}{4}$	$21\frac{2}{3}$	$56\frac{3}{8}$	$24\frac{3}{4}$

7. At the school fair, Edith and Janet sold 8 lb. of candy, in $\frac{1}{4}$-pound packages, at 10¢ a package; 10 lb., in $\frac{1}{2}$-pound packages, at 20¢ a package; and 3 gal. of lemonade, in glasses holding $\frac{1}{4}$ qt., at 5¢ a glass.

(*a*) How many quarter-pound packages did they sell?

(*b*) How many half-pound packages did they sell?

(*c*) How many glasses of lemonade did they sell?

(*d*) How much money did they receive for all their sales?

8. A grocer found that he regularly had orders for about the same number of 1-pound packages of tea, $\frac{1}{2}$-pound packages, and $\frac{1}{4}$-pound packages. One day he put up 10 lb. of tea in quarter-pound packages, 20 lb. of tea in half-pound packages, and 40 lb. of tea in pound packages.

(*a*) How many packages of tea did he prepare?

(*b*) On Saturday he sold 38 quarter-pound packages at 13¢ a package, 37 half-pound packages at 25¢ a package, and 35 pound packages at 50¢ a package. How much did he receive for tea that day?

(*c*) How many pounds of tea were sold that day?

9. With compasses draw a circle 4 in. in diameter. Divide the circle into quarters. Divide one of the quarters into 2 equal parts, another into 4 equal parts, and another into 8 equal parts. By comparing the quarters thus divided, complete this equation: $\frac{1}{4} = \frac{}{8} = \frac{}{16} = \frac{}{32}$

Reducing Fractions to a Least Common Denominator

The **least common denominator** (L. C. D.) of several fractions is the smallest denominator to which the several fractions may be reduced.

Illustration. Reduce $\frac{1}{2}$, $\frac{1}{3}$, $\frac{1}{4}$ to equivalent fractions having their least common denominator.

The smallest number that will contain the denominators 2, 3, and 4 is 12. Hence 12 is the L. C. D.

Then $\frac{1}{2} = \frac{1 \times 6}{2 \times 6} = \frac{6}{12}$; $\quad \frac{1}{3} = \frac{1 \times 4}{3 \times 4} = \frac{4}{12}$; $\quad \frac{1}{4} = \frac{1 \times 3}{4 \times 3} = \frac{3}{12}$

Finding the least common denominator of two or more fractions is a very simple operation. For most exercises it may be found by *inspection*. By using the following steps apply *inspection* to the above illustration:

a. If the largest denominator is not divisible by all the denominators, multiply it by 2.

b. If the result is not divisible by all the denominators, multiply the largest denominator by 3.

c. If this result is divisible by all the denominators, it is the *least common denominator*.

d. If necessary, continue multiplying, using 4, 5, etc. as the multiplier, until you find a number that is exactly divisible by each of the given denominators.

ADDING AND SUBTRACTING FRACTIONS

Fractions cannot be added or subtracted unless they are reduced to fractions having the same denominator.

When several fractions have the same denominator, they are said to have a **common denominator**. Thus, $\frac{1}{16}$, $\frac{3}{16}$, $\frac{5}{16}$, and $\frac{11}{16}$ are fractions having the common denominator 16.

One of the laws of arithmetic is:

Only like things or parts of like things may be added or subtracted.

3 quarts and 2 apples cannot be added.

$\frac{1}{2}$ foot cannot be subtracted from $\frac{1}{3}$ pint.

In adding or subtracting parts of like things, as $\frac{1}{4}$ hr., $\frac{1}{2}$ hr., and $\frac{1}{3}$ hr., not only must the things (hours in this case) be like, but the parts of the thing must be expressed in fractions having the same denominator.

When fractions have been reduced to equivalent fractions having their least common denominator, adding them or subtracting them consists of adding or subtracting their numerators and carrying forward the least common denominator.

Illustration. Add $\frac{3}{8}$, $\frac{3}{4}$, and $\frac{5}{6}$.

$$\frac{3}{8} + \frac{3}{4} + \frac{5}{6} = \frac{9}{24} + \frac{18}{24} + \frac{20}{24} = \frac{47}{24} = 1\frac{23}{24}$$

Problems

Reduce the fractions to a common denominator and perform the indicated operation:

1. $\frac{1}{2} + \frac{3}{4} + \frac{5}{8}$	11. $\frac{5}{8} - \frac{1}{4}$	21. $\frac{3}{4} + \frac{5}{8} - \frac{1}{2}$
2. $\frac{1}{3} + \frac{1}{2} + \frac{5}{6}$	12. $\frac{5}{6} - \frac{2}{3}$	22. $\frac{2}{3} + \frac{7}{12} - \frac{3}{4}$
3. $\frac{3}{4} + \frac{2}{3} + \frac{5}{12}$	13. $\frac{7}{12} - \frac{1}{4}$	23. $\frac{5}{6} + \frac{2}{3} - \frac{5}{12}$
4. $\frac{5}{8} + \frac{1}{3} + \frac{1}{6}$	14. $\frac{11}{12} - \frac{5}{8}$	24. $\frac{7}{16} - \frac{1}{4} + \frac{3}{8}$
5. $\frac{7}{8} + \frac{3}{4} + \frac{1}{2}$	15. $\frac{9}{16} - \frac{3}{8}$	25. $\frac{9}{16} - \frac{3}{8} + \frac{3}{4}$
6. $\frac{2}{5} + \frac{1}{2} + \frac{7}{10}$	16. $\frac{15}{16} - \frac{3}{4}$	26. $\frac{11}{16} + \frac{2}{3} - \frac{5}{12}$
7. $\frac{3}{4} + \frac{1}{2} + \frac{5}{8}$	17. $\frac{11}{12} - \frac{5}{6}$	27. $\frac{4}{5} + \frac{1}{2} - \frac{7}{10}$
8. $\frac{2}{3} + \frac{5}{6} + \frac{11}{12}$	18. $\frac{7}{8} - \frac{1}{3}$	28. $\frac{3}{4} + \frac{5}{6} - \frac{7}{12}$
9. $\frac{1}{2} + \frac{5}{6} + \frac{7}{12}$	19. $\frac{9}{16} - \frac{1}{3}$	29. $\frac{11}{12} - \frac{1}{3} - \frac{1}{4}$
10. $\frac{1}{3} + \frac{3}{4} + \frac{3}{8}$	20. $\frac{11}{12} - \frac{3}{4}$	30. $\frac{15}{16} - \frac{1}{8} - \frac{3}{4}$

If the least common denominator is not readily discovered by *inspection,* proceed as in the following illustrations.

Illustration. Add $\frac{3}{5}$, $\frac{11}{12}$, and $\frac{17}{32}$.

2)	5	12	32
2)	5	6	16
	5	3	8

$$\frac{3}{5} + \frac{11}{12} + \frac{17}{32} = \frac{288}{480} + \frac{440}{480} + \frac{255}{480} = \frac{983}{480} = 2\frac{23}{480}$$

The least common denominator is the product of all the divisors and all the final quotients, when they are prime to each other.

$$2 \times 2 \times 5 \times 3 \times 8 = 480$$

480 = 96 × 5. Therefore the first numerator is 96 × 3 = 288
480 = 40 × 12. Therefore the second numerator is 40 × 11 = 440
480 = 15 × 32. Therefore the third numerator is 15 × 17 = 255
Adding gives $\frac{983}{480}$, which equals $2\frac{23}{480}$.

Illustration. From $5\frac{1}{2}$ subtract $3\frac{2}{3}$.

$5\frac{1}{2} = 4\frac{3}{2} = 4\frac{9}{6}$ Since $\frac{2}{3}$ cannot be subtracted from $\frac{1}{2}$, change $5\frac{1}{2}$
$3\frac{2}{3} = 3\frac{2}{3} = 3\frac{4}{6}$ to $4\frac{3}{2}$ and then subtract.
$1\frac{5}{6}$ The result is $1\frac{5}{6}$.

Problems

Perform the following indicated operations:

1. $\frac{2}{3} + \frac{1}{5} + \frac{3}{4}$
2. $\frac{3}{8} + \frac{1}{5} + \frac{3}{4}$
3. $\frac{9}{16} + \frac{5}{12} + \frac{1}{4}$
4. $\frac{7}{8} + \frac{2}{3} - \frac{3}{4}$
5. $\frac{11}{12} + \frac{5}{8} - \frac{1}{4}$
6. $\frac{15}{16} - \frac{1}{4} - \frac{1}{8}$
7. $\frac{9}{10} + \frac{1}{3} + \frac{1}{5}$
8. $\frac{7}{15} + \frac{2}{3} - \frac{1}{5}$
9. $\frac{11}{15} + \frac{3}{5} - \frac{3}{15}$
10. $\frac{9}{16} - \frac{3}{8} + \frac{3}{4}$
11. $\frac{1}{12} + \frac{1}{3} + \frac{1}{4}$
12. $\frac{7}{15} - \frac{1}{3} + \frac{1}{4} - \frac{1}{5}$
13. $\frac{5}{16} + \frac{5}{8} - \frac{3}{4} + \frac{1}{2}$
14. $\frac{7}{8} - \frac{5}{12} + \frac{2}{3} - \frac{1}{4}$
15. $\frac{11}{16} - \frac{1}{2} + \frac{3}{4} + \frac{1}{8}$
16. $\frac{1}{2} + \frac{3}{8} + \frac{3}{4} - \frac{5}{8}$

17. On a picnic four boys brought oranges as follows: $\frac{1}{2}$ doz., $\frac{2}{3}$ doz., $\frac{3}{4}$ doz., and $\frac{5}{6}$ doz. There were 15 boys in the group. If each boy ate 2 oranges, what part of a dozen oranges was left?

18. Pieces of cloth containing $3\frac{3}{8}$ yd., $4\frac{3}{4}$ yd., and $6\frac{1}{2}$ yd. were used to make costumes requiring $3\frac{1}{2}$ yd., $4\frac{3}{4}$ yd., and $5\frac{1}{4}$ yd., respectively. How much cloth was left?

MULTIPLYING FRACTIONS

There are four types of operations involved in **multiplying fractions.**

1. *Multiplying a fraction by an integer*
2. *Multiplying a mixed number by an integer*
3. *Multiplying a fraction or a mixed number by a fraction*
4. *Multiplying a mixed number by a mixed number*

To Multiply a Fraction by an Integer

Illustration. **Multiplying the Numerator.** Each of 5 boys had a quarter of a dollar. How many quarter dollars did all 5 boys have?

$$5 \times \$\tfrac{1}{4} = \$\tfrac{5}{4}$$

Illustration. **Dividing the Denominator.** If each of 4 boys contributes $\frac{3}{4}$ of a dollar to help buy athletic supplies, how much do they all contribute?

$$\overset{1}{\cancel{4}} \times \$\frac{3}{\underset{1}{\cancel{4}}} = \$3$$

These illustrations show two ways of multiplying a fraction by an integer:

1. **Multiply the numerator of the fraction by the integer.**
2. **Divide the denominator of the fraction by the integer.**

Problems

Multiply by inspection. Reduce each answer to its simplest form:

	a	*b*	*c*	*d*	*e*
1.	$5 \times \frac{2}{3}$	$7 \times \frac{3}{7}$	$3 \times \frac{3}{8}$	$12 \times \frac{2}{5}$	$15 \times \frac{3}{5}$
2.	$6 \times \frac{1}{5}$	$8 \times \frac{5}{8}$	$7 \times \frac{5}{4}$	$16 \times \frac{3}{16}$	$13 \times \frac{2}{13}$

Notice that when a fraction is multiplied by its denominator, the product is its numerator.

Thus, $7 \times \frac{3}{7} = 3$; $4 \times \frac{1}{4} = 1$; $8 \times \frac{7}{8} = 7$, etc.

To Multiply a Mixed Number by an Integer

Illustration. At $16\frac{1}{2}$¢ a gallon, how much will 12 gal. of gasoline cost?

$$\begin{array}{r} 16\tfrac{1}{2}¢ \\ \underline{12} \\ 6 \\ \underline{192} \\ 198¢ \end{array} = \$1.98, \text{ cost}$$

The mixed number $16\frac{1}{2}$¢ must be multiplied by the integer 12.

Multiply each part of the mixed number separately and add the results, thus: $12 \times \frac{1}{2} = 6$.

$12 \times 16 = 192$. $192 + 6 = 198$, the number of cents. Therefore the cost is \$1.98.

Problems

Find the products:

1. $14 \times 3\frac{1}{2}$	5. $8 \times 15\frac{3}{5}$	9. $24 \times 17\frac{2}{3}$
2. $16 \times 5\frac{3}{8}$	6. $9 \times 17\frac{1}{4}$	10. $32 \times 5\frac{5}{6}$
3. $15 \times 3\frac{3}{4}$	7. $12 \times 13\frac{3}{8}$	11. $27 \times 16\frac{3}{4}$
4. $12 \times 3\frac{3}{5}$	8. $13 \times 8\frac{3}{4}$	12. $33 \times 21\frac{2}{3}$

13. A boy worked $6\frac{3}{4}$ hr. at 20¢ an hour. How much did he earn?

14. What is the cost of $2\frac{1}{2}$ doz. eggs at 34¢ a dozen?

15. A newsboy sold 48 papers each day for 6 days. He paid $1\frac{3}{4}$¢ each for the papers and sold them for 3¢ each. What was his profit?

16. A grocer sells eggs at 33¢ a dozen. By so doing he makes $\frac{1}{2}$¢ on each egg. How much do the eggs cost him per dozen?

17. A school lunchroom bought a box of 96 apples for $1.68. 72 apples were sold at 3¢ each and the remainder at the rate of 2 apples for 5¢. How much was made on the box of apples?

18. A tub of butter weighs $53\frac{3}{4}$ lb. If the empty tub weighs $5\frac{1}{2}$ lb., how much is the butter worth at 32¢ a pound?

19. A baker uses $\frac{3}{4}$ lb. of baking powder daily. At $.30 a pound, what is the cost of the baking powder he uses in 26 days?

To Multiply a Fraction by a Fraction

Illustration. How much is $\frac{1}{2}$ of a half dollar?

$$\frac{1}{2} \text{ of } \$\frac{1}{2} = \$\frac{1}{4}$$

Examine these diagrams:

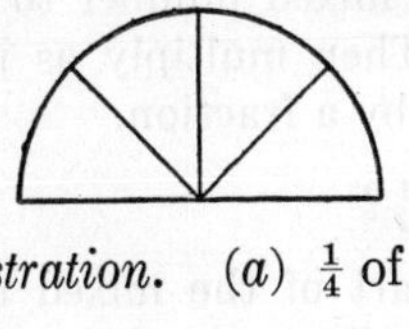

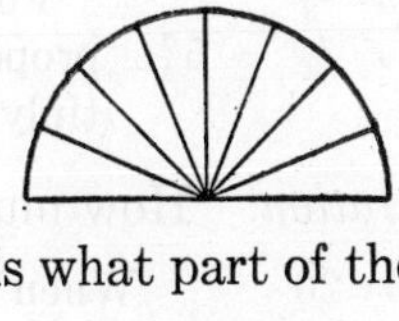

Illustration. (*a*) $\frac{1}{4}$ of $\frac{1}{2}$ of a circle is what part of the whole circle?

(*b*) $\frac{1}{8}$ of $\frac{1}{2}$ of a circle is what part of a whole circle?

(*a*) $\frac{1}{4}$ of $\frac{1}{2} = \frac{1}{8}$ (*b*) $\frac{1}{8}$ of $\frac{1}{2} = \frac{1}{16}$

Cancellation should be used where practicable.

To multiply two or more fractions together, multiply the numerators together for a new numerator and the denominators together for a new denominator.

Illustration. Multiply $\frac{5}{8} \times \frac{3}{4} \times \frac{8}{9} \times \frac{16}{25}$.

$$\frac{\overset{1}{\cancel{5}}}{\underset{1}{\cancel{8}}} \times \frac{\overset{1}{\cancel{3}}}{\underset{1}{\cancel{4}}} \times \frac{\overset{1}{\cancel{8}}}{\underset{3}{\cancel{9}}} \times \frac{\overset{4}{\cancel{16}}}{\underset{5}{\cancel{25}}} = \frac{4}{15}$$

Mental Drills

	a	*b*	*c*	*d*
1.	$\frac{3}{8} \times \frac{1}{2}$	$\frac{3}{4} \times \frac{3}{5}$	$\frac{4}{5} \times \frac{5}{8}$	$\frac{1}{3} \times \frac{3}{8}$
2.	$\frac{4}{5} \times \frac{3}{7}$	$\frac{3}{8} \times \frac{2}{3}$	$\frac{5}{6} \times \frac{6}{7}$	$\frac{1}{4} \times \frac{5}{9}$
3.	$\frac{5}{6} \times \frac{1}{3}$	$\frac{5}{8} \times \frac{3}{4}$	$\frac{3}{4} \times \frac{3}{8}$	$\frac{1}{8} \times \frac{1}{9}$
4.	$\frac{1}{2} \times \frac{3}{9}$	$\frac{2}{3} \times \frac{6}{7}$	$\frac{3}{7} \times \frac{1}{2}$	$\frac{1}{7} \times \frac{2}{5}$

Problems

Find the products:

1. $\frac{3}{4} \times \frac{5}{8} \times \frac{6}{7} \times \frac{12}{25}$

2. $\frac{5}{6} \times \frac{8}{15} \times \frac{3}{4} \times \frac{9}{2}$

3. $\frac{3}{7} \times \frac{7}{8} \times \frac{16}{21} \times \frac{14}{15}$

4. $\frac{5}{9} \times \frac{9}{10} \times \frac{11}{12} \times \frac{6}{7}$

5. $\frac{5}{7} \times \frac{3}{8} \times \frac{8}{3} \times \frac{7}{5}$

6. $\frac{3}{4} \times \frac{4}{5} \times \frac{5}{2} \times \frac{2}{7}$

7. $\frac{7}{8} \times \frac{11}{16} \times \frac{8}{11} \times \frac{32}{7}$

8. $\frac{5}{16} \times \frac{8}{3} \times \frac{4}{15} \times \frac{15}{2}$

To Multiply a Mixed Number by a Fraction

Illustration. How much is $\frac{3}{4}$ of $7\frac{2}{3}$?

$7\frac{2}{3} = \frac{23}{3}$

$\frac{\cancel{3}}{4}$ of $\frac{23}{\cancel{3}} = \frac{23}{4} = 5\frac{3}{4}$

First reduce the mixed number to an improper fraction. Then multiply as in multiplying a fraction by a fraction.

Illustration. How much is $\frac{5}{8}$ of $32\frac{1}{2}$?

$\frac{5}{8}$ of $32 = 20$

$\frac{5}{8}$ of $\frac{1}{2} = \frac{5}{16}$

$20\frac{5}{16}$

When the integer part of the mixed number can be multiplied mentally, as in this case, multiply the integer first, and then multiply the fraction separately, and add the two results.

Problems

Multiply:

1. $\frac{3}{5} \times 5\frac{2}{3}$
2. $\frac{2}{3} \times 7\frac{1}{2}$
3. $\frac{5}{6} \times 4\frac{1}{2}$
4. $\frac{3}{8} \times 9\frac{3}{5}$
5. $\frac{4}{5} \times 8\frac{3}{4}$
6. $\frac{2}{3} \times 24\frac{1}{2}$
7. $\frac{3}{4} \times 36\frac{3}{8}$
8. $\frac{3}{7} \times 28\frac{2}{3}$
9. $\frac{7}{8} \times 56\frac{3}{4}$
10. $\frac{4}{5} \times 35\frac{3}{4}$
11. $\frac{2}{3} \times 13\frac{1}{2}$
12. $\frac{3}{5} \times 31\frac{3}{4}$
13. $\frac{5}{6} \times 23\frac{4}{5}$
14. $\frac{3}{4} \times 41\frac{1}{4}$
15. $\frac{7}{8} \times 17\frac{3}{5}$

To Multiply a Mixed Number by a Mixed Number

Illustration. What is the cost of $8\frac{1}{4}$ yd. of ribbon at $\$.16\frac{1}{2}$ a yard?

$$\begin{array}{r} \$.16\frac{1}{2} \\ \underline{8\frac{1}{4}} \\ 4\frac{1}{8} \\ 4 \\ \underline{1\ 28} \\ \$1.36\frac{1}{8}\text{, or \$1.36, cost} \end{array}$$

(1) $\frac{1}{4}$ of $\frac{1}{2} = \frac{1}{8}$
(2) $\frac{1}{4}$ of $16 = 4$
(3) $8 \times \frac{1}{2} = 4$
(4) $8 \times 16 = 128$

NOTE. The four steps are explained at the right to illustrate the method. They should not be written in practice.

The four-step method is shorter than the method of reducing the mixed numbers to improper fractions. Compare the two methods shown below.

Illustration. Multiply $56\frac{1}{4}$ by $23\frac{3}{8}$.

Four-step Method

$$\begin{array}{r} 56\frac{1}{4} \\ \underline{23\frac{3}{8}} \\ \frac{3}{32} \\ 21 \\ 5\frac{3}{4} \\ 168 \\ \underline{112} \\ 1314\frac{27}{32} \end{array}$$

(A total of 30 figures)

Improper-fraction Method

$$56\frac{1}{4} \times 23\frac{3}{8} = \frac{225}{4} \times \frac{187}{8} = \frac{42075}{32}$$

$$\begin{array}{r} 225 \\ \underline{187} \\ 1575 \\ 1800 \\ \underline{225} \\ 42075 \end{array} \qquad \begin{array}{r} 1314\frac{27}{32} \\ 32\overline{)42075} \\ \underline{32} \\ 100 \\ \underline{96} \\ 47 \\ \underline{32} \\ 155 \\ \underline{128} \\ \frac{27}{32} \end{array}$$

(A total of 81 figures)

Problems

Multiply:

1. $28\frac{1}{4} \times 16\frac{1}{2}$	5. $36\frac{2}{3} \times 27\frac{3}{4}$	9. $63\frac{2}{3} \times 45\frac{4}{7}$
2. $27\frac{1}{4} \times 18\frac{1}{3}$	6. $56\frac{3}{4} \times 32\frac{1}{4}$	10. $68\frac{3}{8} \times 32\frac{3}{4}$
3. $54\frac{2}{3} \times 24\frac{1}{2}$	7. $94\frac{1}{6} \times 48\frac{1}{2}$	11. $75\frac{5}{8} \times 28\frac{2}{3}$
4. $47\frac{1}{8} \times 32\frac{1}{2}$	8. $88\frac{3}{4} \times 24\frac{7}{8}$	12. $47\frac{1}{3} \times 25\frac{1}{2}$

13. What is the cost of $7\frac{1}{2}$ doz. eggs at $18\frac{1}{2}$¢ a dozen?

14. A man worked $32\frac{3}{4}$ hr. at $22\frac{1}{2}$¢ an hour. How much did he earn?

15. When the express rate on sheep not crated is \$2.47$\frac{1}{2}$ a hundredweight, how much does it cost to send three uncrated sheep, with a combined weight of $3\frac{3}{4}$ cwt.?

16. On an automobile trip a man bought gas as follows: 12 gal. at $16\frac{1}{2}$¢ a gallon; 16 gal. at $16\frac{1}{2}$¢ a gallon; 14 gal. at $16\frac{1}{2}$¢ a gallon. He also bought 1 qt. of oil for 30¢. The gas tank on his car when he started registered 14 gal., which had been bought at $16\frac{1}{2}$¢ a gallon. When he reached home, he had 8 gal. of gas left. The speedometer registered 28,244 mi. at the beginning of the trip and 28,964 mi. at the end. With the man were his wife and two children.

(*a*) Find the total quantity of gas used on the trip.

(*b*) Find the cost of gas and oil.

(*c*) Find the total number of miles traveled.

(*d*) To the nearest tenth of a mill, what was the average cost a mile per person for the trip?

(*e*) Find the average number of miles per gallon of gas.

17. On the shelves of a store there were 4 pieces of taffeta containing $48\frac{1}{2}$ yd., $47\frac{3}{4}$ yd., $49\frac{1}{4}$ yd., and $51\frac{3}{4}$ yd. What was the value of the taffeta at $93\frac{3}{4}$¢ a yard?

18. A young man worked 8 hr. on Monday, $6\frac{1}{2}$ hr. on Tuesday, and $7\frac{1}{4}$ hr. on Wednesday. If he received \$.32$\frac{1}{2}$ an hour, how much did he earn?

19. From a bolt of cloth containing $42\frac{3}{4}$ yards, a merchant sold $17\frac{1}{2}$ yd. at \$.22$\frac{1}{2}$ a yard; $12\frac{3}{4}$ yd. at \$.22$\frac{1}{2}$ a yard, and the remainder at \$.19$\frac{1}{2}$ a yard. How much did he receive for all?

Short Methods

Illustration. Multiply $16\frac{1}{2}$ by $4\frac{1}{2}$.

$$\begin{array}{r} 16\frac{1}{2} \\ 4\frac{1}{2} \\ \hline 10\frac{1}{4} \\ 64 \\ \hline 74\frac{1}{4} \end{array}$$

The "four steps" are here reduced to three steps.

(1) $\frac{1}{2}$ of $\frac{1}{2} = \frac{1}{4}$
(2) $\frac{1}{2}$ of $(16 + 4) = 10$
(3) $4 \times 16 = 64$

If the two fractions are alike, the integers may be added in the second step and their sum multiplied by one of the fractions.

Illustration. Multiply $17\frac{2}{3}$ by $19\frac{2}{3}$.

$$\begin{array}{l} 17\frac{2}{3} \\ 19\frac{2}{3} \\ \hline \quad\frac{4}{9} \\ 24 \\ 153 \\ 17 \\ \hline 347\frac{4}{9} \end{array}$$

(1) $\frac{2}{3}$ of $\frac{2}{3} = \frac{4}{9}$
(2) $\frac{2}{3}$ of $(17 + 19) = 24$
(3) $19 \times 17 = 323$

Apply the short method of calculation when possible. In the dry-goods trade, small figures placed like an exponent are used to indicate quarters. For example, 19^3 yd. means $19\frac{3}{4}$ yd.; 21^2 yd. means $21\frac{2}{4}$ yd., or $21\frac{1}{2}$ yd., etc.

Problems

Find the total cost of each group of items:

1.		2.		3.	
	19^3 yd. @ $17\frac{3}{4}$¢		54^2 yd. @ $34\frac{1}{2}$¢		$8\frac{1}{2}$ A. @ \$65
	21^2 yd. @ $19\frac{1}{2}$¢		49^1 yd. @ $27\frac{1}{4}$¢		$13\frac{1}{4}$ bu. @ \$.75
	33^1 yd. @ $21\frac{1}{4}$¢		38^3 yd. @ $26\frac{3}{4}$¢		$56\frac{1}{4}$ M @ \$12.25
	45^3 yd. @ $23\frac{3}{4}$¢		41^2 yd. @ $27\frac{1}{2}$¢		$63\frac{3}{4}$ lb. @ \$.05$\frac{3}{4}$
	13^2 yd. @ $47\frac{1}{2}$¢		53^1 yd. @ $31\frac{1}{4}$¢		$74\frac{1}{2}$ lb. @ \$.14$\frac{1}{2}$

DIVIDING FRACTIONS

Four types of operations are involved in dividing fractions.

1. *Dividing a fraction by an integer*
2. *Dividing a mixed number by an integer*
3. *Dividing an integer, a fraction, or a mixed number by a fraction*
4. *Dividing by a mixed number*

To Divide a Fraction by an Integer

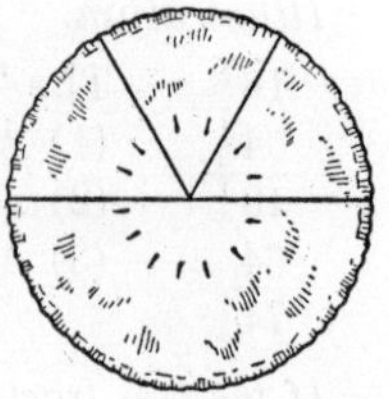

Illustration. **Multiplying the Denominator.** If $\frac{1}{2}$ of a pie is divided into 3 equal parts, what part of the whole pie will one of the pieces be?

Notice that the more pieces there are, the smaller each piece is.

If each half of the pie is divided into 3 pieces, there will be 6 pieces in the entire pie. Hence each piece is $\frac{1}{6}$ of the pie.

That is, $\frac{1}{2} \div 3 = \frac{1}{6}$.

Illustration. **Dividing the Numerator.** If $\frac{5}{8}$ of a gallon of milk is divided equally among 5 children, what part of a gallon will each child receive?

This gallon jar is $\frac{5}{8}$ full. If the filled portion, $\frac{5}{8}$, is divided into 5 equal parts, each part is $\frac{1}{8}$ of a gallon.

That is, $\frac{5}{8} \div 5 = \frac{1}{8}$.

These illustrations show two ways of dividing a fraction by an integer.

1. **Multiplying the denominator of the fraction divides the fraction.**
2. **Dividing the numerator of the fraction divides the fraction.**

Mental Drills

Give the quotients orally:

	a	*b*	*c*	*d*	*e*
1.	$\frac{1}{8} \div 2$	$\frac{3}{8} \div 5$	$\frac{9}{16} \div 3$	$\frac{4}{5} \div 4$	$\frac{5}{9} \div 3$
2.	$\frac{3}{4} \div 3$	$\frac{5}{7} \div 2$	$\frac{8}{15} \div 5$	$\frac{3}{16} \div 4$	$\frac{4}{5} \div 4$
3.	$\frac{5}{6} \div 2$	$\frac{6}{11} \div 3$	$\frac{7}{12} \div 4$	$\frac{3}{10} \div 5$	$\frac{15}{16} \div 5$

To Divide a Mixed Number by an Integer

Illustration. If $2\frac{2}{3}$ yd. of ribbon are cut into 4 equal parts, how long will each part be?

Change $2\frac{2}{3}$ yd. to $\frac{8}{3}$ yd. and then divide by 4.

$$\frac{8}{3} \text{ yd.} \div 4 = \frac{2}{3} \text{ yd.}$$

Illustration. A tailor bought a piece of cloth containing $30\frac{3}{8}$ yd. From it he made 9 suits of clothes. What was the average number of yards per suit?

$$\begin{array}{l} \quad 3 \\ 9\overline{)30\frac{3}{8}} \\ \underline{\quad 27} \\ \quad 3\frac{3}{8}, \text{ remainder } = \frac{27}{8} \\ \frac{27}{8} \div 9 = \frac{3}{8} \\ 3 \text{ yd.} + \frac{3}{8} \text{ yd.} = 3\frac{3}{8} \text{ yd.} \end{array}$$

When the integer in the dividend is larger than the divisor, do not change the dividend to an improper fraction. Divide as shown at the left. Then change the remainder, $3\frac{3}{8}$, to an improper fraction and divide as illustrated.

The remainder should in most cases be changed mentally to an improper fraction and divided mentally by the integer.

Problems

Divide:

1. $3\frac{3}{4} \div 5$	6. $128\frac{8}{9} \div 8$	11. $276\frac{5}{6} \div 8$
2. $2\frac{1}{3} \div 6$	7. $134\frac{3}{5} \div 7$	12. $322\frac{5}{8} \div 7$
3. $5\frac{1}{4} \div 8$	8. $154\frac{1}{8} \div 6$	13. $545\frac{5}{8} \div 5$
4. $48\frac{3}{5} \div 7$	9. $328\frac{3}{4} \div 5$	14. $328\frac{3}{8} \div 9$
5. $52\frac{3}{8} \div 6$	10. $316\frac{3}{7} \div 6$	15. $432\frac{1}{16} \div 7$

To Divide an Integer, a Mixed Number, or a Fraction by a Fraction

Illustration. If $\frac{3}{4}$ of a dozen oranges cost \$.27, how much will a dozen oranges cost?

(*a*) $\frac{3}{4}$ of cost = \$.27
$\frac{1}{4}$ of cost = $\frac{1}{3}$ of \$.27 = \$.09
$\frac{4}{4}$ of cost = 4 × \$.09 = \$.36

(*b*) \$.27 ÷ $\frac{3}{4}$ = \$.27 × $\frac{4}{3}$ = \$.36, cost of a dozen

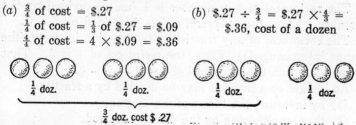

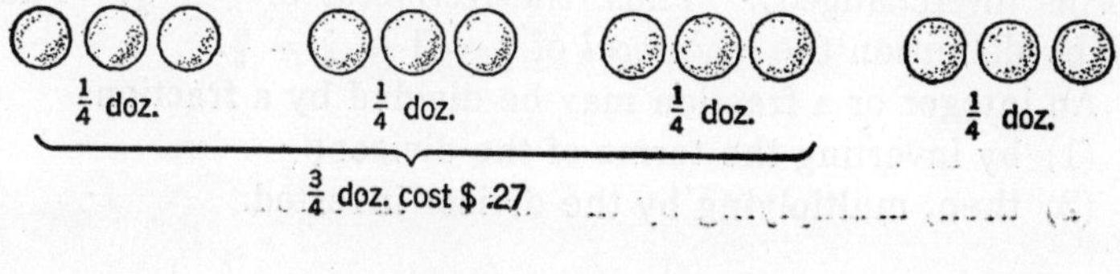

From the illustration it is evident that if $\frac{3}{4}$ of a dozen oranges cost \$.27, $\frac{1}{4}$ of a dozen will cost $\frac{1}{3}$ of \$.27, or \$.09. If $\frac{1}{4}$ of a dozen costs \$.09, a whole dozen will cost 4 times \$.09, or \$.36.

This solution is called the **unitary-analysis solution.** It is so called because the first step is to find the value of a *fractional unit* of the quantity and then to multiply that value by the number of fractional units in the quantity.

In the problem given above, the quantity is 1 dozen, $\frac{3}{4}$ of which cost \$.27. Since the dozen is broken up into fourths, *each one of the fourths*, that is ($\frac{1}{4}$), is called a *fractional unit.* Since 3 of those fractional units, that is, $\frac{3}{4}$ (of a dozen), cost \$.27, 1 fractional unit costs $\frac{1}{3}$ of \$.27, or \$.09. The four fractional units (that is, $\frac{4}{4}$) into which the dozen was divided will cost 4 times \$.09, or \$.36.

Problems

Divide, using the *unitary-analysis* plan:

1. $18 \div \frac{2}{3}$	**10.** $35 \div \frac{7}{8}$	**19.** $51 \div \frac{3}{4}$
2. $24 \div \frac{3}{4}$	**11.** $36 \div \frac{9}{2}$	**20.** $54 \div \frac{9}{7}$
3. $27 \div \frac{9}{8}$	**12.** $39 \div \frac{3}{4}$	**21.** $56 \div \frac{8}{3}$
4. $16 \div \frac{4}{5}$	**13.** $42 \div \frac{6}{7}$	**22.** $58 \div \frac{2}{3}$
5. $22 \div \frac{2}{5}$	**14.** $44 \div \frac{4}{5}$	**23.** $64 \div \frac{4}{5}$
6. $26 \div \frac{2}{7}$	**15.** $45 \div \frac{5}{3}$	**24.** $66 \div \frac{3}{4}$
7. $28 \div \frac{7}{4}$	**16.** $48 \div \frac{4}{5}$	**25.** $78 \div \frac{2}{5}$
8. $35 \div \frac{5}{7}$	**17.** $46 \div \frac{2}{3}$	**26.** $39 \div \frac{3}{5}$
9. $33 \div \frac{3}{4}$	**18.** $49 \div \frac{7}{9}$	**27.** $28 \div \frac{4}{7}$

The reciprocal of any number is 1 (unity) divided by the number. Thus, the *reciprocal* of 7 is, 1 divided by 7 = $\frac{1}{7}$.

The reciprocal of any fraction is the fraction inverted (the terms interchanged). Thus, the *reciprocal* of $\frac{5}{8}$ is $\frac{8}{5}$. That is, by definition the *reciprocal* of $\frac{5}{8} = 1 \div \frac{5}{8} = \frac{8}{5}$.

An integer or a fraction may be divided by a fraction
(1) by inverting the terms of the divisor;
(2) then, multiplying by the divisor inverted.

Problems

Divide by multiplying the *dividend* by the *reciprocal* of the divisor:

1. $11\frac{2}{3} \div \frac{5}{6}$	**6.** $\frac{2}{3} \div \frac{2}{9}$	**11.** $228 \div \frac{1}{4}$
2. $14\frac{2}{3} \div \frac{4}{9}$	**7.** $31\frac{3}{4} \div \frac{3}{8}$	**12.** $165 \div \frac{4}{5}$
3. $\frac{3}{4} \div \frac{7}{8}$	**8.** $36\frac{4}{5} \div \frac{4}{5}$	**13.** $196 \div \frac{3}{8}$
4. $\frac{1}{4} \div \frac{5}{8}$	**9.** $\frac{3}{5} \div \frac{3}{10}$	**14.** $244 \div \frac{5}{7}$
5. $23\frac{3}{4} \div \frac{5}{16}$	**10.** $125 \div \frac{4}{5}$	**15.** $387 \div \frac{5}{8}$

Illustration. A girl bought 18 yd. of ribbon for a certain purpose. When she had completed her work with the ribbon, she found she had purchased twice as much ribbon as she needed. How much ribbon did she need?

If she had twice as much ribbon as she needed, the amount needed is found by dividing 18 yd. by 2. 18 yd. ÷ 2 = 9 yd., the amount she needed.

Illustration. Another girl bought $8\frac{1}{3}$ yd. of ribbon with which to tie 15 Christmas packages. When she had wrapped and tied 10 packages, she had used all her ribbon. What part of her packages had she tied? The ribbon she had bought was what fractional part of the ribbon she needed? How much ribbon should she have bought?

Since she had wrapped only 10 of her packages, she had wrapped $\frac{10}{15}$, or $\frac{2}{3}$ of her packages. Hence she had purchased $\frac{2}{3}$ as much ribbon as she needed. To find the quantity of ribbon she needed, divide $8\frac{1}{3}$ by $\frac{2}{3}$.

$$8\tfrac{1}{3}\text{ yd.} \div \frac{2}{3} = \frac{25}{\underset{1}{\cancel{3}}}\text{ yd.} \times \frac{\overset{1}{\cancel{3}}}{2} = \frac{25}{2}\text{ yd.} = 12\tfrac{1}{2}\text{ yd., amount needed}$$

In the above solution, notice that the dividend is not exactly divisible by the numerator of the divisor. The dividend was therefore changed to an improper fraction and multiplied by the *reciprocal* of the divisor.

Problems

Use the unitary-analysis method of solution wherever possible in solving the following problems.

1. In $\frac{4}{5}$ hr. a shopworker did 24 pieces of work. At that rate, how many pieces would he complete in 8 hr.?

Since in $\frac{4}{5}$ hr. he did 24 pieces of work, in $\frac{1}{5}$ hr. he would do $\frac{1}{4}$ of 24 pieces, or 6 pieces. In 1 hr. he would do 5×6 pieces, or 30 pieces. In 8 hr. he would do 8×30 pieces, or 240 pieces.

2. A young man spent $\frac{2}{7}$ of his savings for a used car, for which he paid $150. How much money had he saved?

3. 36 is $\frac{3}{8}$ of what number?

4. A student paid $.25 for a quarter gross of steel pens. At the same rate how much would 3 gross cost?

5. A man paid $4500 for a plot of ground containing $\frac{3}{8}$ of an acre. How much would an acre cost at the same rate?

6. A high-school baseball team lost 4 games, which was $\frac{2}{5}$ of the number of games they won. How many games did they play?

7. The average number of days without frost in a year in Alberta, Canada, is 90, which is $\frac{3}{8}$ of the average number of days without frost in southern Georgia. How many days without frost are there in a year in southern Georgia?

To Divide by a Mixed Number

Illustration. At 15\frac{7}{8}$ a share, how many shares of stock can be bought for $7620?

```
15⅞) 7620
 8      8
─────────
127 )60960(480, number of shares
     508
     ────
     1016
     1016
     ────
        0
```

(1) Set up the exercise as for division by an integer.

(2) Clear of fractions by multiplying both divisor and dividend by the denominator of the fraction in the divisor.

(3) Divide as in whole numbers.

Illustration. If a grain bag holds $2\frac{3}{8}$ bu. of grain, how many bags will be required to contain $308\frac{3}{4}$ bu.?

```
2 3/8) 308 3/4
8        8
------------------
19 )2470 (130, number of bags
    19         required
    --
     57
     57
     --
      0
```

(1) Set up the exercise as for division by an integer.

(2) Clear of fractions by multiplying both divisor and dividend by the L. C. D. of the two fractions.

(3) Divide as in whole numbers.

Problems

Using the method just explained, divide:

1. $47 \div 3\frac{2}{3}$	**7.** $84\frac{1}{3} \div 9\frac{1}{4}$	**13.** $475 \div 22\frac{3}{4}$
2. $38 \div 5\frac{1}{2}$	**8.** $76\frac{3}{4} \div 8\frac{1}{8}$	**14.** $328\frac{2}{3} \div 31\frac{1}{3}$
3. $56 \div 7\frac{3}{4}$	**9.** $98\frac{3}{7} \div 13\frac{1}{2}$	**15.** $446\frac{3}{8} \div 28\frac{1}{2}$
4. $69 \div 8\frac{3}{4}$	**10.** $85\frac{5}{8} \div 17\frac{1}{8}$	**16.** $536 \div 32\frac{1}{4}$
5. $76 \div 9\frac{1}{3}$	**11.** $93\frac{2}{3} \div 11\frac{1}{2}$	**17.** $637 \div 46\frac{2}{3}$
6. $85 \div 9\frac{3}{4}$	**12.** $99\frac{5}{16} \div 6\frac{1}{4}$	**18.** $938\frac{2}{3} \div 45\frac{1}{4}$

19. A man exchanged $2\frac{3}{4}$ doz. eggs worth 24¢ a dozen for $3\frac{2}{3}$ yd. of bleached muslin. What was the value of the muslin per yard?

20. A stone wall is 792 ft. long. How much did it cost to lay the wall at $\$4\frac{1}{4}$ a rod?

21. A man invested $\frac{2}{5}$ of his capital in 84 shares of stock at $\$74\frac{3}{8}$ a share. Find the amount of his capital.

22. At $\$2\frac{3}{8}$ a yard, how many yards of silk can be bought for $\$85\frac{1}{2}$?

23. If $8\frac{3}{4}$ tons of coal cost $\$122\frac{1}{2}$, how much will $14\frac{1}{4}$ tons cost at the same rate?

24. Mrs. Hall bought the following: 2 doz. oranges at 8 for 25¢, 6 grapefruit at 2 for 15¢, 14 lb. of sugar at $3\frac{1}{2}$ lb. for 18¢, 12 lb. of potatoes at 4 lb. for 10¢, and $2\frac{1}{2}$ lb. of bacon at 25¢ a pound. She gave \$5 in payment. How much change should she receive?

25. A dealer sold $\frac{2}{5}$ of his stock of flour at $\$13\frac{3}{4}$ a barrel. If he received $880, how many barrels of flour did he sell? How many barrels of flour had he left?

26. A man was engaged to do a day's work, but was taken ill and was unable to work longer than $\frac{5}{8}$ of a day. For his labor he was paid $1.75. What was the daily wage?

27. A merchant sold an article for $\frac{5}{4}$ of what he paid for it. If he sold it for $17.50, how much did he pay for it? How much did he gain?

28. A damaged article was sold for $\frac{3}{4}$ of its cost. If the selling price was $\$11\frac{1}{4}$, what was the cost? the loss?

29. The market price of corn per bushel for 6 days was $\$.58\frac{1}{2}$, $\$.58\frac{1}{4}$, $.59, $\$.59\frac{3}{8}$, $\$.58\frac{7}{8}$, and $\$.58\frac{1}{2}$. Find the average price.

30. At $\$46\frac{7}{8}$ a share, how many shares of stock can I buy for $6750?

31. An article was sold for $6.30, which was $\frac{1}{6}$ more than it cost. How much did it cost?

32. The net income from a business block for a year was $15,840. If the income was equal to $\frac{1}{8}$ of the value of the block, find the value of the property.

33. A shop-worn rug was sold for $19.60, which was $\frac{1}{3}$ less than it cost. How much did the rug cost? How much was the loss? The loss was equal to what part of the selling price?

34. A sum of money amounting to $2925 was left to three persons as follows: For each dollar received by A, B was to receive $1\frac{1}{4}$ dollars, and C was to receive $1\frac{1}{2}$ dollars. How much did each receive?

35. A woman bought a remnant of cloth containing $4\frac{1}{4}$ yd. for $1.02. At that rate, find the price per yard. If the regular price was $.42 a yard, her saving was what part of the regular price?

ALIQUOT PARTS

The word that characterizes the activity of modern business life is *speed*. Many millions of dollars have been spent to make possible greater speed on the railroads, on airplanes which can cross the continent in a single day, and in increasing the output of machinery.

The student who becomes proficient in arithmetic must make use of those devices in calculating that enable him to obtain accurate results most readily.

Skill in the use of **aliquot parts** develops speed in calculating many kinds of problems. Operations may thereby be materially shortened.

An aliquot part of a number is an exact divisor of the number. For example, 10, $12\frac{1}{2}$, 20, 25, and $33\frac{1}{3}$ are all aliquot parts of 100 because each number is contained in 100 an exact number of times.

Aliquot parts, expressed in terms of fractions, have 1 for a numerator. Thus, 10 is $\frac{1}{10}$ of 100, $12\frac{1}{2}$ is $\frac{1}{8}$ of 100, 20 is $\frac{1}{5}$ of 100, 7 is $\frac{1}{3}$ of 21, 9 is $\frac{1}{5}$ of 45, etc.

In the following table are important aliquot parts of 100.

Aliquot Parts of 100

$12\frac{1}{2} = \frac{1}{8}$ of 100	$25 = \frac{1}{4}$ of 100
$16\frac{2}{3} = \frac{1}{6}$ of 100	$33\frac{1}{3} = \frac{1}{3}$ of 100
$20 = \frac{1}{5}$ of 100	$50 = \frac{1}{2}$ of 100

The principle of aliquot parts can be used in many kinds of computation, but it is especially useful in billing, in inventory work, and in merchandising transactions where the salesperson has very many mental calculations to make at top speed. These transactions involve the elements, *quantity*, *price*, and *cost* (amount of the sale). Every sale is based on \$1, so the salesperson should be familiar with all possible divisors of \$1 for quick, mental calculations.

MULTIPLICATION BY ALIQUOT PARTS

Find the Cost (Amount of Sale) When the Quantity and Price Are Given

Quantity × Price = Cost

Illustration. What will 12 yards of goods cost if the price of 1 yard is $16\frac{2}{3}$¢?

The analysis of the solution based on the aliquot-parts principle is as follows.

State the *quantity* and *price* in terms of $1, then multiply. At $1 a yard, 12 yds. will cost $12; hence, at $16\frac{2}{3}$¢, which is $\frac{1}{6}$ of $1, the cost will be $\frac{1}{6}$ of $12, or $2. It is important, of course, that the analysis be understood, but after a reasonable amount of practice, the salesperson merely says $\frac{1}{6}$ of $12 = $2. She has familiarized herself with the aliquot parts of $1 and knows instantly that $16\frac{2}{3}$¢ is $\frac{1}{6}$ of $1.

Problems

Using aliquot parts, find the total cost of each group:

1. 16 lb. @ 25¢
   24 lb. @ 25¢
   28 lb. @ 25¢
   36 lb. @ 25¢
2. 14 lb. @ 50¢
   16 lb. @ 50¢
   22 lb. @ 50¢
   24 lb. @ 50¢
3. 28 yd. @ 50¢
   32 yd. @ 25¢
   36 yd. @ 50¢
   24 yd. @ $16\frac{2}{3}$¢
4. 8 lb. @ 25¢
   12 lb. @ 25¢
   32 lb. @ 25¢
   44 lb. @ 25¢
5. 12 lb. @ $16\frac{2}{3}$¢
   18 lb. @ $16\frac{2}{3}$¢
   24 lb. @ $16\frac{2}{3}$¢
   30 lb. @ $16\frac{2}{3}$¢
6. 18 yd. @ 25¢
   21 yd. @ 50¢
   12 yd. @ $16\frac{2}{3}$¢
   13 yd. @ 25¢
7. 12 lb. @ $33\frac{1}{3}$¢
   18 lb. @ $33\frac{1}{3}$¢
   45 lb. @ $33\frac{1}{3}$¢
   30 lb. @ $33\frac{1}{3}$¢
8. 12 yd. @ $12\frac{1}{2}$¢
   16 yd. @ $12\frac{1}{2}$¢
   24 yd. @ $12\frac{1}{2}$¢
   28 yd. @ $12\frac{1}{2}$¢
9. 17 yd. @ 25¢
   19 yd. @ 50¢
   40 yd. @ $12\frac{1}{2}$¢
   60 yd. @ $16\frac{2}{3}$¢

MULTIPLES OF ALIQUOT PARTS

When solving a problem involving a number that is an *aliquot part* of 100 or $1, multiply or divide by the fractional equivalent rather than by the whole number. There are many problems, however, that do not contain *aliquots* of 100, but they contain *multiples of the various aliquots* of 100 or $1. A multiple of a number is any number of times the number. Thus, the *multiples* of $12\frac{1}{2}$ up to 100 are: 25, $37\frac{1}{2}$, 50, $62\frac{1}{2}$, 75, $87\frac{1}{2}$, and 100. For anyone engaged in work that requires rapid calculating, it is necessary to recognize immediately whether the problem contains any *aliquots* or *multiples of aliquots*.

The principle of using *aliquot parts* in multiplying two numbers has been explained; it remains now to explain how the *multiples of aliquots* can be used.

Illustration. Multiply 48 by $.37\frac{1}{2}$.

Having memorized the essential aliquots of 100, we see immediately that $37\frac{1}{2}$ is not an aliquot of 100, but it is a multiple of $12\frac{1}{2}$, which is an aliquot ($\frac{1}{8}$) of 100. That is, $37\frac{1}{2}$ is exactly 3 times greater than $12\frac{1}{2}$, or $\frac{3}{8}$ of 100.

Thus, $48 \times .37\frac{1}{2} = 48 \times \frac{3}{8} = 18$.

Since $37\frac{1}{2}$ is not an aliquot of 100, we found the ratio of $37\frac{1}{2}$ to 100 indirectly to be $\frac{3}{8}$, by using the already-known ratio of $12\frac{1}{2}$ to 100, which is $\frac{1}{8}$. Another method of finding the ratio of $37\frac{1}{2}$ to 100 is to show the relationship in the form of a fraction and reduce the fraction to its lowest terms by dividing both terms by a number that is a factor common to both terms.

Thus, $37\frac{1}{2} : 100 = \frac{37\frac{1}{2}}{100}$. Reduce the fraction to its lowest terms by dividing both numerator and denominator by $12\frac{1}{2}$ (a factor of both $37\frac{1}{2}$ and 100) which gives us the fraction $\frac{3}{8}$.

A thorough knowledge of multiples of aliquots is very important in rapid figuring; the principles are easily understood and applied.

Illustration. Find the cost of 16 yards of goods at $62\frac{1}{2}$ cents a yard.

You know that $62\frac{1}{2}$¢ is a multiple of $12\frac{1}{2}$¢, which is an aliquot of $1. Visualize the ratio of $62\frac{1}{2}$¢ to $1 in the form of a fraction $\frac{62\frac{1}{2}¢}{100}$. Reduce the fraction to its lowest terms by dividing the numerator and denominator by $12\frac{1}{2}$, which is $\frac{5}{8}$.

Now, stating the quantity and price in terms of *dollars*, 16 yds. at $1 will cost $16; hence at $62\frac{1}{2}$¢, which is $\frac{5}{8}$ of $1, the cost will be $\frac{5}{8}$ of $16, or $10.

We have stated the solutions and principles in full to give the pupil the reason for each step in the solution. Pupils have difficulty also in placing the decimal point correctly in the quotient; we, therefore, suggest that the *quantity* and *price* be thought of in terms of *dollars*. In actual practice, however, the salesperson performs merely the mental calculations.

Thus, $\frac{62\frac{1}{2}¢ \div 12\frac{1}{2}}{100 \div 12\frac{1}{2}} = \frac{5}{8} \times \$16 = \$10$

When reducing the fraction divide by the largest aliquot possible. Be sure to learn the fractional equivalents of the aliquot parts of 100 or $1, as well as their multiples. Practice will enable you to handle them quickly and effectively.

Problems

1. Name consecutively the multiples of $6\frac{1}{4}$ up to and including 100.

2. What multiple of $6\frac{1}{4}$ is $31\frac{1}{4}$? is $62\frac{1}{2}$? is $87\frac{1}{2}$? is 100?

3. Name consecutively the multiples of $8\frac{1}{3}$ up to and including 100.

4. What multiple of $8\frac{1}{3}$ is $16\frac{2}{3}$? is $58\frac{1}{3}$? is $83\frac{1}{3}$? is 100?

Problems

State orally the cost of each of the following. Solve by aliquot parts and their multiples.

	a	*b*	*c*
1.	12 yd. @ 25¢	24 yd. @ $12\frac{1}{2}$¢	32 yd. @ 25¢
2.	16 yd. @ $12\frac{1}{2}$¢	24 yd. @ $66\frac{2}{3}$¢	32 yd. @ 50¢
3.	18 yd. @ 50¢	24 yd. @ 75¢	32 yd. @ 75¢
4.	20 yd. @ 75¢	32 yd. @ $12\frac{1}{2}$¢	32 yd. @ $37\frac{1}{2}$¢
5.	22 yd. @ 50¢	34 yd. @ 25¢	32 yd. @ $87\frac{1}{2}$¢
6.	26 yd. @ 25¢	34 yd. @ 50¢	32 yd. @ $62\frac{1}{2}$¢
7.	28 yd. @ 75¢	36 yd. @ 75¢	32 yd. @ 75¢
8.	40 yd. @ $37\frac{1}{2}$¢	36 yd. @ $16\frac{2}{3}$¢	48 yd. @ $87\frac{1}{2}$¢

9.	40 yd. @ $62\frac{1}{2}$¢	48 yd. @ $58\frac{1}{3}$¢	56 yd. @ $12\frac{1}{2}$¢
10.	40 yd. @ 75¢	48 yd. @ $37\frac{1}{2}$¢	56 yd. @ 25¢
11.	40 yd. @ $87\frac{1}{2}$¢	48 yd. @ $62\frac{1}{2}$¢	56 yd. @ $37\frac{1}{2}$¢
12.	64 yd. @ $12\frac{1}{2}$¢	72 yd. @ 25¢	72 yd. @ $12\frac{1}{2}$¢
13.	72 yd. @ 50¢	64 yd. @ $37\frac{1}{2}$¢	64 yd. @ 25¢
14.	80 yd. @ $62\frac{1}{2}$¢	56 yd. @ 50¢	56 yd. @ $62\frac{1}{2}$¢
15.	91 yd. @ 25¢	96 yd. @ $83\frac{1}{3}$¢	88 yd. @ $37\frac{1}{2}$¢
16.	56 lb. @ 25¢	88 lb. @ 25¢	144 yd. @ 25¢
17.	56 lb. @ $12\frac{1}{2}$¢	88 lb. @ 50¢	144 yd. @ $12\frac{1}{2}$¢
18.	56 lb. @ $37\frac{1}{2}$¢	88 lb. @ $12\frac{1}{2}$¢	144 yd. @ 50¢
19.	56 lb. @ 50¢	88 lb. @ $87\frac{1}{2}$¢	144 yd. @ $37\frac{1}{2}$¢
20.	72 lb. @ 25¢	96 lb. @ $37\frac{1}{2}$¢	160 yd. @ $37\frac{1}{2}$¢
21.	72 lb. @ $12\frac{1}{2}$¢	96 lb. @ $62\frac{1}{2}$¢	160 yd. @ $62\frac{1}{2}$¢
22.	72 lb. @ $62\frac{1}{2}$¢	96 lb. @ $87\frac{1}{2}$¢	160 yd. @ $87\frac{1}{2}$¢

Another Method of Multiplying by Multiples

Illustration. Find the cost of 344 yd. at $18\frac{3}{4}$¢ a yard.

$344		= cost of 344 yd. at $1 a yard
$86		= cost of 344 yd. at $.25 a yard
21	50	= cost of 344 yd. at $$.06\frac{1}{4}$ a yard
$64	50	= cost of 344 yd. at $$.18\frac{3}{4}$ a yard

$$.18\frac{3}{4}$ is $\frac{3}{4}$ of $.25. Hence we first find the value of 344 yd. at $.25 a yard and then deduct $\frac{1}{4}$ of the result.

This plan changes a division by 16 into two easy divisions by 4.

Illustration. Find the cost of $27\frac{1}{4}$ yd. at $31\frac{1}{4}$¢ a yard.

$27	25	= cost of $27\frac{1}{4}$ yd. at $1 a yard
$6	8125	= cost of $27\frac{1}{4}$ yd. at $.25 a yard
1	7031	= cost of $27\frac{1}{4}$ yd. at $$.06\frac{1}{4}$ a yard
$8	5156	= cost of $27\frac{1}{4}$ yd. at $$.31\frac{1}{4}$ a yard

Ans. $8.52

$$.31\frac{1}{4}$ is $\frac{1}{4}$ more than $.25. Hence we first find the cost of $27\frac{1}{4}$ yd. at $.25 a yard and then add $\frac{1}{4}$ of the result.

Problems

Using the plans outlined in the foregoing illustrations, find the cost of each of the following:

1. 133 yd. at $18\frac{3}{4}$¢ a yard	6. $121\frac{1}{2}$ yd. @ $18\frac{3}{4}$¢
2. 147 yd. at $18\frac{3}{4}$¢ a yard	7. $131\frac{3}{4}$ yd. @ $31\frac{1}{4}$¢
3. 155 yd. at $31\frac{1}{4}$¢ a yard	8. $243\frac{1}{4}$ yd. @ $18\frac{3}{4}$¢
4. 167 yd. at $31\frac{1}{4}$¢ a yard	9. $327\frac{1}{2}$ yd. @ $18\frac{3}{4}$¢
5. 183 yd. at $18\frac{3}{4}$¢ a yard	10. $341\frac{3}{4}$ yd. @ $31\frac{1}{4}$¢

Find the total cost of:

11. 524 yd. at 25¢ a yard	12. $481\frac{1}{2}$ yd. @ 25¢
648 yd. at $6\frac{1}{4}$¢ a yard	$481\frac{1}{2}$ yd. @ $18\frac{3}{4}$¢
324 yd. at $18\frac{3}{4}$¢ a yard	$481\frac{1}{2}$ yd. @ $31\frac{1}{4}$¢
324 yd. at $31\frac{1}{4}$¢ a yard	572 yd. @ $12\frac{1}{2}$¢
440 yd. at $37\frac{1}{2}$¢ a yard	572 yd. @ $6\frac{1}{4}$¢

DIVISION BY ALIQUOT PARTS

Find the Quantity When the Cost and Price Are Given

$$\frac{\text{Cost}}{\text{Price}} = \text{Cost} \div \text{Price} = \text{Quantity}$$

Illustration. How many yards of goods can be bought for \$2 if the price of 1 yard is $16\frac{2}{3}$¢?

Analysis of the solution based on the aliquot-parts principle.

At \$1 a yard, 2 yds. can be bought for \$2; hence at $16\frac{2}{3}$¢, which is $\frac{1}{6}$ of \$1, as many yards can be bought as $\frac{1}{6}$ is contained times in 2 yards or 12 yards. That is, 2 yds. $\div \frac{1}{6} = 2 \times \frac{6}{1} = 12$ yds.

Here again, instead of performing the complete analysis, the salesperson will quickly multiply the cost by the aliquot part inverted (the *reciprocal* of the fraction).

Mental Drills

Using aliquot parts (or their multiples where convenient) in the following problems with *Cost* and *Price*, state orally the *Quantity* that can be bought.

	Cost	Price	Cost	Price	Cost	Price
1.	\$3	25¢ per yd.	\$2	$6\frac{1}{4}$¢ per yd.	\$15	25¢ per doz.
2.	\$2	$12\frac{1}{2}$¢ per yd.	\$8	25¢ per yd.	\$25	$16\frac{2}{3}$¢ per doz.
3.	\$9	50¢ per yd.	\$7	20¢ per yd.	\$12	$12\frac{1}{2}$¢ per doz.
4.	\$2	$8\frac{1}{3}$¢ per yd.	\$10	$41\frac{2}{3}$¢ per yd.	\$35	$58\frac{1}{3}$¢ per doz.
	(Divide \$2 by $\frac{1}{12}$. Why?)		(Divide \$10 by $\frac{5}{12}$. Why?)		(Divide \$35 by $\frac{7}{12}$. Why?)	
5.	\$12	$37\frac{1}{2}$¢ per yd.	\$36	75¢ per yd.	\$48	$66\frac{2}{3}$¢ per doz.

Find the Price When the Cost and Quantity Are Given

$$\frac{\text{Cost}}{\text{Quantity}} = \text{Cost} \div \text{Quantity} = \text{Price}$$

Illustration. You bought 12 yds. of goods for \$2. What was the price per yard?

Analysis of the solution based on the aliquot-parts principle.

$$\$\tfrac{2}{12} = \tfrac{1}{6} \text{ of } \$1, \text{ or } 16\tfrac{2}{3}¢, \text{ the price}$$

The salesperson should be alert to observe that, when dividing *Cost* by *Quantity*, if the quotient is an aliquot part of \$1, she merely reads the equivalent of the aliquot part in cents.

Illustration. If 25 yards of cloth cost \$6.25, what is the price per yard?

$$\$6.25 \div 25 = 25 \text{ cents, price per yd.}$$

Since 25 is an aliquot ($\frac{1}{4}$) of 100, another method is to divide 6.25 by $\frac{1}{4}$. Thus, $6.25 \div \frac{1}{4} = 6.25 \times \frac{4}{1} = 25$. Therefore the price of 1 yd. is 25 cents.

Mental Drills

Using aliquot parts in the following problems where the *Cost* and *Quantity* are given, state orally the *Price* per unit.

	Cost	Quantity	Cost	Quantity	Cost	Quantity
1.	\$48	96 yds.	\$9	27 lbs.	\$12	96 gross
2.	\$6	24 yds.	\$6	8 lbs.	\$4	24 gross
3.	\$5	40 yds.	\$10	15 doz.	\$49	56 gross
4.	\$3	60 yds.	\$27	54 doz.	\$15	60 gross
5.	\$20	50 yds.	\$20	80 doz.	\$3	30 gross

DECIMAL FRACTIONS

Comparing Common Fractions and Decimals

One difference between a *common fraction* and a *decimal fraction* is that a common fraction must be written with a denominator, while a decimal fraction does not require a written denominator.

Thus, the *common-fraction form* is $\frac{5}{10}$ and the corresponding *decimal-fraction form* is .5. The *denominator* of a *decimal fraction* is not expressed, but is *signified* by the **decimal point** placed at the left of the numerator. The *denominator* of a decimal fraction is always 10 or some power* of 10, as 100, 1000, etc. It may be stated, therefore, that the denominator of a decimal fraction, expressed or understood, is 1 followed by as many zeros as there are figures or digits following the decimal point in the numerator. For example, .5 is read $\frac{5}{10}$ (five tenths), .25 is read $\frac{25}{100}$ (twenty-five hundredths), .125 is read $\frac{125}{1000}$ (one hundred twenty-five thousandths), etc. Note that tenths occupies 1 decimal place; hundredths, 2 decimal places; and thousandths, three decimal places, etc.

Writing Decimals in Their Common Fraction Form

Illustration. Change .3125 to a common fraction.

$.3125 = \frac{3125}{10000}$ (1) Write the decimal in its equivalent common-fraction form by writing its denominator under the numerator.

$25 \mid \frac{3125}{10000} = 25 \mid \frac{125}{400} = \frac{5}{16}$ (2) Reduce the common fraction to its lowest terms.

NOTE. It is always easy to tell whether 25 is a divisor of any given number. 25 will exactly divide any number whose two right-hand figures are zeros or 25, 50, or 75.

*The power of a number is the number multiplied by itself one or more times as, $10 \times 10 = 100$; $10 \times 10 \times 10 = 1000$, etc.

Illustration. Reduce $.71\frac{3}{7}$ to a common fraction.

$.71\frac{3}{7} = \frac{71\frac{3}{7}}{100}$ (1) Write the decimal in its equivalent common-fraction form.

(2) Multiply both numerator and denominator by the denominator of the fraction in the numerator.

$\frac{71\frac{3}{7} \times 7}{100 \times 7} = \frac{500}{700} = \frac{5}{7}$ (3) Reduce the resulting common fraction to its lowest terms.

Problems

Change the following decimals to equivalent common fractions:

	a	*b*	*c*	*d*
1.	.13	.04159	.0207	.0278
2.	.052	.0005	.00345	.06
3.	.3845	.004725	.020	.592875
4.	.004	.6	.0045	.0605

5. $.1875$	**9.** $.26\frac{2}{3}$	**13.** $.583\frac{1}{3}$	**17.** $.133\frac{1}{3}$
6. $.41\frac{2}{3}$	**10.** $.777\frac{7}{9}$	**14.** $.128$	**18.** $.045$
7. $.0125$	**11.** $.005$	**15.** $.432$	**19.** $.055$
8. $.0025$	**12.** $.0075$	**16.** $.375$	**20.** $.93\frac{3}{4}$

Writing Common Fractions in Their Decimal Form

Illustration. If we wish to write $\frac{5}{100}$ (five hundredths) in its decimal form, we write it .05.

That is, when there are not enough figures in the *numerator* to indicate the order required in the *denominator*, zeros are inserted between the decimal point and the first integer of the numerator to fill out the required number of places or figures.

Illustration. Change $\frac{3}{8}$ to a decimal fraction.

$$8\overline{)3.000}\quad = .375$$

Hence $\frac{3}{8} = .375$

Place a decimal point at the right of the numerator, annex zeros, and divide by the denominator.

In some cases the division is not *exact.* The number of places to carry out the division should be indicated as "Reduce to the nearest hundredth" or Reduce to the nearest thousandth" or "Find the exact decimal equivalent of . . ."

Illustration. Find the exact decimal equivalent of $\frac{4}{7}$.

$$7\overline{)4.00}\quad .57\tfrac{1}{7}$$

Hence $\frac{4}{7} = .57\frac{1}{7}$

Illustration. Reduce $\frac{4}{11}$ to a decimal fraction, to the nearest thousandth.

$$11\overline{)4.0000}\quad .3636$$

Hence $\frac{4}{11} = .364$

It is necessary to find the quotient to ten-thousandths. Since the last figure, 6, is more than 5, the digit 3 in thousandths' place is changed to 4 and the 6 is dropped. Hence $\frac{4}{11} = .364$, to the nearest thousandth.

Illustration. Reduce $.18\frac{3}{7}$ to a decimal of four places of exact value.

$.18\frac{3}{7}$ is a two-place decimal. (The fraction $\frac{3}{7}$ does not count as a place.) To make it a four-place decimal, the fraction $\frac{3}{7}$ must be changed to a two-place decimal and annexed to .18. Dividing, we find that $\frac{3}{7} = .42\frac{6}{7}$. Hence $.18\frac{3}{7} = .1842\frac{6}{7}$.

NOTE. The $\frac{3}{7}$ in $.18\frac{3}{7}$ is in reality $.00\frac{3}{7}$. Reducing $.00\frac{3}{7}$ to a four-place decimal gives $.0042\frac{6}{7}$, thus: $.00\frac{3}{7} = \frac{\frac{3}{7}}{100} = \frac{3}{700} = .0042\frac{6}{7}$. Hence what is actually done is to add .18 and $.0042\frac{6}{7}$, which gives $.1842\frac{6}{7}$.

Problems

Write the following fractions in their equivalent decimal form:

	a	*b*	*c*	*d*
1.	$\frac{4}{10}$	$\frac{125}{1000}$	$\frac{32}{100}$	$\frac{3}{100}$
2.	$\frac{5}{100}$	$\frac{307}{10000}$	$\frac{46}{1000}$	$\frac{7}{1000}$
3.	$\frac{35}{100}$	$\frac{42}{10000}$	$\frac{15}{100000}$	$\frac{16}{10000}$
4.	$\frac{15}{1000}$	$\frac{11}{100}$	$\frac{128}{1000000}$	$\frac{625}{10000}$

Reduce to decimal fractions, as indicated:

To Exact Equivalent	*To Nearest Hundredth*	*To Nearest Thousandth*
1. $\frac{1}{3}$	**6.** $\frac{5}{9}$	**11.** $\frac{2}{3}$
2. $\frac{9}{16}$	**7.** $\frac{4}{15}$	**12.** $\frac{5}{16}$
3. $\frac{11}{20}$	**8.** $\frac{5}{11}$	**13.** $\frac{6}{7}$
4. $\frac{5}{6}$	**9.** $\frac{2}{7}$	**14.** $\frac{5}{12}$
5. $\frac{3}{7}$	**10.** $\frac{3}{16}$	**15.** $\frac{1}{12}$

ADDING AND SUBTRACTING DECIMALS

Decimals are *added* and *subtracted* just as whole numbers are added and subtracted. **In writing decimals for addition or subtraction, place the decimal points directly under one another.**

Illustration. Add 4.5, .025, 15.05, 1.02565, and 7.602.

By placing the decimal points under one another, *tenths* are written *under tenths; hundredths, under hundredths; thousandths, under thousandths,* and so on, so that when the numbers are added, digits of like decimal order are added together.

```
     4.5
      .025
    15.05
     1.02565
     7.602
    ________
    28.20265
```

Illustration. From 4.02 subtract 2.4563.

In subtraction, as in addition, the numbers must be written so that the decimal points are in a vertical column.

```
    4.02
    2.4563
    ______
    1.5637
```

The minuend 4.02 might be written 4.0200 without changing its value. Then the numbers would appear like this:

```
    4.0200
    2.4563
    ______
```

It is not customary to write the extra zeros, but the subtraction is done just as though they were expressed.

Problems

1. From the sum of 5.25, .375, and 9.0275 subtract the sum of 3.028, .025, and 7.35965.

2. From the sum of .0325, .00158, and 16.1 subtract the sum of 5.5, 2.037, and 4.056254.

Extend each of the following pairs of numbers to a column of ten numbers and add as directed on page 155. Subtract the total of problem 4 from the total of problem 3; the total of problem 6 from the total of problem 5.

3. 428.36	**4.** 3.276	**5.** 40.5	**6.** .9472
297.4	15.259	16.275	.05265

Addition and Subtraction Involving Both Common Fractions and Decimal Fractions

Illustration. Add $4\frac{3}{4}$, $17.33\frac{1}{3}$, and 2.0252.

Reduce the common fractions to their decimal-fraction form. Since one of the addends, 2.0252, has four decimal places, each of the other decimals must be carried out to four places unless, as in the case of $\frac{3}{4} = .75$, the decimal terminates in less than four places. When the decimals have been reduced, the addition is easily made.

$$\begin{aligned} 4\tfrac{3}{4} &= 4.75 \\ 17.33\tfrac{1}{3} &= 17.3333\tfrac{1}{3} \\ 2.0252 &= 2.0252 \\ \hline & 24.1085\tfrac{1}{3} \end{aligned}$$

Illustration. From $15.14\frac{2}{7}$ subtract $7.168\frac{2}{3}$.

Change the decimals so that each has the same number of decimal places. Then subtract as in ordinary subtraction of mixed numbers in common fractions.

$$\begin{array}{rcr|c} 15.14\frac{2}{7} & = & 15.142\frac{6}{7} & \frac{18}{21} \\ 7.168\frac{2}{3} & = & 7.168\frac{2}{3} & \frac{14}{21} \\ \hline & & 7.974 & \frac{4}{21} \end{array}$$

Problems

Add:

1.	**2.**	**3.**	**4.**
$4.32\frac{1}{3}$	3.4755	.4275	42.85
6.578	.0568	.5	3.026
2.0256	$1\frac{5}{8}$	6.	$.52\frac{1}{3}$
1.0025	$7\frac{2}{9}$	$\frac{1}{3}$	$7.33\frac{2}{3}$
$.0048\frac{1}{3}$	$16\frac{5}{12}$	$4\frac{3}{8}$	$\frac{7}{8}$
$7\frac{1}{6}$	$18.04\frac{1}{3}$	$.01\frac{2}{3}$	$13\frac{3}{7}$
$9\frac{2}{3}$	$5.77\frac{7}{9}$	$.45\frac{1}{4}$	.325
.45	16.	8.005	1.1

5. From $14\frac{1}{3}$ subtract 11.275.
6. From $5.02\frac{1}{4}$ subtract 3.9675.
7. From $14.55 - 2\frac{1}{3}$ subtract $18\frac{1}{12} - 9.33\frac{1}{6}$.

MULTIPLYING DECIMALS

In multiplying decimals point off as many decimal places in the product as there are decimal places in both the multiplicand and the multiplier.

A Mixed Decimal by a Mixed Decimal

Illustration. Multiply 4.135 by 2.7.

Multiply exactly as with whole numbers. Since there are 3 decimal places in the multiplicand and 1 decimal place in the multiplier, (3 + 1) places, or 4 places, are pointed off in the product.

```
  4.135
    2.7
 ------
 2 8945
 8 270
-------
11.1645
```

A Decimal by a Decimal

Illustration. Multiply .0125 by .023.

If the product does not contain as many figures as the sum of the number of places in both multiplier and multiplicand, zeros must be written at the left of the product to make up the required number of places.

```
   .0125
    .023
   -----
     375
    250
--------
.0002875
```

Problems

Multiply and point off the product correctly:

1. 3.278 × .145	6. 5.025 × 4.26
2. 5.026 × .0003	7. .004525 × 3.7
3. 11.458 × .0123	8. $1.16\frac{2}{3}$ × .3456
4. 1.005 × 475.50	9. 9.3 × $.475\frac{1}{3}$
5. 1.0025 × 3000	10. $8\frac{3}{4}$ × 9.648

DIVIDING DECIMALS

Moving the decimal point of any number one place to the right is the same as multiplying the number by 10; moving it two places to the right is the same as multiplying by 100, and so on.

Moving the decimal point in both divisor and dividend the same number of places to the right does not affect the quotient.

This law may be stated in this way:

Multiplying both divisor and dividend by the same number does not change the quotient.

A Mixed Decimal by a Decimal

Illustration. Divide 45.28 by .4.

Write the dividend and divisor as for division of whole numbers. Move the decimal point in the divisor as many places to the right as necessary to make the divisor a whole number. Move the decimal point in the dividend the same number of places to the right. Before dividing, place the decimal point for the quotient directly above the new decimal point in the dividend. Then divide as in whole numbers, placing the figures in the quotient directly above the figures in the dividend, figure for figure. If the quotient figures are correctly placed, the decimal point will be in its proper place.

```
   11 3.2
‸4.)45‸2.8
```

A Decimal by a Whole Number

Illustration. Divide .03125 by 125.

Since the divisor is a whole number, the decimal points are not moved. Place the decimal point for the quotient directly above the decimal point in the dividend. Divide as in whole numbers, placing the first figure of the quotient, 2, above the 2 of the dividend. Since there are three places between the decimal point and the quotient figure 2, fill in those places with zeros.

```
     .00025
125).03125
       250
       ---
       625
       625
       ---
```

A Whole Number by a Decimal

Illustration. Divide 525 by .035.

Before dividing, move the decimal point in the divisor three places to the right (that is, multiply it by 1000), as indicated. The decimal point in the dividend must also be moved three places to the right. Place the decimal point for the quotient directly above the *new* decimal point in the dividend. Divide as in whole numbers, filling in the place between the quotient figures, 15, and the decimal point with zeros, giving a quotient of 15,000.

```
        15 000.
‸035.)525‸000.
      35
      ---
      175
      175
      ---
```

Problems

Find the quotients:

1. 5.64 ÷ .8	**9.** .162 ÷ 180
2. 93.6 ÷ 6	**10.** 4800 ÷ .016
3. 1.44 ÷ .12	**11.** 55 ÷ .75 (to 3 places)
4. 172.8 ÷ .144	**12.** 15.52 ÷ 96
5. 30.25 ÷ 55	(to nearest ten-thousandth)
6. 43.75 ÷ .0125	**13.** 23.925 ÷ 16.5
7. .7864 ÷ 80	**14.** 444.67$\frac{1}{2}$ ÷ 23.1
8. 57.6 ÷ .048	**15.** .01 ÷ 1000

16. The circumference of a circle is 3.1416 times its diameter. Find the circumference of a circle whose diameter is 12.5 feet.

17. The market price of a share of stock was $46.875. A broker charged $.15 a share for buying the stock for a customer. How much was the total cost of 125 shares of the stock?

18. The man who bought the stock in problem 17 sold it 3 mo. after he bought it for $7187.50. Find the selling price per share.

19. At $.15 a yard, how many yards of ribbon can be bought for $4.95?

20. A commission merchant sold a quantity of potatoes and received $125 for selling them. If his commission was $.02 a bushel, how many bushels of potatoes did he sell?

21. If 4$\frac{1}{2}$ doz. eggs were given in exchange for 2$\frac{1}{2}$ lb. of tea at $.36 a pound, how much were the eggs worth a dozen?

22. Andrews and Company in 6 mo. used 5784 gal. of gasoline and 384 qt. of oil in their trucks. Gasoline cost $.13$\frac{1}{2}$, plus a tax of $.04, a gallon. Oil cost $.22$\frac{1}{2}$ a quart. Find the total cost of gasoline and oil for the 6 mo.

23. At $.43$\frac{3}{4}$ a yard how many yards of Pongee Silk can be purchased for $344.75?

COUNTING TIME

In reckoning time between two dates more than one month apart, three distinct methods are employed: *Compound Time, Exact Time,* and *Banker's Time.*

Compound time reckons every month as having 30 days.

Illustration. Find the compound time from April 15 to September 10.

September is the *ninth* month	9 mo.	10 da.
April is the *fourth* month	4	15
Time from April 15 to September 10 =	4 mo.	25 da.

Then, 30 da. + 10 da. − 15 da. = 25 da.
Thus 8 mo. − 4 mo. = 4 mo.

"Borrow" a month (30 days) from the 9 mo. Add this 30 da. to 10 da., making 40 da., and subtract 15 da., leaving 25 da. Then subtract 4 mo. from 8 mo. The compound time is 4 mo. 25 da.

Illustration. Express 4 mo. 25 da. as days.

4 mo. = 120 da.
120 da. + 25 da. = 145 da.

Exact time is reckoned in days (or in years and days if the time is greater than 1 yr.).

Illustration. Find the exact time from April 15 to September 10.

The remaining days in April are	15 da.
The days in May are	31
The days in June are	30
The days in July are	31
The days in August are	31
The 10 days in September are	10
Total	148 da.

Exact time gives 3 days more than compound time, owing to the fact that May, July, and August each have 31 days.

Banker's time reckons whole months (at 30 days each) for the number of *whole months* in the period of time and exact days for any part of a month beyond the whole months.

Illustration. Find the banker's time from April 15 to September 10.

From April 15 to August 15 is	4 mo.	
From Aug. 15 to Sept. 10, count exact days:		
The remaining days in August are 31 da. − 15 da. or		16 da.
The 10 days in September are		10
Total	4 mo.	26 da.

Converting the banker's time of 4 mo. 26 da. to days gives 146 da. Hence we find that the time from April 15 to September 10 by the three methods gives:

By compound time,	145 days
By exact time,	148 days
By banker's time,	146 days

In the illustration given above, the time reckoned by the three methods varies from 1 da. to 3 da. This discrepancy, however, does not exist in every case; in some cases it will be greater and in other cases, less. For instance, the time from January 25 to May 15 is identical by all three methods, except in leap year, when the exact time is 1 day more.

Problems

Find the time (*a*) by compound time, (*b*) by exact time, and (*c*) by banker's time:

1. From Feb. 15 to Aug. 30
2. From Jan. 10 to Sept. 15
3. From April 1 to Oct. 7
4. From May 28 to Dec. 14
5. From June 18 to Nov. 5
6. From Feb. 4 to Oct. 1
7. From Nov. 18 to Feb. 15
8. From Dec. 30 to May 8
9. From Oct. 8 to May 3
10. From Aug. 31 to Feb. 28

11. A note was issued on February 13 and was paid on December 10 following. Find the time it had run by (*a*) compound time; (*b*) by exact time; and (*c*) by banker's time.

MEASUREMENTS

Without a system of measurements it would be impossible to carry on any kind of business.

Milk is purchased by the quart, sugar by the pound, ribbon by the yard, oranges by the dozen, land by the acre, and so on. It is important, therefore, that everyone should know the common measures and understand how to measure with them.

Originally there were no standards, such as the foot, the pound, or the gallon. The manner in which our common units of measure came into use is interesting. Some of them are as follows:

Yard. At one time it was said that a *yard* was the distance around a man's body. Not all men have the same sized bodies. Later King Henry I of England, in the twelfth century, A.D., decreed that the yard should be the distance from the end of his nose to the end of his thumb when his arm was outstretched.

Foot. Originally a *foot* was the length of a man's foot. Men's feet differ in size. Then there came an attempt to standardize the foot and the rod came into use.

Rod. Sixteen men were stood one in front of another with one foot of each man placed in front of the foot of the man behind him. The combined length of the sixteen feet was to be the official *rod*, and $\frac{1}{16}$ of the rod was to be the *foot*.

Inch. The word "inch" is derived from the Latin *uncia*, meaning one-twelfth part. Hence, we have 12 inches in a foot. In early times the inch was divided into barleycorns.

Barleycorns. A statute provided that the inch should be equal to "three grains of barley dry and round," placed end to end. Hence, we have the measure "3 barleycorns equal 1 inch." The barleycorn is used by shoemakers in indicating the size of shoes. After size 8, which is eleven inches long, each size adds $\frac{1}{3}$ of an inch to the length of the shoe.

Hand. This unit is used in measuring the height of a horse. It has come to be regarded as 4 inches. Originally, the measure was the distance across a man's hand, from which the unit takes its name.

Cubit. This unit of measure is not in common use. It is found in the Bible and in some of our older literature. There is no fixed length of the cubit. The average of the several lengths assigned to it is about 18 inches. Originally it was the distance from a man's elbow to the end of his middle finger.

Pace. From the Latin *passus*, a pace, or step. Originally the *pace* was the length of two steps, that is, the "distance from the heel of one foot to the heel of the same foot when it next touched the ground in walking." This was called the Roman pace, and was reckoned as 5 feet. As used today, the pace is one step. In ordinary walking it is about $2\frac{1}{2}$ feet. It is used in the country by farmers in making rough estimates of distances. A tall man may count a pace as three feet. Why?

Mile. From the Latin *millia passum*, a thousand paces. While a thousand paces today would not make a mile, the word "mile" is a fixture in the language.

MEASURING LINES OR DISTANCES

Linear Measure

Linear measure is used to measure *lines* or *distances.*

12 inches (in.)	= 1 foot (ft.)
3 feet	= 1 yard (yd.)
$5\frac{1}{2}$ yards	= 1 rod (rd.)
320 rods	= 1 mile (mi.)

1 mi. = 320 rd. = 1760 yd. = 5280 ft. = 63,360 in.

Other linear measures are:

1 hand	= 4 in.	(Used in measuring the height of horses)
1 fathom	= 6 ft.	(Used in measuring depths at sea)
1 knot	= 1 nautical mile = 1 geographical mile = $1.152\frac{2}{3}$ mi.	

Important Facts to Remember

12 in. = 1 foot	$16\frac{1}{2}$ ft. = 1 rod
36 in. = 1 yard	320 rd. = 1 mile
3 ft. = 1 yard	5280 ft. = 1 mile

MEASURING SURFACES OR AREAS

The area of a given surface is the number of **area units** in the surface.

Units of area are *square inches, square feet, square yards, square rods, acres* (1 acre = 160 sq. rd.), etc.

Square Measure

Square measure is used to measure surfaces or areas.

144 square inches (sq. in.)	= 1 square foot (sq. ft.)
9 square feet	= 1 square yard (sq. yd.)
$30\frac{1}{4}$ square yards	= 1 square rod (sq. rd.)
160 square rods	= 1 acre (A.)
640 acres	= 1 square mile (sq. mi.)

1 A. = 160 sq. rd. = 4840 sq. yd. = 43,560 sq. ft.

A square = 100 sq. ft. (Used in roofing)

Shapes of Surfaces

For measurement purposes surfaces are thought of, or divided up into definite forms, such as the *parallelogram*, *rectangle*, and *square*, etc.

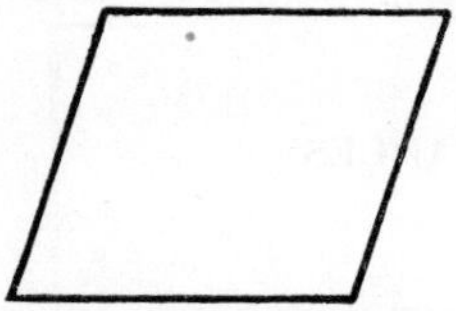

PARALLELOGRAM

A **parallelogram** is a plane surface having four sides, the opposite sides being parallel to each other.

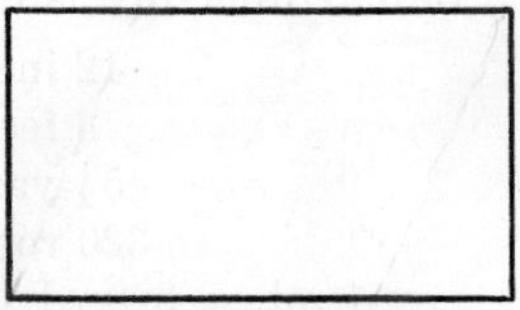

RECTANGLE

A **rectangle** is a parallelogram whose angles are right angles.

SQUARE

A square is a rectangle whose four sides are equal.

1. How many small squares are shown in the rectangle at the right?

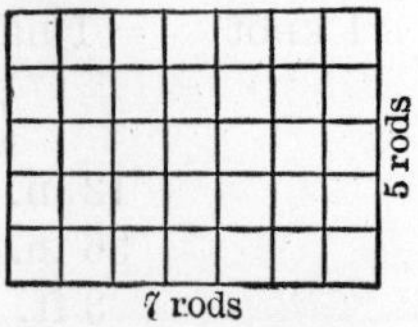

2. How can you find the number of small squares without counting all of them?

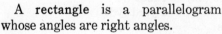

3. How many small squares are there in one row of squares? How many rows of small squares are there?

Area of a Parallelogram

The **area** of a parallelogram is the number of **units of area** within its plane surface.

The *length* of a parallelogram is frequently called its **base,** and its *width* is called its **height.**

The area of a parallelogram is equal to the product of its base by its height.

If the *base* is indicated by the letter b, the *height* by the letter h, and the *area* by the letter A, we may express the rule in terms of a formula as

$$b \times h = A \quad \text{or} \quad bh = A$$

Memorize this formula for finding the area of a parallelogram.

Perimeter of a Parallelogram

A distinction must be made between *area* and *perimeter*. The **perimeter** of a plane surface is the distance around it; the **area** is the number of *units of area* within the *perimeter* of the plane surface.

What is the *perimeter* of the plane figure shown at the right? What is its *area?*

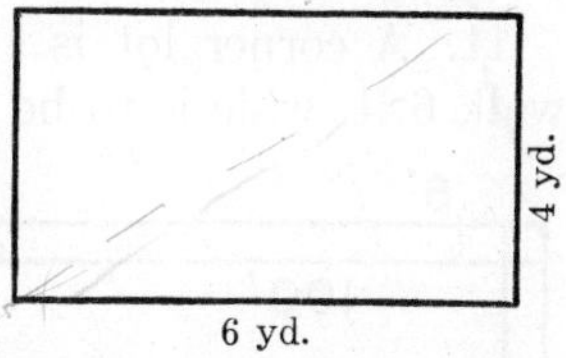

Observe the rectangle shown at the right and notice that there are 2 sides each 6 yd. long, and 2 sides each 4 yd. long. The perimeter may be expressed as (when l = length and w = width)

$$(2 \times l) + (2 \times w) \quad \text{or as} \quad 2\,l + 2\,w.$$

Substitute the figures in the dimensions of the rectangle shown above for the letters in this formula, and see what the result is:

$$2 \times (l + w)$$

How does it differ from $2\,l + 2\,w$?

Problems

Find (*a*) the *area,* and (*b*) the *perimeter*, of parallelograms whose dimensions are as follows:

1. Base 6 ft., height 3 ft.

2. Base 9 ft., height 4 ft.

3. Base 15 ft., height 8 ft.

4. Base 20 in., height 9 in.

5. Base 7 yd., height 9 ft.

6. Base 40 rd., height 8 rd.

7. If you know that a rectangle is divided into 56 small squares and that there are 8 small squares in a row, how can you tell how many rows of squares there are in the rectangle?

Area ÷ base	= height	$A \div b = h$
Area ÷ height	= base	$A \div h = b$

8. A section of street 40 rods long has an area of 120 sq. rd. How wide is it?

9. If it takes 48 sq. yd. of linoleum to cover a hallway 24 yards long, how wide is the hallway?

10. A roofer estimates it will take 14 squares (1400 sq. ft.) of roofing material to cover a roof 35 ft. wide. How long is the roof?

11. A corner lot is 100 ft. on each side. A cement sidewalk 6 ft. wide is to be built on two sides of the lot, but not on the lot. If the cost is $.10 a square foot, how much will it cost?

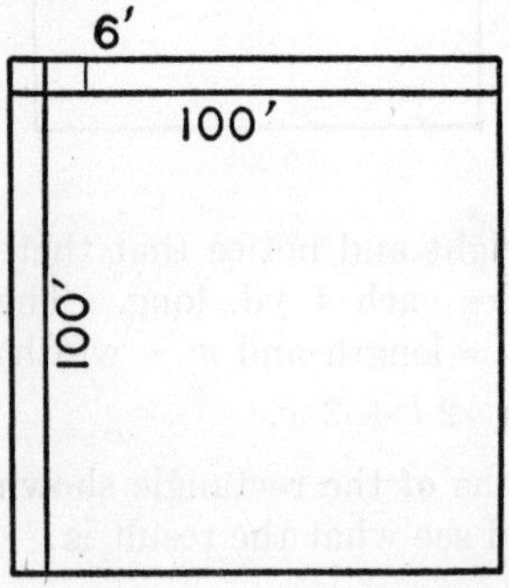

Study the diagram at the left and observe that the total length of the walk is 100′ + 100′ + 6′.

12. Draw a similar diagram and show the sidewalk *on* the lot. Use the same dimensions as in problem 11. What is the length of the sidewalk?

Area of a Triangle

A triangle is a plane figure having 3 sides and 3 angles.

Illustration. The square at the right is 6 yd. on each side. The diagonal divides the square into 2 equal parts. Each part is a triangle.

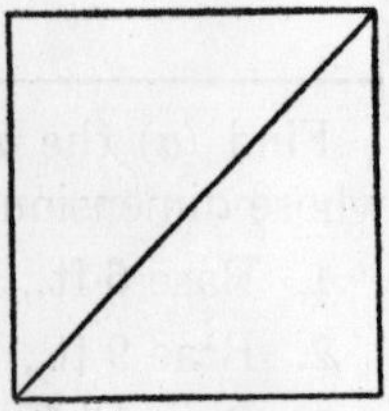

What is the area of the square? What is the area of one of the triangles?

Finding the Area of a Triangle When the Base and Height Are Given

The area of a triangle is equal to one half of the product of its base and height.

$$A = \frac{1}{2} \times (b \times h) \quad \text{or} \quad A = \frac{b \times h}{2}$$

Thus, $\frac{6 \times 6}{2} = 18$ yd., area of 1 triangle (Page 212)

Diagonal. Observe the forms of parallelograms shown here, and note the effect of drawing a diagonal through each of them.

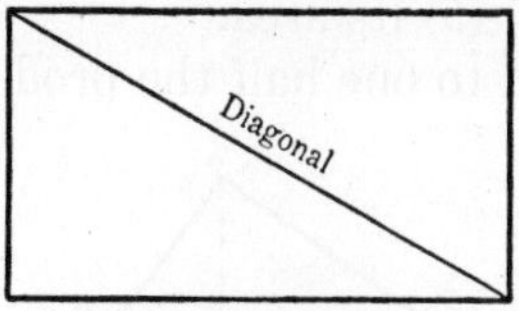

RECTANGLE

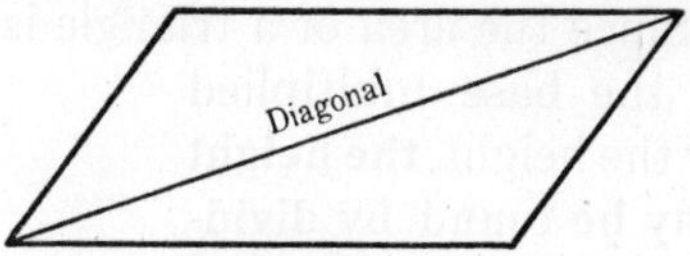

PARALLELOGRAM

The **diagonal** of a parallelogram divides the parallelogram into two equal triangles.

The **height, or altitude,** of a triangle is the perpendicular distance from its base to the highest point opposite. In the triangle at the right the line *CD* is the *height.*

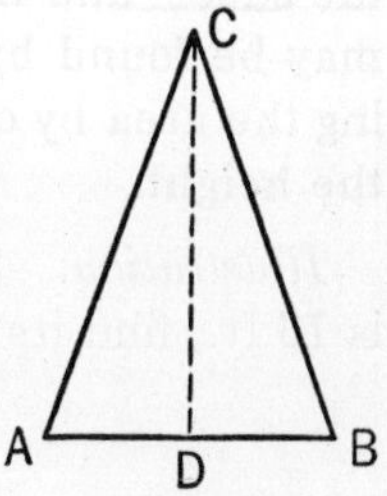

TRIANGLE

Problems

Find the area of triangles whose dimensions are as follows:

1. Base 13 in., height 12 in.
2. Base 8 ft., height 4 ft.
3. Base 6 yd., height 8 ft.
4. Base 16 rd., height 10 rd.
5. Base 40 ft., height 12 ft.
6. The end of a building has dimensions like those shown in the diagram, page 214. It is to be painted at a cost

of $.25 a square yard. Reckoning to the nearest whole square yard, find the cost of painting.

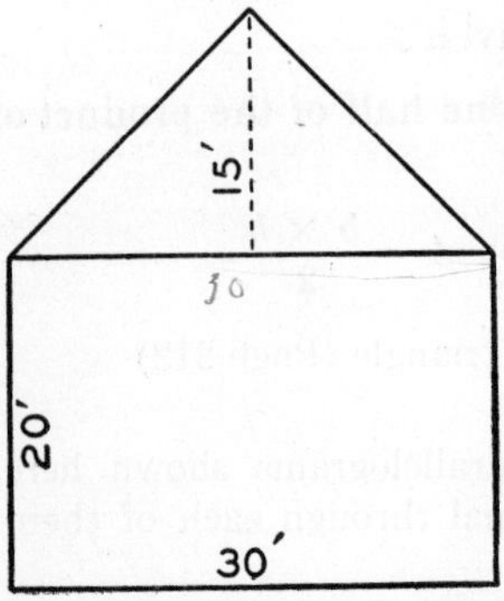

7. A rectangular garden plot is $7\frac{1}{2}$ rods long and 5 rods wide. Around it is a picket fence. Find (*a*) the length of the fence; (*b*) the area of the garden.

8. A triangular plot of ground has the shape and dimensions shown in the diagram below. Find (*a*) its perimeter; (*b*) its area.

Since the area of a triangle is equal to one half the product of the base multiplied by the height, **the height may be found by dividing the area by one half the base; and the base may be found by dividing the area by one half the height.**

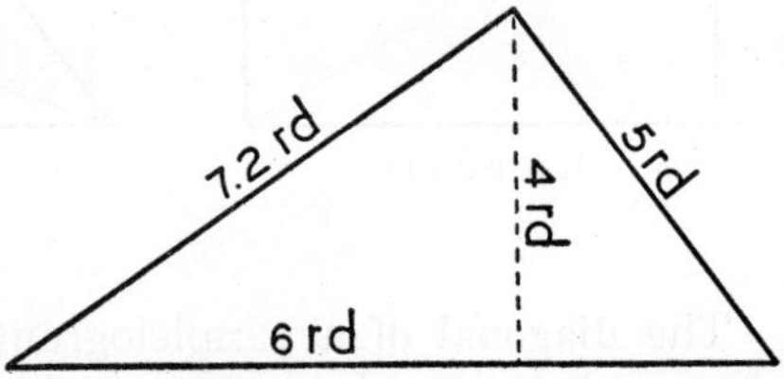

Illustration. The area of a triangle is 48 sq. ft. If its base is 16 ft., find its height.

$$h = \frac{A}{\frac{1}{2}b} = A \div \frac{1}{2}b$$

Therefore, $48 \div 8 = 6$, feet in height

Illustration. The area of a triangle is 108 sq. in. Its height is 18 in. Find its base.

$$b = \frac{A}{\frac{1}{2}h} = A \div \frac{1}{2}h$$

$108 \div 9 = 12$, inches in the base.

The principle used in finding the height or the base of a triangle is the same as that stated on page 13; namely, The product of two factors divided by either factor gives the other factor. Thus, since $A = b \times h/2$, or $A = h \times b/2$, it follows that $b = A \div h/2$, and $h = A \div b/2$.

Problems

Find the missing part in each of the following:

	AREA OF TRIANGLE	BASE	HEIGHT
1.	64 sq. in.	16 in.	?
2.	72 sq. ft.	?	12 ft.
3.	108 sq. ft.	8 yd.	?
4.	?	14 yd.	16 yd.
5.	88 sq. ft.	22 ft.	?
6.	1 Acre (160 sq. rd.)	?	32 rd.
7.	10 Acres	40 rd.	?

MEASUREMENT OF A CIRCLE

Observe the circle at the right. What is the *circumference?* The *diameter?* The *radius?*

How does the length of the radius compare with the length of the diameter?

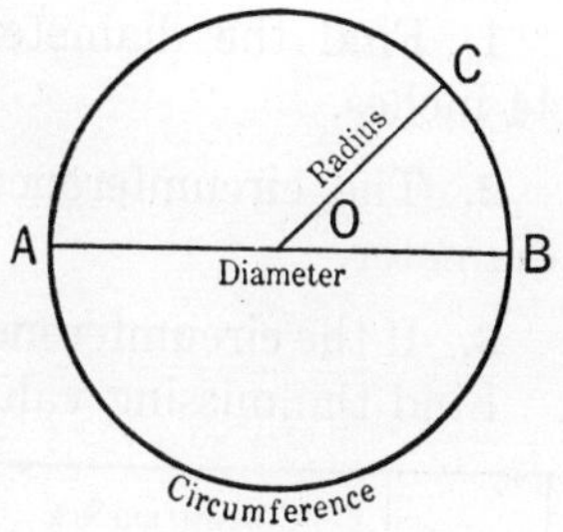

By actual measurement it is found that the circumference of a circle is 3.1416 times the diameter. (3.1416 is very nearly $3\frac{1}{7}$, hence, unless an exact measure is required, use $3\frac{1}{7}$ instead of 3.1416.)

It is customary to call 3.1416, or $3\frac{1}{7}$, by the Greek name of *pi*, and to write the value by means of the Greek letter *p*, which is π.

Finding the Circumference of a Circle When the Diameter Is Given

Since the *circumference* of a circle is $3\frac{1}{7}$ times its *diameter*, the expression, or formula, for finding the circumference of a circle is

$$C = \pi d. \quad \text{That is, } C = \pi \times d.$$

Problems

1. Find the circumference of a circle whose diameter is 14 ft.

2. Find the circumference of a circle whose diameter is 66 ft.

3. Find the circumference of a circle whose diameter is 36 inches.

Finding the Diameter of a Circle When the Circumference Is Given

Since the *circumference* of a circle is equal to the *diameter* multiplied by π, **the diameter may be found by dividing the circumference by π.** That is, $d = \frac{C}{\pi} = C \div \pi$

Problems

1. Find the diameter of a circle whose circumference is 44 inches.

2. The circumference of a circle is 66 inches. Find its diameter.

3. If the circumference of a circle is 11 ft., find its diameter.

Find the missing value in each of the following:

	Circumference	Diameter	Radius
4.	88 inches	?	?
5.	?	35 feet	?
6.	?	?	21 inches
7.	154 feet	?	?
8.	?	10 feet 6 inches	?
9.	?	?	3 feet 6 inches
10.	110 feet	?	?
11.	?	28 feet	?

Finding the Area of a Circle

To find the area of a circle think of the circle as being divided into many triangles like this illustration. It is readily seen that the circumference of the circle is equal to the sum of the bases of all the small triangles which make up the circle.

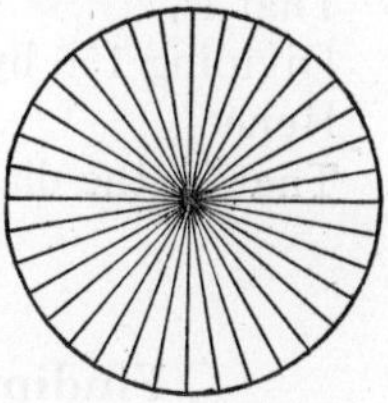

If we were to take any one of the triangles, its area would be equal to the product of its base by half of its height. *The height of one of the triangles is the radius of the circle.*

Since the bases of all the triangles in the circle are equal to the circumference of the circle, **the area of the circle may be found by multiplying the circumference by one half the radius.**

That is, $A = c \times \frac{r}{2}$

Since $c = \pi \times d$, and $d = 2 \times r$

Then, $A = \pi \times 2 \times r \times \frac{r}{2} = \pi r^2$

That is, $A = \pi r^2$

Illustration. Find the area of a circle whose diameter is 42 inches.

The radius is $\frac{1}{2}$ of 42 inches = 21 inches.
Using the formula,

$$A = \pi r^2$$
$$\text{Area} = 3\tfrac{1}{7} \times 21 \times 21 = 1386 \text{ sq. ft.}$$

Problems

Similarly, find the areas of circles whose diameters are:

1. 28 inches
2. 56 inches
3. 70 feet
4. 14 yards

Find the area of circles whose radii are:

5. 5 inches
6. 7 inches
7. 12 feet
8. 3 yards

Finding the Diameter of a Circle

Illustration. The area of a circle is 156 sq. ft. Find its diameter.

$$A = \pi r^2$$

That is, $156 = 3\frac{1}{7} \times r^2$

Dividing 156 by $3\frac{1}{7}$ gives 49

Hence $r^2 = 49$ and $r = 7$

That is, the diameter is 2×7 ft., or 14 ft.

SQUARE ROOT

Finding the Square Root of a Number

As applied to plane figures, the term *square* refers to *area* and the term *square root* refers to *dimension,* that is, to one side of the square.

Thus, in a square 5 in. on each side, the area is 25 sq. in. because the *square* of 5 is 25. Conversely, the side of the square is 5 in. because the *square root* of 25 is 5.

A square is a product, of which the **square root** is one of the two equal factors.

The *perfect squares* from 1 to 100 are 1, 4, 9, 16, 25, 36, 49, 64, 81, 100. The *square roots* of these squares are 1, 2, 3, 4, 5, 6, 7, 8, 9, 10.

Solving problems relating to the circle requires a knowledge of square root.

The **method of finding square root** may be illustrated thus:

Illustration. Let the entire square in the figure at the left, *ABCD,* represent 576 sq. ft. Then one side of the square is equal to the square root of 576.

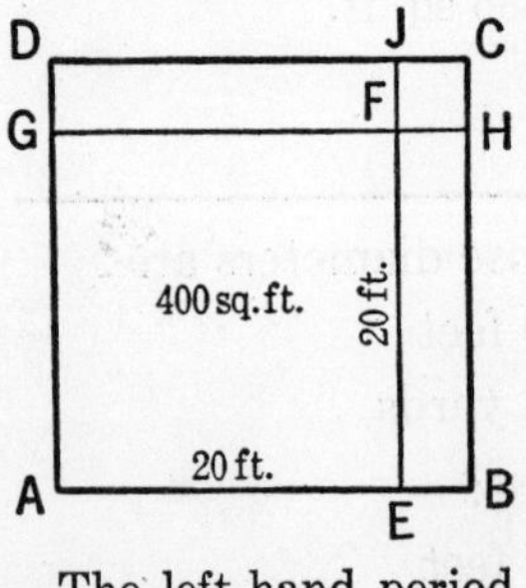

1. Divide the number 576 into periods or groups of two figures each, beginning at units. There are two periods. This shows that the root will have two digits.

	$\sqrt{5'76}$	= 20
	4 00	4
40	1 76	24
44	1 76	

The left-hand period is 5. The largest square less than 5 is 4. The square root of 4 is 2.

2. Since there are two periods in the power (576), write the zero after the 2 in the root, because the root is to have two digits. $20 \times 20 = 400$. Write 400 under 576 and subtract, leaving 176.

In the figure, notice that a square 20 ft. on a side, *AEFG*, has been formed. Its area is 400 sq. ft. The remaining area of 176 sq. ft. is in the two narrow strips on the sides of the square and in the little square in the corner.

3. The length of each of the long strips is 20 ft. Together they are 40 ft. long. This is the reason for doubling the root first found. Notice that nearly all the area of 176 sq. ft. is contained in these two narrow strips. All that remains is the little square in the corner, *FHCJ*. The length of the little square is the same as the width of one of the strips.

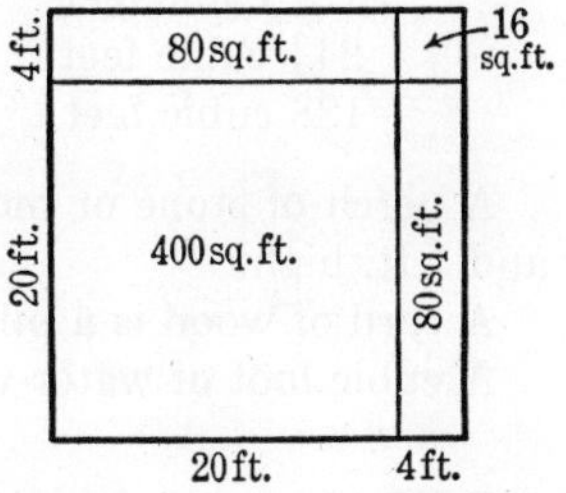

4. Dividing 176 by 40 gives 4. 4 is the width of the narrow strips and the length of each side of the little square.

5. Adding 4 to 40 gives 44, the total length of the two strips and the little square.

6. Multiplying the total length, 44, by 4 gives 176, which shows that 4 is the exact width of the strips on the side of the square.

7. Adding 20 and 4 gives 24.

Therefore, the square root of 576 is 24.

Problems

Find the square root of each of the following numbers:

	a	*b*	*c*	*d*	*e*
1.	16	36	4	100	144
2.	9	49	81	121	400

3. 289 5. 441 7. 256 9. 156.25

4. 324 6. 625 8. 729 10. 992.25

11. The area of a circle is $78\frac{4}{7}$ sq. in. Find its radius.

12. A circular flower plot contains $201\frac{1}{7}$ sq. ft. of ground. Find its diameter.

13. A circular silo is 12 ft. in diameter. A cement floor is laid in it at a cost of \$.25 a square foot. Find its cost.

Important Facts to Remember

144 sq. in. = 1 sq. ft. $3\frac{1}{7} \times$ diameter = circumference
9 sq. ft. = 1 sq. yd. πr^2 = area of a circle

MEASURING VOLUME OR CAPACITY

Cubic measure is the measure of *volume* or *capacity.*

1728 cubic inches (cu. in.)	=	1 cubic foot (cu. ft.)
27 cubic feet	=	1 cubic yard (cu. yd.)
$24\frac{3}{4}$ cubic feet	=	1 perch (P.)
128 cubic feet	=	1 cord (cd.)

A perch of stone or masonry is $16\frac{1}{2}$ ft. (1 rd.) long, $1\frac{1}{2}$ ft. wide, and 1 ft. high.

A cord of wood is a pile 8 ft. long, 4 ft. wide, and 4 ft. high.

A cubic foot of water weighs $62\frac{1}{2}$ lb.

Solids have three dimensions — *length, breadth,* and *thickness.*

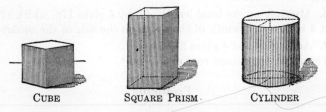

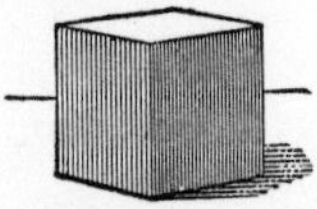

CUBE

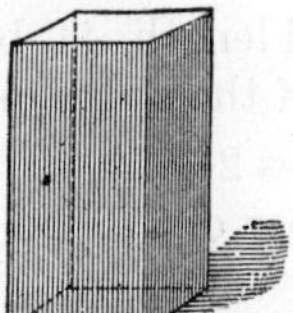

SQUARE PRISM

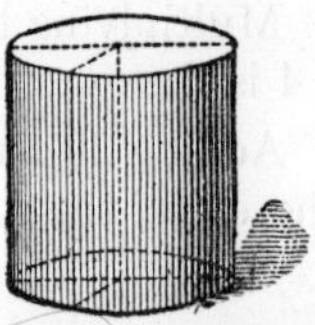

CYLINDER

The volume of a solid is measured in cubic units, as *cubic inches, cubic feet, cubic yards,* etc.

A cubic inch is a *cube* each of whose edges measures *1 inch.*

What is a cubic foot? A cubic yard?

Illustration. A block of wood is 4 ft. long, 2 ft. wide, and 1 ft. thick. How many cubic feet are there in it?

$4 \times 2 \times 1 = 8$, number of cubic feet.

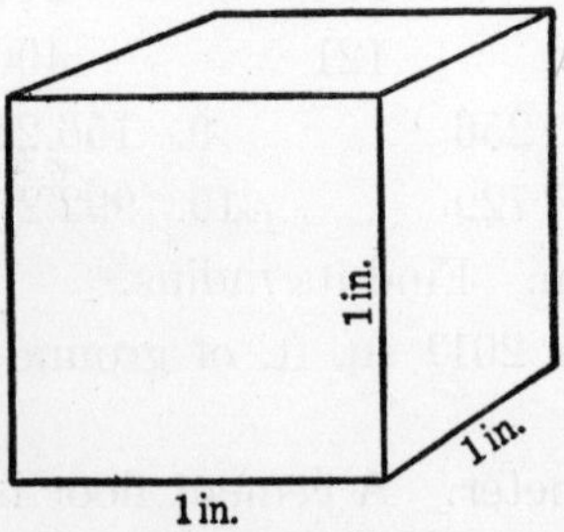

CUBIC INCH

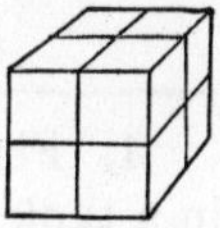

(1) If each small cube in this illustration measures 1 foot on each edge, how many cubic feet are there in the whole cube?

(2) If each small cube in this illustration measures 1 cubic yard, how many cubic yards are there in the whole block?

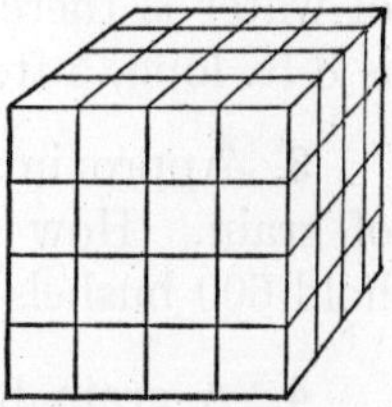

Volume refers to the number of *cubic inches, cubic feet, cubic yards,* etc., of solids, as blocks of marble, walls of masonry, sand and gravel, etc. **Capacity** refers to the contents of containers, such as tanks, barrels, cisterns, reservoirs, etc.

Capacity may be spoken of as cubic inches, cubic feet, etc., but it is more common to refer to capacity as *quarts, gallons, bushels,* etc.

The volume of a rectangular solid is equal to the product of its three dimensions — length, width, and height.

Hence, $V = lwh$. That is, $V = l \times w \times h$

Illustration. Find the volume of a solid 6 ft. long, 4 ft. wide, and 3 ft. high.

$6 \times 4 \times 3 = 72$, number cubic feet.

The capacity of a tank or bin is first found in terms of cubic inches, cubic feet, etc., and then changed to gallons, bushels, etc., as required. Cubic inches, cubic feet, etc., of capacity, are found just the same as cubic units of volume are found. That is,

V (of capacity) $= lwh$

The relations existing between cubic units of volume and capacity are as follows:

231 cu. in. = 1 gallon
1 cu. ft. = $7\frac{1}{2}$ gallons (very nearly)
1 cu. ft. = .8 of a bushel of grain
1 cu. ft. = .63 of a bushel of potatoes, apples, or corn on the cob, etc.

Illustration. How many gallons of water will a water tank 8 ft. long, 3 ft. wide, and 2 ft. deep hold?

$8 \times 3 \times 2 = 48$, no. cu. ft. in contents.

$48 \times 7\frac{1}{2}$ gal. = 360 gal. in the tank.

Problems

1. Find the number of gallons of water that can be held in a tank 30 ft. long, 4 ft. wide, and 3 ft. deep.

2. Water weighs $62\frac{1}{2}$ lb. to the cubic foot. What weight of water is there in a sprinkling cart full of water, if the tank is 8 ft. long, 5 ft. wide, and 4 ft. deep?

3. Approximately $1\frac{1}{4}$ cubic feet of space will hold 1 bushel of grain. How many cubic feet of capacity are required to hold 600 bushels of grain? 1000 bushels of grain?

4. A grain bin is 16 ft. long, 6 ft. wide, and 5 ft. deep. How many bushels of grain will it hold?

5. How many gallons of water will a cistern 5 ft. square and 7 feet deep hold?

6. Mr. Avery wishes to build a grain bin to hold at least 850 bushels of grain. If he can make the bin 24 ft. long and $7\frac{1}{2}$ ft. wide, how deep must it be? (Give answer in whole feet.)

7. A potato bin is 16 ft. long, 6 feet wide, and is filled to a depth of 5 feet. How many bushels of potatoes are in it?

8. A corn crib is 18 ft. long and 6 ft. wide. To what depth will 550 bushels of corn on the cob fill it? (Answer in whole feet.)

9. A contractor plans to build a concrete wall 1 foot thick and 9 feet high along two sides of a courtyard 60 feet long and 40 feet wide. If the measurements are inside measurements, find how many cubic yards of concrete are required.

10. A truckman agreed to haul the dirt from an excavation which measured 36 feet long, 30 feet wide, and 6 feet deep, at $1.75 a load. His truck carries 3 cubic yards to a load. How much did it cost to haul the dirt away? If the truckman drew 8 loads a day, and it cost him $2.50 a day to run his truck, find his profit on the job.

MISCELLANEOUS MEASURES

Liquid Measure

4 gills (gi.) = 1 pint (pt.)
2 pints = 1 quart (qt.)
4 quarts = 1 gallon (gal.)
1 gal. = 4 qt. = 8 pt. = 32 gi.

The technical barrel of $31\frac{1}{2}$ gal. is little used. Barrels, casks, and hogsheads are of various sizes, with the capacity of each marked on it.

The wine gallon of 231 cu. in. is the standard unit of capacity. A wine gallon of water weighs very nearly $8\frac{1}{3}$ lb.

The imperial gallon of England contains 277.274 cu. in. and is very nearly equal to $1\frac{1}{5}$ wine gallons. An imperial gallon of water weighs 10 lb.

Apothecaries' Fluid Measure

These measures are used by druggists in putting up prescriptions of liquid medicines.

60 minims (m) = 1 fluid drachma (f ʒ)
8 fluid drachmas = 1 fluid ounce (f ℥)
16 fluid ounces = 1 pint (O)
8 pints = 1 gallon (Cong.)

The gallon of this measure is the same as the *wine gallon.*

Dry Measure

2 pints (pt.) = 1 quart (qt.)
8 quarts = 1 peck (pk.)
4 pecks = 1 bushel (bu.)

1 bu. = 4 pk. = 32 qt. = 64 pt.
1 bu. = 2150.42 cu. in.
The heaped bushel = 2747.71 cu. in.

The imperial bushel of England = 2218.192 cu. in. It is 8 times the *imperial gallon.*

Liquid and Dry Measures Compared

	Gallon	*Quart*	*Pint*
Liquid:	231 cu. in.	$57\frac{3}{4}$ cu. in.	$28\frac{7}{8}$ cu. in.
Dry:	$268\frac{4}{5}$ cu. in. ($\frac{1}{2}$ peck)	$67\frac{1}{5}$ cu. in.	$33\frac{3}{5}$ cu. in.

MEASURES OF WEIGHT

Three systems of weight are in use in the United States — *troy weight, apothecaries' weight,* and *avoirdupois weight.* In each system the *pound* is differently divided. The origin of the common terms, *pound, grain,* and *ounce,* is as follows:

Pound. From the Latin *pondus,* a weight. The avoirdupois pound is considered equal to 7000 grains of wheat.

Grain. It is from the above fact that we have the unit of weight called the *grain.* Grain is of uniform weight in the three systems of weight.

Ounce. Originally the *ounce* was one twelfth (Latin *uncia*) of a Roman pound. In modern times the ounce is $\frac{1}{16}$ of the avoirdupois pound, and $\frac{1}{12}$ of the troy and apothecary pounds.

Troy Weight

Troy weight is used by the government in weighing coins at the mint and by jewelers in weighing gold, silver, and precious stones.

24 grains (gr.)	= 1 pennyweight (pwt.)
20 pennyweight	= 1 ounce (oz.)
12 ounces	= 1 pound (lb.)

1 lb. = 12 oz. = 240 pwt. = 5760 gr.

1 carat (or karat) as a weight = 3.168 gr. As a degree of fineness it is $\frac{1}{24}$ part. Gold marked 18K (18 carats) is $\frac{18}{24}$ gold and $\frac{6}{24}$ alloy.

Apothecaries' Weight

These weights are used by druggists in compounding medicines.

20 grains (gr.)	= 1 scruple (Sc. or ℈)
3 scruples	= 1 dram (dr. or ʒ)
8 drams	= 1 ounce (oz. or ℥)
12 ounces	= 1 pound (lb. or ℔)

1 lb. = 12 ℥ = 96 ʒ = 288 ℈ = 5760 gr.

Avoirdupois Weight

Avoirdupois weight is used for weighing all sorts of coarse, heavy articles.

16 ounces (oz.)	= 1 pound (lb.)
100 pounds	= 1 hundredweight (cwt.)
20 hundredweight	= 1 ton (T.)

1 T. = 20 cwt. = 2000 lb. = 32,000 oz.

Long Ton Weight

The long ton (or gross ton) is used at the United States Custom House in determining duty on merchandise taxed by the ton. Coal and iron are sold wholesale at the mines by the long ton.

16 ounces (oz.)	=	1 pound (lb.)
28 pounds	=	1 quarter (qr.)
4 quarters (112 lb.)	=	1 hundredweight (cwt.)
20 hundredweight	=	1 ton (T.)

1 T. = 20 cwt. = 80 qr. = 2240 lb. = 35,840 oz.

Comparison of Weights

	Pound	*Ounce*	*Grain*
Troy:	5760 gr.	480 gr.	1 gr.
Apothecaries':	5760 gr.	480 gr.	1 gr.
Avoirdupois:	7000 gr.	$437\frac{1}{2}$ gr.	1 gr.

CIRCULAR OR ANGULAR MEASURE

Circular or angular measure is used in measuring angles or arcs of circles as applied to surveying, civil engineering, astronomical calculations, latitude, longitude, etc.

60 seconds (″)	=	1 minute (′)
60 minutes	=	1 degree (°)
360 degrees	=	1 circle (cir.)

1 cir. = 360° = 21,600′ = 1,296,000″

A quadrant = 90°; a sextant = 60°; a sign = 30°.

TIME MEASURE

Time is called the measure of duration. The common units of time are *year, day, hour, minutes,* and *seconds.*

60 seconds (sec.)	=	1 minute (min.)	52 weeks	=	1 year (yr.)
60 minutes	=	1 hour (hr.)	12 months	=	1 year
24 hours	=	1 day (da.)	365 days	=	1 common year
7 days	=	1 week (wk.)	366 days	=	1 leap year
30 days	=	1 month (mo.)	100 years	=	1 century

The length of the year is determined by the time required for the earth to make one complete revolution around the sun. The exact time is 365 da. 5 hr. 48 min. 46 sec. (very nearly $365\frac{1}{4}$ da.).

It is because of this extra $\frac{1}{4}$ of a day each year that we have a **leap year** once in 4 yr. But an allowance of $\frac{1}{4}$ of a day each year in making a *leap year* each 4 yr. is a little too much time, since the true year is not quite $365\frac{1}{4}$ da. To correct this error, all **centennial years** (1800, 1900, 2100, etc.) not divisible by 400 are not counted as leap years. All other years divisible by 4 are leap years.

The extra day of leap year is added to the month of February.

MONEY

English Money

English money is the legal currency of Great Britain. It includes gold, silver, and copper coins and bills.

4 farthings (far.)	= 1 penny (*d.*)
12 pence	= 1 shilling (*s.*)
20 shillings	= 1 pound, or sovereign (£)

French Money

French money is the legal currency of France. It is a decimal currency.

10 millimes (m.)	= 1 centime (c.)
10 centimes	= 1 decime (dc.)
10 decimes	= 1 franc (F.)

German Money

German money is the legal currency of Germany.

100 pfennige = 1 mark

Paper Measure

24 sheets	= 1 quire (qr.)
20 quires	= 1 ream (rm.)
2 reams	= 1 bundle (bdl.)
5 bundles	= 1 bale (bl.)

Counting

20 units	= 1 score
12 units	= 1 dozen (doz.)
12 dozen	= 1 gross (gro.)
12 gross	= 1 great gross (gr. gro.)

DENOMINATE NUMBERS

REDUCTION

Illustration. **Reduction Descending.** How many pints are there in 2 gal. 3 qt. 1 pt.?

$$\begin{aligned} 2 \text{ gal.} &= 2 \times 4 \times 2 \text{ pt.} &= 16 \text{ pt.} \\ 3 \text{ qt.} &= 3 \times 2 \text{ pt.} &= 6 \text{ pt.} \\ 1 \text{ pt.} & &= \underline{1 \text{ pt.}} \\ \text{Total} & &= 23 \text{ pt.} \end{aligned}$$

Hence 2 gal. 3 qt. 1 pt. = 23 pt.

Illustration. **Reduction Ascending.** How many yards, feet, and inches are there in 784 in.?

$$\begin{array}{l} 12 \text{ in.})\underline{784} \text{ in.} \\ \quad 3)\underline{\ 65}, \text{ number of feet} + 4 \text{ in.} \\ \qquad 21, \text{ number of yards} + 2 \text{ ft.} \end{array}$$

Hence 784 in. = 21 yd. 2 ft. 4 in.

Problems

1. How many ounces are there in 8 lb. 7 oz.?

2. Reduce 3 sq. yd. 5 sq. ft. 80 sq. in. to square inches.

3. A grocer sold 6 gal. 2 qt. 1 pt. of milk at $.06 a pint. How much did he receive for the milk?

4. If 12 lb. 8 oz. of tea was sold in 4-ounce packages at $.13 a package, how much was received for the tea?

5. An automobile wheel 108 in. in circumference made 1000 revolutions between Mr. Abel's home and his office. How many miles, rods, and yards is his office from his home?

6. A rectangular field is 48 rd. long and 24 rd. wide. How many fence posts set 12 ft. apart are required for a fence around the field?

7. A boy picked $2\frac{3}{8}$ bu. of chestnuts and sold them at $.05 a quart. How much did he receive for them?

8. A building plot is 4 rd. wide and 8 rd. long. (*a*) How many building plots can be made from a field of 10 acres if $\frac{1}{5}$ of the area is required for streets? (*b*) What part of an acre is the area of each building plot?

ADDITION AND SUBTRACTION

Illustration. **Addition.** A man worked as follows for 4 days: 7 hr. 20 min., 6 hr. 30 min., 8 hr. 25 min., and 5 hr. 40 min. Find the total time he worked.

7 hr. 20 min.	
6 hr. 30 min.	115 min. = 1 hr. 55 min.
8 hr. 25 min.	Carry 1 hr. to the hour column, making 27 hr.
5 hr. 40 min.	Hence the total time he worked was 27 hr. 55 min.
26 hr. 115 min. = 27 hr. 55 min.	

Illustration. **Subtraction.** From a piece of cloth containing 9 yd. 1 ft. 9 in., a merchant cut 4 yd. 2 ft. 3 in. How much cloth was left?

	3 in. taken from 9 in. leaves 6 in.
9 yd. 1 ft. 9 in.	Since 2 ft. cannot be taken from 1 ft., borrow
4 yd. 2 ft. 3 in.	1 yd. from 9 yd. and change it to feet. 1 yd. =
4 yd. 2 ft. 6 in.	3 ft. 3 ft. + 1 ft. = 4 ft. 4 ft. − 2 ft. = 2 ft.
	8 yd. − 4 yd. = 4 yd.

Hence there were 4 yd. 2 ft. 6 in. of cloth left.

Problems

1. Find the sum of 6 lb. 8 oz., 4 lb. 5 oz., 3 lb. 12 oz., and 9 lb. 15 oz.

2. An irregular field has sides of the following lengths: 28 rd. 3 yd. 2 ft., 32 rd. 4 yd. 1 ft., 40 rd. 5 yd., and 50 rd. 1 ft. Find the length of fence required to enclose the field.

3. A druggist bought 2 lb. 9 oz. 4 drams of quinine and dispensed 1 lb. 11 oz. 6 drams of it. How much quinine was left?

4. A jeweler saved 1 lb. 2 oz. 7 pwt. of gold in fine bits. He used 8 oz. 12 pwt. of it to make articles of jewelry. How much gold was left?

5. A dairyman had 28 gal. 3 qt. 1 pt. of milk from his own cows. He bought 17 gal. 2 qt. 1 pt. from a neighbor and then sold 40 gal. 3 qt. 1 pt. of milk. How much milk was left?

MULTIPLICATION AND DIVISION

Illustration. **Multiplication.** Multiply 6 bu. 3 pk. 4 qt. by 5.

	5 × 4 qt. = 20 qt. 20 qt. = 2 pk. and 4 qt.
6 bu. 3 pk. 4 qt.	Write 4 qt. and carry 2 pk.
5	(5 × 3 pk.) + 2 pk. = 17 pk.
34 bu. 1 pk. 4 qt.	17 pk. = 4 bu. and 1 pk.
	Write 1 pk. and carry 4 bu.
	(5 × 6 bu.) + 4 bu. = 34 bu.

Hence the product is 34 bu. 1 pk. 4 qt.

Illustration. **Division.** A plot of land containing 124 sq. rd. 4 sq. yd. 3 sq. ft. was divided into 6 equal lots. Find the area of each lot.

6)124 sq. rd. 4 sq. yd. 3 sq. ft.
20 sq. rd. 20 sq. yd. 8 sq. ft.

124 sq. rd. ÷ 6 = 20 sq. rd. with a remainder of 4 sq. rd.
4 sq. rd. = 121 sq. yd. 121 sq. rd. + 4 sq. yd. = 125 sq. yd.
125 sq. yd. ÷ 6 = 20 sq. yd. with a remainder of 5 sq. yd.
5 sq. yd. = 45 sq. ft. 45 sq. ft. + 3 sq. ft. = 48 sq. ft.
48 sq. ft. ÷ 6 = 8 sq. ft.

Hence each lot contained 20 sq. rd. 20 sq. yd. 8 sq. ft.

Problems

1. If 1 silver spoon weighs 2 oz. 6 pwt. 12 gr., find the weight of a dozen spoons.

2. A grain bag contains 2 bu. 1 pk. 4 qt. of grain. How much grain can be put into 25 such bags?

3. If it takes 2 bu. 2 pk. 4 qt. of oats to feed 7 horses 1 day, how much grain does each horse get per day?

4. If 39 gal. 1 qt. 1 pt. of ammonia are put into 105 bottles, find the contents of each bottle.

5. Each of six girls furnished 1 yd. 2 ft. 4 in. of ribbon for use in decorating a club room. If the ribbon was cut into equal lengths, 1 ft. 4 in. each, into how many pieces was the ribbon cut?

THE METRIC SYSTEM

The **metric system** is a decimal system of weights and measures. Nearly all the civilized nations of the world except the United States and England use this system.

The fundamental unit of the system is the **meter,** because every other unit of measure or weight is based on it.

The length of the meter was determined by taking one ten-millionth of the distance from the Equator to the pole. 1 meter = 39.37 in.

The advantages of the metric system are:

(1) The decimal relation between the units

(2) The extremely simple relation of the units of length, area, volume, and weight to one another

(3) The uniform and self-defining names of the units

The primary units are as follows:

For length: **1 meter** = 39.37 inches

For capacity: **1** liter = .908 dry quarts = 1.0567 liquid quarts

For weight: **1 gram** = 15.432 grains

There are three Latin prefixes and four Greek prefixes used in the names of the units of the metric system.

The Latin prefixes are:

milli	= $\frac{1}{1000}$	(1 millimeter = $\frac{1}{1000}$ meter)
centi	= $\frac{1}{100}$	(1 centimeter = $\frac{1}{100}$ meter)
deci	= $\frac{1}{10}$	(1 decimeter = $\frac{1}{10}$ meter)

The Greek prefixes are:

deca	= 10	(1 decagram = 10 grams)
hecto	= 100	(1 hectogram = 100 grams)
kilo	= 1000	(1 kilogram = 1000 grams)
myria	= 10,000	(1 myriagram = 10,000 grams)

The United States government requires the use of the metric system of measures in all medical work of the navy and the war departments and in the public health and marine hospital service. Its use is obligatory in Puerto Rico.

For postal purposes "15 grams shall be the equivalent of $\frac{1}{2}$ ounce avoirdupois, and so on in progression."

At the mint, $12\frac{1}{2}$ grams is the weight of a half dollar. The quarter dollar and the dime are in proportion.

Linear Measure

The meter is the unit of *linear measure.*

10 millimeters (mm.)	= 1 centimeter (cm.)
10 centimeters	= 1 decimeter (dm.)
10 decimeters	= 1 meter (m.)
10 meters	= 1 decameter (Dm.)
10 decameters	= 1 hectometer (Hm.)
10 hectometers	= 1 kilometer (Km.)
10 kilometers	= 1 myriameter (Mm.)

It should be observed that the abbreviations of the Latin prefixes begin with *small letters*, while those of the Greek prefixes begin with *capital letters*.

Square Measure

The square meter is the unit of *square measure* for small areas and the are (100 sq. m.) for land areas.

100 square millimeters (sq. mm.)	= 1 square centimeter (sq. cm.)
100 square centimeters	= 1 square decimeter (sq. dm.)
100 square decimeters	= 1 square meter (sq. m.)
100 square meters	= 1 square decameter (sq. Dm.)
100 square decameters	= 1 square hectometer (sq. Hm.)
100 square hectometers	= 1 square kilometer (sq. Km.)

Land Measure

The are is the unit of *land measure.*

100 centares (ca.)	= 1 are (a.)	= 100 sq. m.
100 ares	= 1 hectare (Ha.)	= 10,000 sq. m.

Cubic Measure

The cubic meter is the unit of *volume.*

1000 cubic millimeters (cu. mm.)	= 1 cubic centimeter (cu. cm.)
1000 cubic centimeters	= 1 cubic decimeter (cu. dm.)
1000 cubic decimeters	= 1 cubic meter (cu. m.)

Table of Wood Measure

The stere is the unit of *wood measure.*

10 decisteres (ds.)	= 1 stere (s.) = 1 cu. m.
10 steres	= 1 decastere (Ds.) = 10 cu. m.

Measure of Capacity

The liter is the unit of *capacity* for either *solids* or *liquids.* The *liter* is equal in volume to *1 cu. dm.*

10 milliliters (ml.)	= 1 centiliter (cl.)
10 centiliters	= 1 deciliter (dl.)
10 deciliters	= 1 liter (l.)
10 liters	= 1 decaliter (Dl.)
10 decaliters	= 1 hectoliter (Hl.)
10 hectoliters	= 1 kiloliter (Kl.)

Measure of Weight

The gram is the unit of *weight.* The *gram* is the weight of *1 cu. cm. of distilled water in a vacuum at its greatest density,* 39.2° F. The *gram* weighs 15.4324 gr.

10 milligrams (mg.)	= 1 centigram (cg.)
10 centigrams	= 1 decigram (dg.)
10 decigrams	= 1 gram (g.)
10 grams	= 1 decagram (Dg.)
10 decagrams	= 1 hectogram (Hg.)
10 hectograms	= 1 kilogram (Kg.)
10 kilograms	= 1 myriagram (Mg.)
10 myriagrams	= 1 quintal (Q.)
10 quintals	= 1 tonneau (T.)

Common Metric and English Equivalents

1 meter	= 39.37 inches
1 square meter	= 1.196 square yards
1 cubic meter	= 1.308 cubic yards
1 cubic decimeter	= 1 liter
1 liter	= 1.0567 liquid quarts
1 liter	= .908 dry quarts
1 gram	= 15.432 grains
1 kilogram	= 2.2046 pounds (avoir.)

1 liter of water weighs 1 kilogram

REDUCTION OF METRIC TABLES

Illustration. **Liters to Quarts.** Express 48 liters as liquid quarts.

1 liter = 1.0567 liquid quarts
48 liters = 48 × 1.0567 qt. = 50.7216 qt.

Illustration. **Square Yards to Square Meters.** How many square yards are there in 75 sq. m.?

1 sq. m. = 1.196 sq. yd.
75 sq. m. = 75 × 1.196 sq. yd. = 89.7 sq. yd.

Illustration. A vat of water is 3 m. long, 1 m. wide, and 5 dm. deep. (*a*) How many cubic meters of water does it contain? (*b*) how many cubic decimeters? (*c*) how many liters? (*d*) how many kilograms?

(*a*) 5 dm. = .5 m.; 3 × 1 × .5 × 1 cu. m. = 1.5 cu. m.
(*b*) 1 cu. m. = 1000 cu. dm.; 1.5 × 1000 cu. dm. = 1500 cu. dm.
(*c*) 1 cu. dm. = 1 liter; 1500 × 1 liter = 1500 liters
(*d*) 1 liter of water weighs 1 Kg.; 1500 × 1 Kg. = 1500 Kg.

Problems

1. One train runs at a speed of 50 mi. an hour. Another train runs 80 Km. an hour. Which train runs faster? how many miles per hour faster?

2. A merchant imported 1860 m. of silk. He sold it by the yard. How many yards did he sell?

3. 1 cu. cm. of water weighs 1 g. Gold weighs $19\frac{1}{4}$ times as much as water. Find, to the nearest grain, how many pennyweights and grains 1 cu. cm. of gold weighs.

4. Wheat weighs 60 lb. to the bushel. How many kilograms are there in 1600 bu. of wheat?

5. For postal purposes 15 g. equal $\frac{1}{2}$ oz. avoirdupois. At 3¢ an ounce or fraction thereof, how much postage will be required on a letter weighing 100 g.?

6. A half dollar weighs $12\frac{1}{2}$ g. Find the weight in pounds of $1000 in half-dollar pieces.

7. How many capsules of quinine containing 5 gr. each can be made from 1 Kg. of quinine?

READING THE GAS METER

Relation of the Dials. Illuminating gas is measured by a gas meter in terms of **cubic feet**. As the gas passes through the meter, its quantity is indicated by pointers on dials like the following:

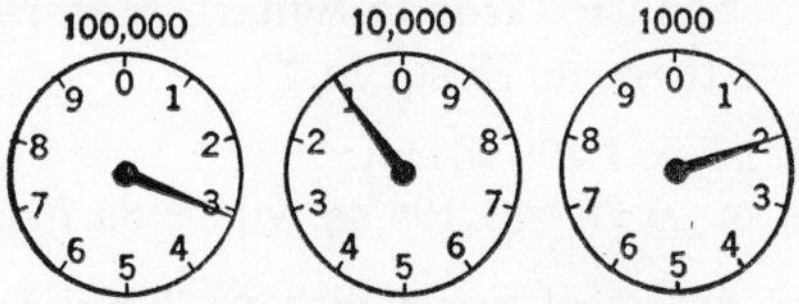

DIALS ON A GAS METER

When the pointer on the right-hand dial has moved from 0 to 1, it shows that 1 hundred cubic feet of gas have passed through the meter. When the pointer has made one complete revolution, 10 hundred or 1 thousand cubic feet of gas have passed through the meter. The pointer on the second dial records the number of thousands of cubic feet of gas, up to 10 thousand, that have passed through the meter. That is, when the pointer on the first dial has made one complete revolution, showing that 1 thousand cubic feet of gas have been used, the pointer on the second dial will point to 1 to record that fact. Similarly, the pointer on the second dial moves up 1 place every time the pointer on the first dial makes a complete revolution and the pointer on the third dial moves from 0 to 1 or from 1 to 2 or from 2 to 3 each time the pointer on the second dial makes a complete revolution.

Reading the Dials. *When the pointer on any dial is between two numbers, the smaller number is read.* On the dials in the illustration above, the reading is 31,200 cu. ft.

To determine the quantity of gas used since the last reading of a meter, find the difference between the two readings. If the preceding reading of the above dials was 28,500 cu. ft., the amount of gas used is the difference between 31,200 cu. ft. and 28,500 cu. ft., or 2700 cu. ft. The price charged for gas generally is quoted at a given rate per 1000 cu. ft.

Illustration. One company's rates are as follows:

For the first 100 cu. ft. of gas, \$.72

For the next 2900 cu. ft. of gas, \$1.20 per 1000 cu. ft.

For all over 3000 cu. ft. of gas, \$.75 per 1000 cu. ft.

At \$.72 for the first 100 cu. ft. and \$1.20 per 1000 cu. ft. for the rest of the gas, the 2700 cu. ft. of gas used since the last reading would cost \$3.84.

For the first 100 cu. ft.	\$ .72
(2600 ÷ 1000) × \$1.20 = 2.60 × \$1.20 =	\$3.12
Total,	\$3.84

Problems

1. Read the meter for each month in the following diagrams. Using the dials on page 234 as the reading for January, find the monthly gas bill at the rate given on page 234.

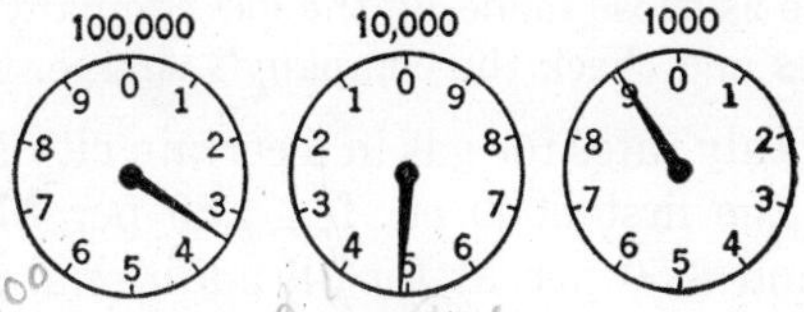

FEBRUARY

MARCH

2. The dials on the gas meter of a manufacturing company using large quantities of gas showed the following readings for two months.

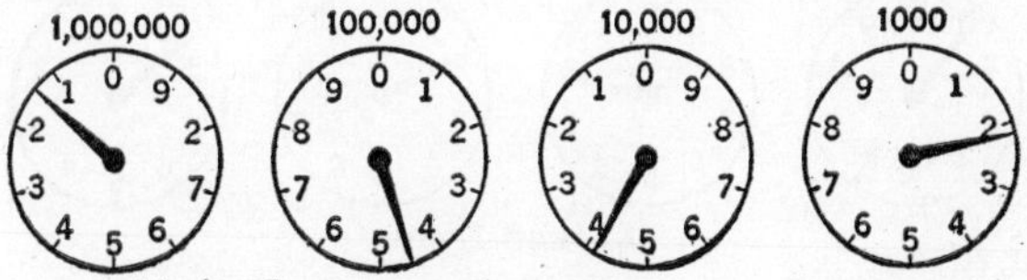

AUGUST

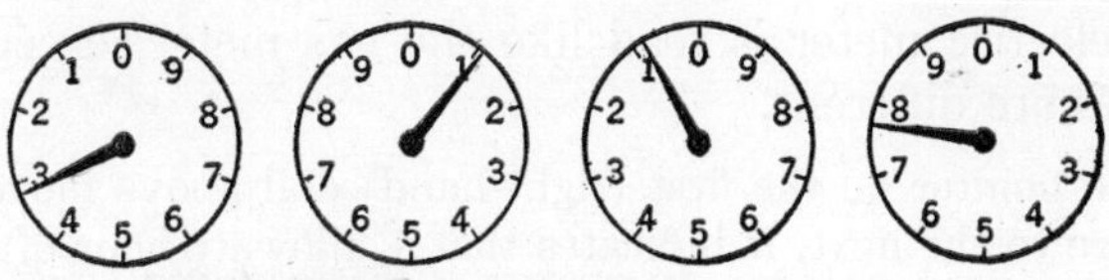
SEPTEMBER

(*a*) Read the meter for each month.

(*b*) Determine the amount of gas used from August to September.

(*c*) Compute the cost of gas used at the rates given on page 234.

3. Prepare a diagram of the dials on your gas meter, showing the latest reading, and bring it to class.

If gas is used in your home, inspect the gas meter and take the readings from the dials. Compare the readings with the gas bills. Your readings should be made the same day and as near the same hour as possible as those made by the gas company. Consult the gas bill for rates and check the company's charge.

4. The monthly rates for gas in a certain city are as follows: $1 per M for the first 5000 cu. ft., $.80 per M for the next 5000 cu. ft., and $.50 per M for all additional gas consumed in a given month. Find the amount of Mr. Robson's gas bill for the month of January if he used 22,150 cu. ft. of gas.

READING THE ELECTRIC METER

Relation of the Dials. Electric current is measured in units called **kilowatt hours.** The quantity of current passing through the meter is indicated by pointers on dials somewhat like those on a gas meter.

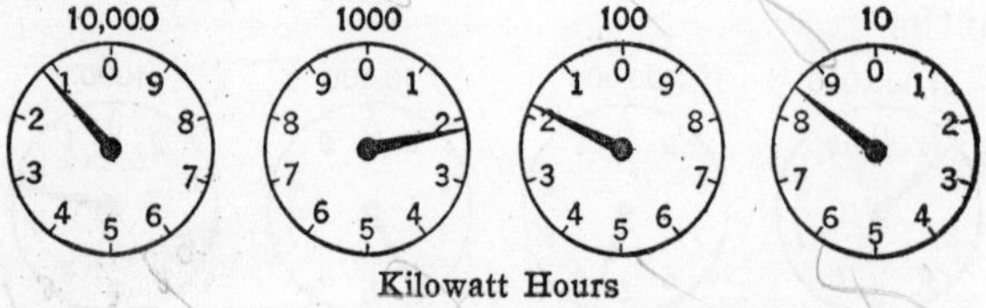

DIALS ON AN ELECTRIC METER

The electric meter is read like the gas meter, except that the units are different.

As the pointer on the first (right-hand) dial above moves from one figure to the next, it indicates that 1 kilowatt hour of current has passed through the meter. When the pointer has made one complete revolution of the first dial, 10 kilowatt hours of current have passed through the meter and the pointer on the second dial will have moved one space, that is, from 0 to 1 or from 1 to 2, and so on.

Problems

1. In the dials shown on page 236, how far will the pointer on the second dial have moved when the pointer on the first dial has made 5 complete revolutions? 10 complete revolutions?

2. When the pointer on the first dial has made 10 complete revolutions, how far will the pointer on the third dial have moved?

3. How many revolutions must the pointer on the first dial make to cause the pointer on the fourth dial to move from 0 to 1?

4. If all pointers are set at 0, how many revolutions must the pointer on the first dial make to bring all pointers to the position shown in the illustration on page 236?

5. Can you read the meter shown on page 236? Begin at the left hand dial and read the smaller of the two numbers between which the pointer lies, continuing to the right till the last dial is read. The reading is 1218 kilowatt hours.

Kilowatt hour is abbreviated *k.w.h.* and is generally called **kilowatt.**

The rate charged for electric current varies in different communities. It usually is based on a given number of cents per kilowatt hour. The rates are often on a sliding scale, which means that after a stated minimum number of kilowatts has been consumed in a given month, a lower rate is charged on the current in excess of the stated minimum and up to another stated amount, and a still lower rate is charged for current in excess of that amount, and so on.

6. The sliding scale of rates per month charged in one community is shown in the following schedule:

First	12 kilowatt hours (or less),	$1.00
Next	10 kilowatt hours,	6¢ per kilowatt hour
Next	28 kilowatt hours,	5¢ per kilowatt hour
Next	150 kilowatt hours,	$4\frac{1}{2}$¢ per kilowatt hour
All over	200 kilowatt hours,	2¢ per kilowatt hour

The electric company charged you for 48 kilowatt hours of electric current for January. Using the rates quoted above, find the amount of your bill.

7. Using the rates in Problem 6, find the total cost of 350 kilowatt hours of electric current.

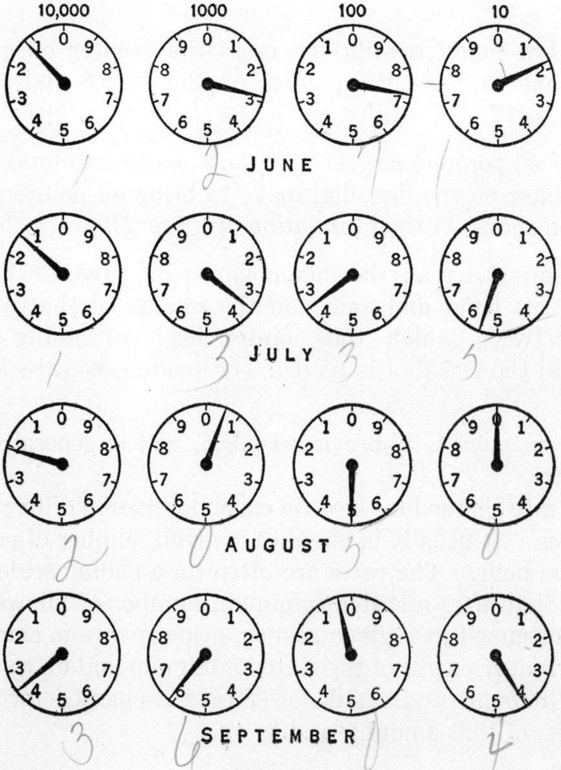

8. Prepare a diagram of the dials of your electric meter (if you use electric current), showing the latest reading, and bring it to class.

9. Assume that the dials shown on page 236 indicate the reading of the meter for May and that the dials shown on page 238 are the readings for successive months. Find the cost of the current for each month, at the rates given in Problem 6.

10. If the charge for electric current is a minimum of $1.25 per month for the first 25 kilowatt hours, and $.04 for each additional kilowatt hour find Mr. Ebling's electric bill if his meter readings for May were 3182 kilowatt hours on May 1, and 3254 kilowatt hours on June 1.

Comprehensive Test in Measurements

1. Find the cost at $1.25 a square yd. of building a sidewalk 8 ft. wide on one side and one end of a lot 120 ft. long and 60 ft. wide, if the walk is on the outside of the lot. (Reckon in nearest whole square yard.)

2. A triangle has a base of 160 in. and an altitude of 72 in. Find its area in square feet.

3. The diameter of a circle is 66 in. Find its area.

4. An excavation 36 ft. long, 27 ft. wide, and $7\frac{1}{2}$ ft. deep cost $.85 a cubic yard. How much did it cost?

5. Allowing $7\frac{1}{2}$ gallons to the cubic foot, how long must a sprinkling cart, 5 ft. wide and 4 ft. deep, be to hold 1500 gallons of water? 1500 ÷ 7½ = 200 4×5=20 200 ÷ 20 = 10' ft long

6. How much will the water required to fill the sprinkling cart in Problem 5 weigh?

7. A jeweler saved all of the fine particles of gold which resulted from his various processes, until he had 150 pwt. of fine (pure) gold. At $35 an ounce, how much was it worth?

8. A brick wall is 60 yd. long, 9 ft. high, and $1\frac{1}{2}$ ft. thick. If it requires 22 bricks for each cubic foot of wall, find how many bricks will be needed for the wall.

9. A field containing 10 acres is 20 rd. wide. How long is it?

10. If the field in Problem 9 has a roadway 4 rd. wide running lengthwise through the middle of it, and the remaining area is cut into building lots measuring 4 rd. by 8 rd., how many building lots will there be?

11. Change 15 Kg. to pounds and ounces avoirdupois.

12. If 25 grams of quinine are put up in 5 grain capsules, how many capsules of quinine will there be?

13. An importation of silk contained 1420 meters. Find the equivalent number of yards.

14. A tank contains 1 cu. m. of water. Find its weight in pounds. (1 cu. dm. of water weighs 1 Kg.)

15. The October reading of your gas meter was 28,500 cu. ft., and the November reading was 31,700 cu. ft. Find the amount of your gas bill at the following rates:

For the first 100 cu. ft., $.76
For the next 1400 cu. ft., $1.10 per 1000 cu. ft.
For all over 1500 cu. ft., $.80 per 1000 cu. ft.

16. Your electric meter read 7299 K.W.H. in March and 7457 K.W.H. in April. Using the rates given below, find the amount of your electric bill.

For the first 11 K.W.H., $.95
For the next 39 K.W.H., $.05 per K.W.H.
For the next 50 K.W.H., $.045 per K.W.H.
For the next 50 K.W.H., $.04 per K.W.H.
For all over 150 K.W.H., $.02 per K.W.H.

PART TWO

OPTIONAL SUBJECTS

GRAPHS

The Purpose of Graphs

One reason for the popularity of the movies is that the "story" is illustrated by pictures with their speaking parts. Without the picture the speaking part would be much less interesting, and more quickly forgotten. It is the picture that makes the lasting impression.

So it is with a series or group of numbers. Few people can remember many numbers and their relation to each other. A series of numbers presented in the form of a picture, or graph, helps the memory to retain the facts represented by the numbers.

A graph may be called a picture of numerical facts. (*Graph* is from a Greek word meaning to write, to make clear or vivid. Mention some English words containing the syllable "graph," and state their meaning.)

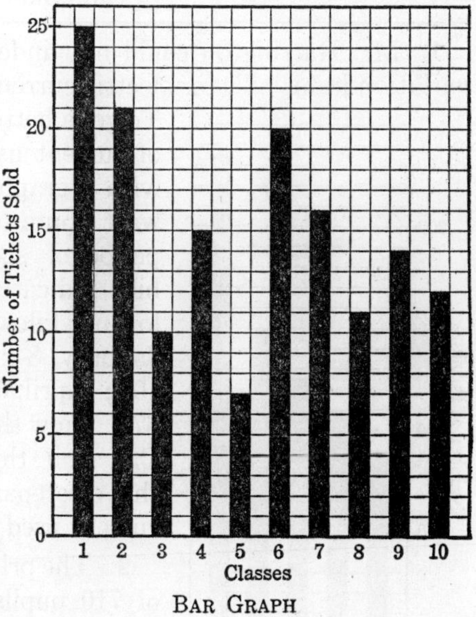

BAR GRAPH

Graphs are commonly employed in business and government circles to show more vividly the relationship of numbers; when so expressed the relationship existing between numbers, or between sets of related numbers, makes a much stronger impression on the mind than the numbers alone.

BAR GRAPHS

One of the simplest forms of graphs is the *bar graph,* that represents each fact by a "bar" or line.

From your study of the bar graph on page 243, answer the following questions:

(*a*) Which class sold the greatest number of tickets? the smallest number of tickets?

(*b*) How many tickets were sold by each class? By the whole school? What amount was paid for all the tickets at $.15 a ticket?

(*c*) A free ticket was given to the sales agent in each class selling more than 15 tickets. The agent in which classes received a free ticket?

Problems

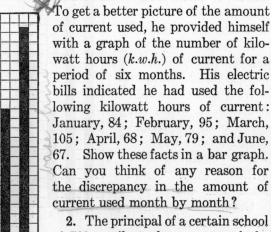

1. Mr. Harrington could not understand what caused the variation in his bills for electric current from month to month. To get a better picture of the amount of current used, he provided himself with a graph of the number of kilowatt hours (*k.w.h.*) of current for a period of six months. His electric bills indicated he had used the following kilowatt hours of current: January, 84; February, 95; March, 105; April, 68; May, 79; and June, 67. Show these facts in a bar graph. Can you think of any reason for the discrepancy in the amount of current used month by month?

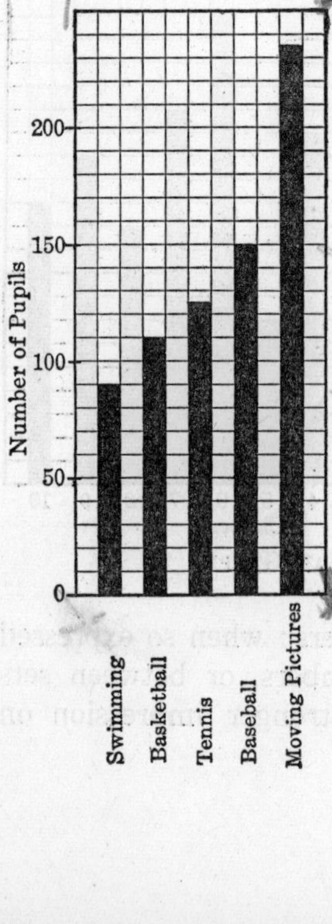

2. The principal of a certain school of 710 pupils took a survey of the school to learn the chief sports and pastimes of the students and to encourage more outdoor exercises. The result of the survey is shown in the accompanying graph. Read the results, as shown in the graph, on page 244, and make a table giving the number of pupils who preferred each sport or pastime.

3. In a school of 400 pupils, at a certain marking period, 64 students were on the honor roll (that is with an average of 85% or more in all subjects); 116 were on the merit roll (that is, with an average between 75% and $84\frac{1}{2}$%); 185 had averages between 65% and $74\frac{1}{2}$%; and the rest had averages below 65%. Show these facts in a bar graph.

4. Gather data similar to that in (3) from your own class and draw a bar graph of the facts.

5. An automobile manufacturer, for the purpose of making a study of sales possibilities in foreign countries, gathered the following facts: In the United States there is 1 automobile for every $4\frac{1}{2}$ persons, in England, 1 automobile for every 20 persons, in Germany 1 automobile for every 49 persons, and in Russia 1 automobile for every 479 persons. Show a bar graph to represent these facts. What conclusions can you draw from these facts?

CIRCLE GRAPHS

A **protractor** is an instrument for measuring angles. A circle has 360°. The measurement of an angle is expressed in degrees. With the protractor an angle of any number of degrees may be measured or constructed. To construct an angle of 70° draw a straight line to represent one side of the angle. The point, 0, is the center point of the protractor.

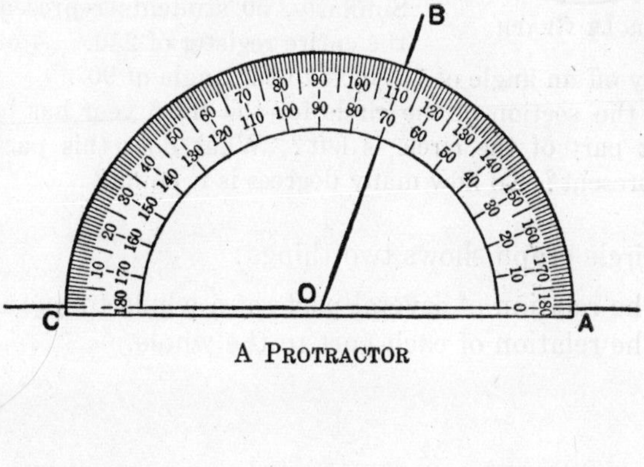

A PROTRACTOR

Place the protractor with its straight side on the straight line with the center point of the protractor at the point 0. Mark the point at 70° and draw a line from 0 to that point. The resulting angle is an angle of 70°.

Using a protractor, construct angles of 40°, 60°, 10°.

With a compass draw a circle. From the center of the circle draw a radius of the circle. (The radius extends from the center of the circle to the circumference.) Letting the center point of the circle be the apex of the angles, and using the protractor, draw angles of 80°, 90°, 45°.

If we wish to show that in a school of 240 students, 90 students are in the first year, 60 are in the second year, 50 are in the third year, and 40 are in the fourth year, we illustrate these facts by means of a **circle graph** shown below.

The whole circle represents the total of 240 students.

To find what part of the circle will represent the 90 students in the first year, find what part 90 students are of the entire register, 240 students. $\frac{90}{240} = \frac{3}{8}$. Since there are 360° in a circle, $\frac{3}{8}$ of a circle is $\frac{3}{8}$ of 360°, which is 135°. With a protractor lay off an angle of 135° at the center of the circle.

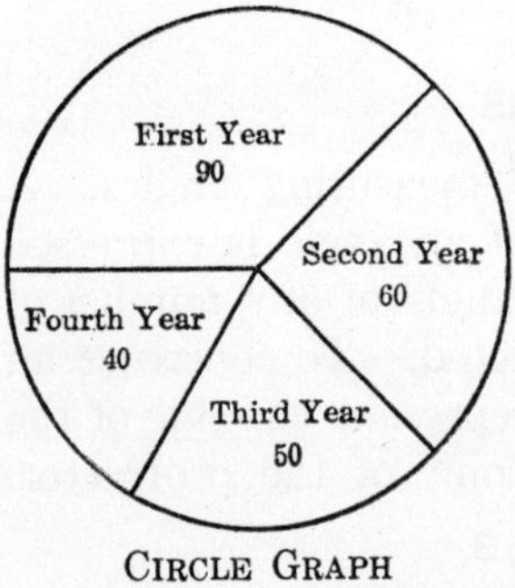

CIRCLE GRAPH

In the same way, 60 students represent $\frac{1}{4}$ of the entire register of 240. $\frac{1}{4}$ of 360° = 90°. With a protractor lay off another section of the circle equal to 90°, adjoining the first section of 135°. Similarly, 50 students represent $\frac{5}{24}$ of the entire register of 240. $\frac{5}{24}$ of 360° = 75°. Lay off an angle of 75° next to the angle of 90°.

When the section of the circle for the third year has been laid off, what part of the circle is left? What does this part of the circle represent? To how many degrees is it equal?

The circle graph shows two things:

(1) The relation of several parts of a whole to one another.

(2) The relation of each part to the whole.

Problems

1. In a certain village a "community chest" of $9000 was distributed as follows: boy scouts, $2000; campfire girls, $1500; the children's hospital, $3000; and the balance for the relief of the needy.

(*a*) How many degrees in a circle will represent the amount the boy scouts received? the amount the campfire girls received? the children's hospital? the needy?

Check your results by adding the number of degrees in each section to see if the total represents a whole circle, 360°.

(*b*) Show by a circle graph the distribution of the fund.

2. A young man earns $18 a week. His board and room cost him $8 a week; he sets aside $1.50 a week for clothes, $1 a week for insurance, $.75 a week for vacation expenses, $1.50 a week for gifts and benevolence, and $2 a week for miscellaneous expenses. He puts the remainder in a savings bank. How much does he save each week? Show these facts in a circle graph.

3. A merchant's statement of profit and loss contained the following facts: Sales of merchandise, $240,000; cost of goods sold, $160,000; rent, $10,000; advertising, $16,000; office and general expenses, $18,000; miscellaneous expenses, $12,000; net profit, $24,000. Make a circle graph to show the distribution of the sales dollar.

"BOX" OR RECTANGLE GRAPHS

A box or rectangle may be used to show much the same facts as are shown in the circle graph.

A board of education prepared a graph like the following to show the distribution of the money required to run the schools of a small city. If the total expenditure was $6,500,000, find the cost of each item of expense.

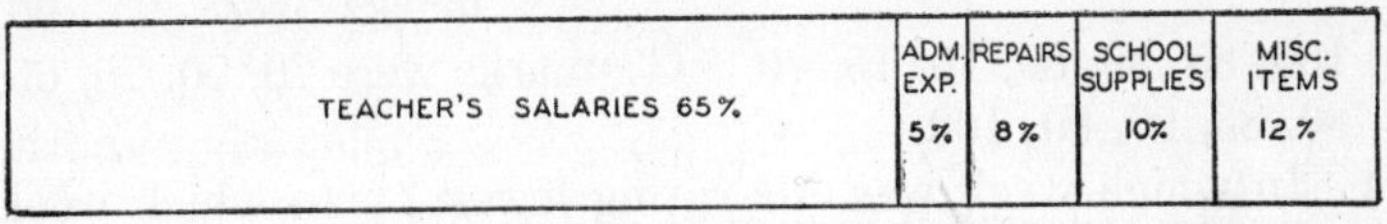

Problems

1. The population of the United States is about 6% of the population of the world. Yet the people of the United States own 70% of the world's automobiles, 50% of all the telephones, and 40% of all the radios. Show each of these facts in a box graph.

2. The expenses of the J. B. Havemeyer Company for one month were as follows: Salaries of executive officers, \$25,000; wages of office clerks, bookkeepers, etc., \$18,750; office supplies, \$2500; postage, \$1250; salesmen's commissions, \$20,000; advertising, \$7500. Find the percentage of each of these items, and show the facts in a bar graph.

3. From the following facts prepare a box graph. A merchant's sales were \$48,000 in one month. The cost of sales was \$28,000; selling wages and commissions, \$6000; store supplies, \$600; delivery expenses, \$1400; and other expenses, \$4000. The remainder of the sales was net profit.

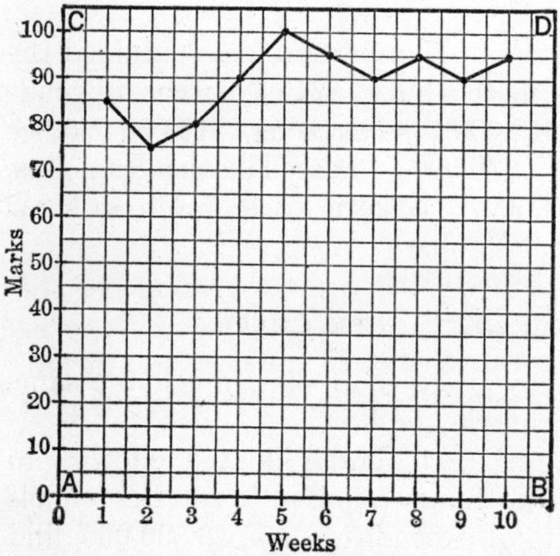

A's Line Graph

LINE GRAPHS

Three students A, B, and C kept a record of their marks in mathematics for a period of 10 weeks. A's marks were 85, 75, 80, 90, 100, 95, 90, 95, 90, 95. B's marks were 95, 90, 95, 100, 85, 80, 80, 75, 75, 70. C's marks were 70, 70, 75, 65, 75, 80, 85, 90, 90, 100.

1. In which week was A's rating lowest? In which week

was it highest? What does this graph show regarding A's progress in mathematics? Was it a steady improvement?

To make A's **line graph** proceed as follows:

1. Notice the number of facts to be shown in the graph. In this case A records his marks for 10 weeks.

2. Draw a horizontal line, as AB, on a sheet of *graph paper* (called also *cross-section paper*) long enough to allow for the number of facts to be represented.

3. Along this base line indicate at equal intervals the dates or times of the several facts. Notice that there are ten uniform spaces along the line AB in the graph to represent the 10 weeks.

4. Estimate the number of spaces to allow on the graph paper for each period of time and the total number of spaces to allow for the total time to be represented. Two squares are allowed on the graph paper for 1 week; therefore each square represents $\frac{1}{2}$ week. Hence 20 squares are required to represent 10 weeks.

5. Observe the "range" or difference between the smallest fact and the largest fact. In this graph, the range is 25 — that is, the difference between the lowest and highest marks is 25. Make allowance for this range in the facts. For example, A's graph would cover the facts if it ran from 70 to 100, instead of from 0 to 100.

6. At the left end of the base line, draw a vertical line the required number of spaces high. (See the line AC on the graph.) At regular intervals mark the ratings, as 10, 20, 30, 40, etc. Complete the rectangle by drawing the line at the top (CD) and the line at the right side (BD).

7. Where the vertical line marked 1 for the first week, and the horizontal line for 85 cross, place a dot, which locates the mark of 85 for the first week. Continue in this way until a dot has been placed on the vertical line for each week at the place where the horizontal line representing the mark for that week crosses it.

8. With a ruler connect these dots in (7) with straight lines. The result is A's graph shown on page 248.

Problems

1. Prepare a line graph similar to A's graph for both B's marks and C's marks (see page 248) and state what each graph shows about each boy's progress.

2. Keep a graph of your own marks in each subject. Note the trend — up or down — of your progress.

3. An agent made a line graph of his monthly sales. If his sales for six months were, for January, \$1975; for February, \$1790; for March, \$2250; for April, \$2380; for May, \$2700; and for June, \$3150, prepare the line graph the agent would have made.

Graphing Temperatures

The Weather Bureau, by means of a self-registering thermometer called a *thermograph*, records and keeps a record of every change of temperature at the place of record.

1. The following readings from a thermograph for each three hours from 6 A.M. one day to 6 A.M. the next day are shown on the graph below.

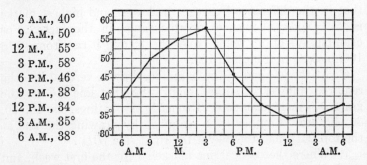

6 A.M., 40°
9 A.M., 50°
12 M., 55°
3 P.M., 58°
6 P.M., 46°
9 P.M., 38°
12 P.M., 34°
3 A.M., 35°
6 A.M., 38°

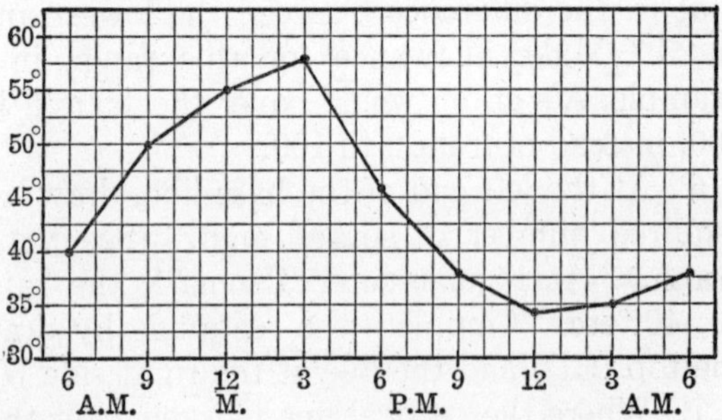

Study this graph before you attempt ex. 2. Notice where the dots for 58°, 46°, 38°, and 34° are placed.

In the line graph changes in values are assumed to be uniform between any two consecutive periods of time. That is, in the graph showing temperatures at various periods of the day the change in temperature most likely is not actually uniform, but is *assumed* to be uniform. Thus in the graph of temperatures in ex. 4, the temperature is indicated as changing from − 9 to − 5 from 6 A.M. to 9 A.M. On the graph it is assumed that the temperature at 7.30 A.M. has risen half way from − 9 to − 5 degrees because the time at 7.30 A.M. is half way between 6 A.M. and 9 A.M. The graph is to give a picture of the general trend of the temperature, and not to give exact temperatures at each moment of time.

Study the graph, and note how an estimate of the temperature is indicated between the periods of time shown on the graph.

2. The hourly readings of a thermometer from 9 A.M. to 9 P.M. are given below. Prepare a line graph of these facts.

9 A.M., 72°	1 P.M., 85°	4 P.M., 85°	7 P.M., 72°
10 A.M., 78°	2 P.M., 86°	5 P.M., 84°	8 P.M., 70°
11 A.M., 81°	3 P.M., 86°	6 P.M., 77°	9 P.M., 66°
12 M., 83°			

3. Draw a graph to show the following changes in temperature one day. Notice that the vertical scale should begin with − 10° instead of 0°, since the lowest temperature to be shown is − 8°. Let each square represent 1°.

4 A.M., − 6°	8 A.M., − 4°	12 M., 4°	4 P.M., 5°
6 A.M., − 8°	10 A.M., 0°	2 P.M., 6°	6 P.M., 3°

4. Make a table showing the temperatures recorded on this graph:

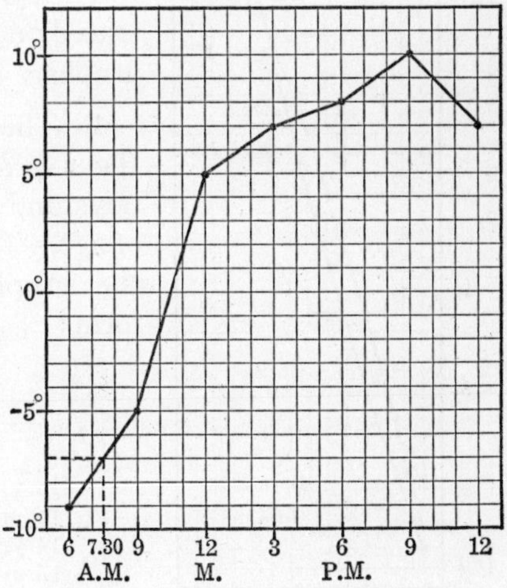

The temperature readings are given only once in 3 hr. The change in temperature from − 9° to − 5° between 6 A.M. and 9 A.M. did not take place all at once, but was a gradual change during the 3 hr.

To estimate the temperature at 7.30 A.M., consider that 7.30 A.M. is halfway between 6 A.M. and 9 A.M. Assuming that the rise in temperature from − 9° to − 5° was uniform during the 3 hr., the temperature at 7.30 A.M. would be halfway between − 9° and − 5°.

To show this on the graph, draw a perpendicular line from the point marked 7.30 A.M. to the temperature line. From the point where this perpendicular touches the temperature line, draw a horizontal line to the left till it touches the margin of the graph. The point at which this line touches the margin shows the approximate temperature reading at 7.30 A.M.

5. Reproduce on cross-section paper the graph in ex. 4 and show on it how you would find the temperature at 10.30 A.M.; at 1.30 P.M.

6. Referring to the graph you made for ex. 5, show how you would find the hour at which the temperature was approximately 3° below zero, or − 3°; 3° above zero.

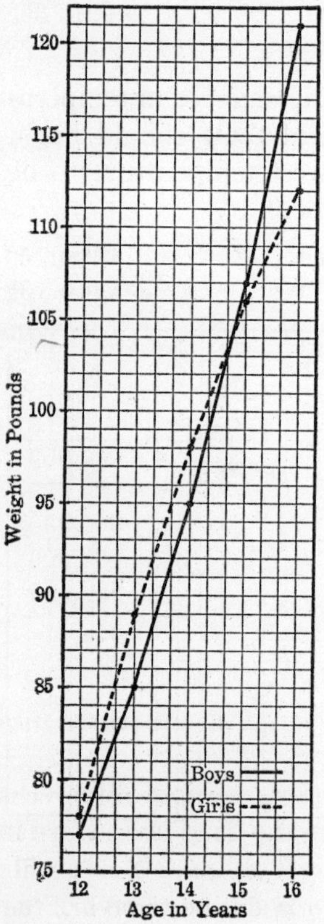

Graphing Two or More Sets of Facts

In some cases more than one set of facts may be shown on one graph. The sets of facts have some relation to each other, which is better illustrated on a single graph than on two graphs.

1. The graph at the left shows the average weights in pounds of boys and girls from 12 to 16 years of age. Tabulate the facts shown in the graph, using a copy of this form:

Ages	Weights of Boys	Weights of Girls
12 yr.	----lb.	----lb.
13 yr.	----lb.	----lb.
14 yr.	----lb.	----lb.
15 yr.	----lb.	----lb.
16 yr.	----lb.	----lb.

2. Show how to find from the graph on page 252 the approximate weight of a boy $13\frac{1}{2}$ yr. old.

3. At what age should a girl's approximate weight be 102 lb.?

4. Prepare a graph, similar to the graph on page **252**, of heights of boys and girls from the following facts:

Ages	Heights of Boys	Heights of Girls
12 yr.	60 in.	56 in.
13 yr.	62 in.	58 in.
14 yr.	64 in.	60 in.
15 yr.	65 in.	61 in.
16 yr.	66 in.	62 in.

How do you explain the fact that the weight increases more rapidly than the height?

5. For a period of five years a certain corporation reported, in round millions of dollars, the following annual sales and amounts paid for taxes. Show all these facts on the same graph, called a **several-line** graph.

	Sales	*Taxes*
First year	$228,000,000	$26,000,000
Second year	$237,000,000	$29,000,000
Third year	$239,000,000	$31,000,000
Fourth year	$231,000,000	$33,000,000
Fifth year	$222,000,000	$36,000,000

PROFILE GRAPHS

Engineers often need to know the depth of the water in a river — where it is shallow and where it is deep — when they wish to build a bridge over the river or a tunnel under the river. Navigators need to know where the deep waters are in navigable rivers. To show these facts on paper, a **profile** graph is made of the river bed, together with the shores of the river.

The graph below represents a river bed and the shores for a short distance from the water's edge. The numbers along the vertical line indicate feet above and below water level.

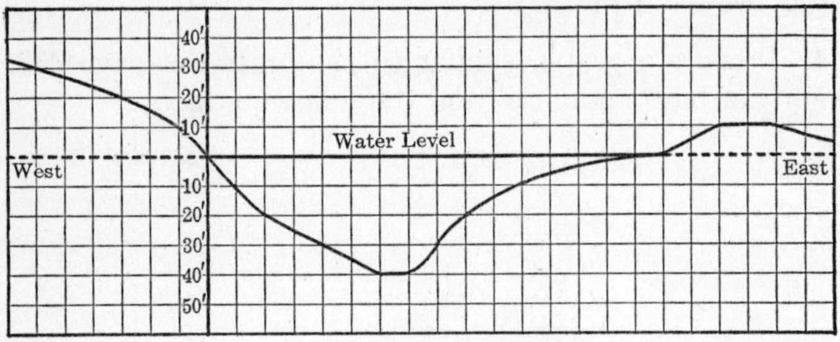

A PROFILE GRAPH

Problems

1. (*a*) If each horizontal space represents 10 ft., how wide is the river?

(*b*) How deep is the water 10 ft. from the west shore?

(*c*) How far from the west shore is the water the deepest?

(*d*) How deep is the water at the deepest place?

(*e*) How far from the east shore is the water 10 ft. deep?

(*f*) How high is the west shore 60 ft. from the water's edge?

(*g*) At what height would the water overflow the east bank?

2. From the following facts, prepare a graph showing the height of the shores and the depth of the water in a river:

North Shore	*South Shore*
100 ft. from water, 200 ft. high	100 ft. from water, 20 ft. high
60 ft. from water, 150 ft. high	80 ft. from water, 15 ft. high
30 ft. from water, 100 ft. high	40 ft. from water, 10 ft. high
10 ft. from water, 20 ft. high	10 ft. from water, 5 ft. high

The River Bed, 120 ft. Wide

10 ft. from north shore, 15 ft. deep
20 ft. from north shore, 40 ft. deep
30 ft. from north shore, 50 ft. deep
40 ft. from north shore, 30 ft. deep
80 ft. from north shore, 20 ft. deep
100 ft. from north shore, 5 ft. deep

STUDIES IN RETAILING

MARKUP

The term **markup,** sometimes called **mark-on,** is used to indicate the difference between the gross cost and the retail selling price of goods. The term **retail** is used instead of *marked price,* or *selling price,* to indicate the price at which goods are sold.

Finding the Markup Rate When the Markup and Retail Are Known

Illustration. Find the markup rate on the cost and on the retail of goods for the following periods:

	Gross Cost	*Retail*
For the week ended April 15	$3000	$4600
For the week ended April 22	$3600	$5300
Totals	$6600	$9900

The markup for the period is $9900 − $6600 = $3300

Hence, $3300 ÷ $6600 = .50 = 50%, markup on cost

and $3300 ÷ $9900 = $.33\frac{1}{3}$ = $33\frac{1}{3}$%, markup on retail

Problems

Markup ÷ Cost = Rate of Markup on Cost

Markup ÷ Retail = Rate of Markup on Retail

Find the markup rate (*a*) on cost, (*b*) on retail, for each of the following purchase and sales figures:

		Gross Cost	*Retail*
1.	For week ended May 8	$15,000	$21,000
	For week ended May 15	$16,500	$22,000

		Gross Cost	*Retail*
2.	Inventory, January 1	$11,500	$15,000
	For the week ended January 8	$ 8,900	$10,500
	For the week ended January 15	$ 9,600	$12,500

3. A purchase of goods amounted to \$17,400, and freight charges were \$375. These goods were marked to retail at \$21,330. Determine the rate of markup based on (*a*) cost; (*b*) on retail. (Freight is added to purchases.)

Finding the Cost When the Retail and Markup Rate Are Known

Illustration. The retail of goods for a given period is \$450, and the markup rate is 25% of retail. Find the cost.

Since the rate is based on the retail,

The retail	=	100% of retail
The markup rate	=	25% of retail
The cost (the difference)	=	75% of retail
Therefore, 75% of \$450	=	\$337.50, cost

Problems

Retail × (100% − Markup Rate) = Cost

1. An article was marked to retail at \$7.50, which was at a markup rate of 20%. Find the cost.

2. A merchant's stock of goods was marked to retail for \$13,200. The markup rate was $16\frac{2}{3}$%. Find the cost.

3. A dealer paid \$350 freight on a bill of goods which were marked to retail at \$20,000. The markup rate was 10%. Find (*a*) the gross cost of the goods; (*b*) the prime cost of the goods.

Finding the Retail When the Cost and Markup Are Known

Illustration. The cost of goods for a certain period was \$1950. Find the retail if the markup was 35% of retail.

Since the rate is based on the retail,

The retail	=	100% of retail
The markup rate	=	35% of retail
The cost (the difference)	=	65% of retail
Therefore, \$1950	=	65% of retail
Hence, \$1950 ÷ .65	=	\$3000, retail

Problems

Cost ÷ (100% − Markup Rate) = Retail

Unless otherwise specified the markup rate is based on retail and not on cost.

1. The purchases for a week amounted to $3750. Find the retail if they were marked to retail at a markup of 25%.

2. On goods invoiced at $1460, buying expenses of $40 were paid by the purchaser. Find the retail if they were sold at a markup rate of 20%.

3. A quantity of goods cost $2250, plus freight and other charges of $90. Find the retail if the markup rate was 22%.

CUMULATIVE MARKUP

The markup may be for a single week, for several weeks, or for any length of time desired. The markup for a relatively long period of time is called **cumulative markup.**

Illustration. The stock on hand at the beginning of a three months' period was $5000, marked to retail at $7500. Purchases and retail prices for the next three months were:

	Gross Cost	*Retail*
First month	$6500	$8500
Second month	$5800	$8000
Third month	$7200	$9400

Find the cumulative markup rate (*a*) on retail; (*b*) on cost for the whole period.

$5000 + $6500 + $5800 + $7200 = $24,500, total cost
$7500 + $8500 + $8000 + $9400 = $33,400, total retail
$33,400 − $24,500 = $8900, total markup

(*a*) $8900 = ?% of $33,400
$8900 ÷ $33,400 = .266 = 26.6%, cumulative markup on retail

(*b*) $8900 = ?% of $24,500
$8900 ÷ $24,500 = .363 = 36.3%, cumulative markup on cost

25

Problems

Markup ÷ Retail = Rate of Markup on Retail
Markup ÷ Cost = Rate of Markup on Cost

1. Mr. Hobbs's inventory of merchandise on July 1 was $6500, which he had marked to retail for $8000. For the next four months his purchases and retail prices were as follows:

	Gross Cost	*Retail*
July	$3800	$5400
August	$4400	$6600
September	$5300	$7600
October	$5700	$8000

Find the cumulative markup (*a*) on the retail; (*b*) on cost.

2. A hat sells for $3.50 when the markup on retail is 40%. Find its cost.

3. A suit of clothes was sold for $28. If the markup on retail was 30%, how much did the dealer pay for the suit?

4. Lamps cost $4.80 each. If the markup rate is 28%, find the retail.

5. A dozen office chairs cost $56.40. Freight charges were $3.60. At what price should each chair retail to get a markup of $33\frac{1}{3}$% of the retail?

6. At the beginning of the month a merchant had on hand goods which cost him $7400, and which he had marked to retail for $9500. During the following four weeks goods were purchased and marked to retail as follows:

	Gross Cost	*Retail*
First	$3750	$5200
Second	$4125	$5500
Third	$4250	$5700
Fourth	$4675	$6200

(*a*) Find the markup rate for the original stock, and for each week separately. (Based on retail.)

(*b*) Find the cumulative markup rate on the retail for the entire stock to date.

7. Shoes which cost \$4.50 were marked to retail at \$7.50. To meet competition the retail was dropped to \$6.00. Find (*a*) the original markup rate on the retail basis; and (*b*) the markup rate based on retail after the retail was reduced.

NOTE: This latter markup rate (that is, after the retail is reduced) is called the maintained markup.

COMPARISON OF RATES ON COST AND RETAIL

A merchant should know two things to be able to calculate the selling prices of his goods.

1. The rate of gross profit based on retail, or sales price, required to pay expenses, and have enough left over to have a reasonable profit.

2. The corresponding rate based on cost, which will give him the same dollar markup as in 1.

Knowing those two things he can readily calculate the retail price of his goods for sale directly from the cost price.

Illustration. A dealer wishes to make a gross profit of 30% of his retail to pay expenses and have left a net profit of 10% of his retail. How much above cost should he mark his stock? For how much should he sell a quantity of goods which cost him \$3500?

Calculate first the rate of markup on cost equivalent to a 30% markup on retail.

Since the given rate is based on retail,

Let retail	=	100% of retail
The markup	=	30% of retail
The cost	=	70% of retail

The question now is, The markup is what per cent of cost?

That is, $.30 = ?\%$ of $.70$

Hence $.30 \div .70 = .42\frac{6}{7} = 42\frac{6}{7}\%$, the equivalent rate on cost

Since the cost is \$3500, and the rate of markup on cost is $42\frac{6}{7}\%$ of cost, the retail is found thus:

$$42\tfrac{6}{7}\% = \tfrac{3}{7}$$

$\frac{3}{7}$ of \$3500 = \$1500, the markup in dollars

\$3500 + \$1500 = \$5000, the retail

Problems

Find the markup rate on cost equivalent to the following markup rates on retail, and calculate the retail price of goods costing the amounts indicated:

	Retail Markup	*Cost*		*Retail Markup*	*Cost*
1.	10%	$1200	5.	20%	$428.72
2.	$12\frac{1}{2}$%	$21.70	6.	40%	$2150
3.	15%	$3.00	7.	25%	$3.75
4.	$16\frac{2}{3}$%	$1575	8.	35%	$55

Finding the Rate of Markup on Retail Equivalent to a Given Rate of Markup on Cost

Illustration. Find the markup rate based on retail equivalent to a markup of 16% on cost, and find the gross profit on stock sold for $150.

Since the given rate is based on cost,

Let cost = 100% of cost
The markup = 16% of cost
The retail = 116% of cost

The question, then, is

16% = ?% of 116%

Hence .16 ÷ 1.16 = .138 = 13.8%, equivalent rate on retail

Since the stock sold for $150, the gross profit is

13.8% of $150 = $20.70, profit

Problems

Find the rates of markup on retail equivalent to the following rates of markup on cost, and find the gross profit on sales as indicated:

	Markup on Cost	*Retail*		*Markup on Cost*	*Retail*
1.	$12\frac{1}{2}$%	$50	5.	30%	$2000
2.	15%	$250	6.	50%	$1875
3.	20%	$300	7.	40%	$4550
4.	25%	$1540	8.	60%	$3200

Finding the Rate of Markup on Cost Equivalent to a Given Rate of Markup on Retail

In many instances it is possible to find mentally the rate of markup on cost equivalent to a given rate of markup on retail, or vice versa.

Illustration. Find the rate of markup on cost equivalent to a rate of 20% on retail.

Think as indicated at the right.

Retail	=	100% of retail
Markup	=	20% of retail
Cost	=	80% of retail

The question now is, What per cent of cost is the markup?

That is, 20% = ?% of 80%

.20 ÷ .80 = .25 = 25%, markup rate on cost

Think over carefully this whole process, and you will find it may be done mentally quicker than the figures can be made on paper.

Problems

Practice on the following, doing all work mentally.

Find the rate of markup on cost, and the retail of goods costing the amounts indicated, when the retail markup is as follows:

	Retail Markup	*Cost*		*Retail Markup*	*Cost*
1.	$12\frac{1}{2}$%	\$2.10	**4.**	25%	\$4.50
2.	$16\frac{2}{3}$%	\$12.50	**5.**	40%	\$6.30
3.	30%	\$1.40	**6.**	$37\frac{1}{2}$%	\$25

Finding the Rate of Markup on Retail Equivalent to a Rate of Markup on Cost

Illustration. The rate of markup on cost is 20%. Find the equivalent rate on retail.

Think as indicated at the right.

Cost	=	100% of cost
Markup	=	20% of cost
Retail	=	120% of cost

The question now is, What per cent of the retail is the markup?

That is, 20% = ?% of 120%

.20 ÷ 1.20 = $.16\frac{2}{3}$ = $16\frac{2}{3}$%, markup on retail

Problems

Practice on the following, doing all work mentally:

Find the rate of markup on retail, and the gross profit on stock selling as indicated, when the rate of markup on cost is as follows:

	Markup Rate on Cost	*Retail*		*Markup Rate on Cost*	*Retail*
1.	25%	$1.50	**4.**	$33\frac{1}{3}$%	$6.40
2.	$16\frac{2}{3}$%	$2.80	**5.**	60%	$3.20
3.	30%	$2.60	**6.**	100%	$9.80

7. Assume you are a price-marking clerk in a large department store. In such a store rates of markup vary in different departments. It is your duty to calculate correct retail prices, using the various rates of markup (on retail) for the several departments. In preparation for determining the retail prices you set up a table to show the rates of markup on cost which correspond to the rates on retail. Prepare a table to show rates of markup on cost equivalent to the following rates on retail:

5%	12%	$17\frac{1}{2}$%	$27\frac{1}{2}$%	$37\frac{1}{2}$%
$7\frac{1}{2}$%	$12\frac{1}{2}$%	20%	30%	40%
8%	15%	$22\frac{1}{2}$%	$33\frac{1}{3}$%	45%
10%	$16\frac{2}{3}$%	25%	35%	50%

8. Using the rates found in Problem 7, find the retail price of articles costing the amounts indicated, and on which it is desired to make the rates of gross profit as stated:

	Cost	Rate of Profit on Retail		Cost	Rate of Profit on Retail
a.	$5.00	$12\frac{1}{2}$%	*f.*	$3.35	20%
b.	$6.50	15%	*g.*	$1.95	35%
c.	$7.50	$17\frac{1}{2}$%	*h.*	$.72	$27\frac{1}{2}$%
d.	$8.40	20%	*i.*	$2.19	40%
e.	$9.50	$22\frac{1}{2}$%	*j.*	$1.68	45%

MERCHANDISE TURNOVER

Merchandise turnover is a term used to indicate the number of times in a year, or any fiscal period, that a sum of money may be invested in merchandise and the merchandise sold. Thus, if a man purchases $100 worth of goods, then sells the goods, takes the $100 and buys more goods and sells them, continuing this process for a year, the number of times he can buy and sell the goods in a year is his *merchandise turnover*. If he can repeat the process once each month, his merchandise turnover will be 12 in one year.

Other things being equal, the more times a merchant can sell his goods and buy more in the course of a year, the better is his business condition. Thus, if he should buy $1200 worth of goods at the beginning of the year instead of buying $100 worth, and sell them by the end of the year, he might have the same amount of profit at the end of the year as if he had bought $100 each month, but his turnover would be 1 instead of 12. The rate, or speed, at which money is working is an important factor in the success of the business. The more rapid the turnover the less working capital is required. In the illustration only $100 is required for a turnover once a month, or 12 times a year, while $1200 is required for a turnover of 1.

Estimating Merchandise Turnover on Cost Basis

In business a merchant does not sell all his merchandise before buying more. Purchases are made whenever any kind of stock is getting low, and new kinds of stock are purchased as requirements need. At no time during the year is all merchandise sold; therefore, there is merchandise on hand at the beginning of the year and also at the end of the year. The following formula may be used in arriving at the merchandise turnover:

$$\text{Rate of Merchandise Turnover} = \frac{\text{Cost of Goods Sold}}{\frac{1}{2}\text{ of (Inventory at Beginning} + \text{Inventory at the End of Year)}}$$

Illustration. A statement of profit and loss shows the cost of goods sold to be $35,350, and the beginning and ending inventories to be $4500 and $5600 respectively. What is the merchandise turnover?

$$\frac{\$35{,}350}{\frac{1}{2}\text{ of }(\$4500 + \$5600)} = \frac{\$35{,}350}{\$5050} = 7$$

In other words, each dollar spent for merchandise was used, on the average, 7 times during the year.

Problems

For four successive years Mr. Hart's statements of profit showed the following inventories and cost of goods sold. Determine the rate of turnover for each year. Prepare a line graph of the several rates of turnover. What would you conclude as to the condition of Mr. Hart's business?

	Inventory at Beginning of Year	*Inventory at End of Year*	*Cost of Goods Sold*
1.	$7,840	$6,960	$66,600
2.	$6,960	$14,710	$70,427.50
3.	$14,710	$11,238	$136,227
4.	$11,238	$7,456	$121,511

The following four problems are assumed to be taken from the same business for four years. Prepare the statements of profit and loss, calculate the turnover, and estimate the percentages for each of the following, using the net sales as the basis: (*a*) cost of goods sold; (*b*) gross profit; (*c*) total operating expenses; and (*d*) net profit. Prepare a several-line graph to show the trend of the business indicated in the several percentages found in the statements. The graph on page 266 shows the several percentages of gross profit for the four problems. Copy this graph, and add to it the lines representing the graph of each of the other items. Also prepare a graph of the several rates of turnover.

1. On Dec. 31, 19— Marvin Duff's records showed the following facts concerning his business: Merchandise inven-

tory, Jan. 1, \$3500; at the end of the year other accounts showed office furniture, \$975; delivery, \$1350; purchases, \$37,675; buying expense, \$325; sales, \$58,555; return sales, \$475; cash balance, \$21,130; notes receivable (notes due from others), \$4500; accounts receivable (accounts due from others), \$5500; notes payable (notes due others), \$2800; accounts payable (accounts due others), \$3400; salaries and wages, \$4500; rent, \$3600; heat and light, \$575; general expense, \$650; Marvin Duff, Capital, \$20,000. The inventories on Dec. 31 were: Merchandise, \$5600; office furniture, \$850; delivery equipment, \$950.

MARVIN DUFF

Statement of Profit and Loss

For the Year Ending December 31, 19—

Gross Sales		**\$58,555**	
Less: Return Sales		**475**	
Net Sales		**\$58,080**	**= 100%**
Cost of Goods Sold			
Inventory at Beginning of Year	**\$3,500**		
Add: Purchases for the Year	**37,675**		
Add: Buying Expenses	**325**		
Total Cost of Stock for Sale	**\$41,500**		
Less: Inventory at End of Year	**5,600**		
Cost of Goods Sold		**35,900**	**= 61.8%**
Gross Profit on Sales		**\$22,180**	**= 38.2%**
Operating Expenses			
Salaries and Wages	**\$4,500**		
Rent	**3,600**		
Heat and Light	**575**		
Other Office Expenses	**650**		
Depreciation:			
Office Equipment	**125**		
Delivery Equipment	**400**		
Total Operating Expenses		**9,850**	**= 17%**
Net Profit		**\$12,330**	**= 21.2%**

$$\text{Turnover} = \frac{35900}{\frac{1}{2}\text{ of }(3500 + 5600)} = \frac{35900}{4550} = 7.9\%$$

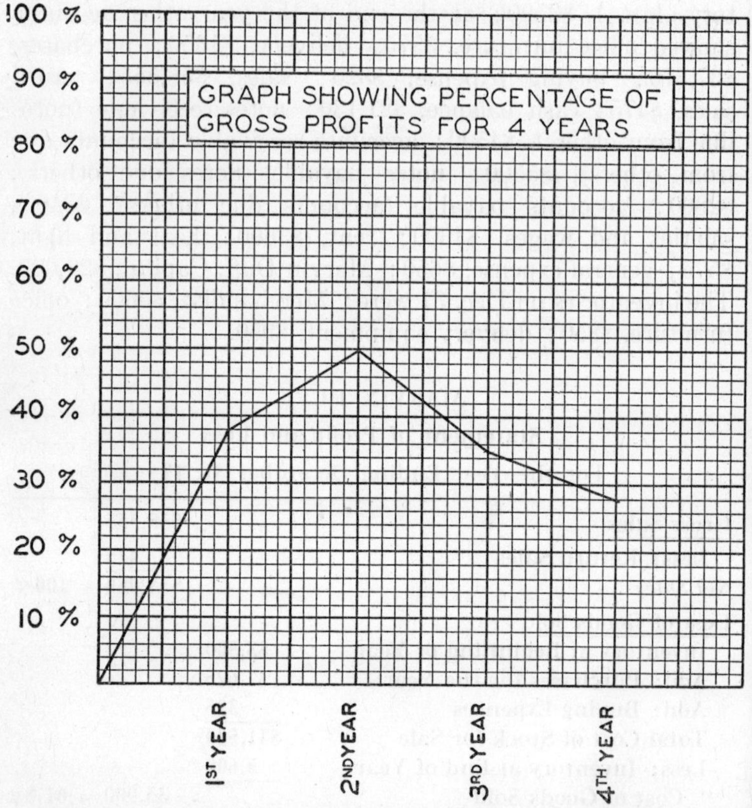

2. Stock on hand at the beginning of the year, $5600; prime cost of purchases, $13,700; buying expenses, $342.50; gross sales, $20,698; return sales, $572; office furniture, $850; delivery equipment, $950; salaries and wages, $3900; rent, $3600; heat and light, $625; general expense, $450; cash, $18,485.50; notes receivable, $3750; accounts receivable, $6250; notes payable, $2565; accounts payable, $3482; Marvin Duff, Capital, $32,330. Inventories at end of year, merchandise, $9800; office furniture, $750; and delivery equipment, $800.

3. Inventory of merchandise at the beginning of the year, $9800; purchases, $19,950; buying expense, $997.50; sales,

$32,680; return sales, $1440; office furniture, $1100; delivery equipment, $800; salaries and wages, $3300; rent, $3400; heat and light, $610; general expense, $1400; cash, $21,836; notes receivable, $2785; accounts receivable, $3665; notes payable, $3125; accounts payable, $1490; Marvin Duff, Capital, $33,788.50. The inventories at the end of the year were: merchandise, $10,500; office furniture, $975; delivery equipment, $600.

4. The inventory of merchandise at the beginning of the year was $10,500; purchases were $21,540; buying expense, $640; sales, $33,600; return sales, $560; office furniture, $975; delivery equipment, $600; salaries and wages, $3500; rent, $3400; heat and light, $590; general expense, $1125; cash, $25,686; notes receivable, $1780; accounts receivable, $3250; notes payable, $1960; accounts payable, $2840; Marvin Duff, Capital, $35,746. The inventories at the end of the year were, merchandise, $8750; office furniture, $800; delivery equipment, $400.

THE FINANCIAL STATEMENT

The **financial statement** or **balance sheet** shows all the *assets* and all the *liabilities* of an individual or firm. This form of report is frequently required when a business concern wishes to borrow money from a bank. It shows whether the applicant owns sufficient assets to pay his debts (liabilities); that is, whether his business is *solvent* or not. The **present worth,** also called **net worth or capital,** is the difference between the total assets and the total liabilities.

When preparing a financial statement one must keep in mind two simple definitions and one equation called the "balance sheet equation." The definitions are:

Assets are things owned which have a money value.
Liabilities are debts owed to others.

The equation is:

Assets − Liabilities = Capital (Present or Net Worth)

Following is a financial statement prepared from the data given in Problem 1, page 264.

MARVIN DUFF
Financial Statement
As of December 31, 19—

Assets		
Cash	**$21,130**	
Accounts Receivable	**5,500**	
Notes Receivable	**4,500**	
Merchandise Inventory 12/31/19—	**5,600**	
Office Furniture	**850**	
Delivery Equipment	**950**	
Total Assets		**$38,530**
Liabilities		
Accounts Payable	**$3,400**	
Notes Payable	**2,800**	
Total Liabilities		**6,200**
Net Worth, December 31, 19—		**$32,330**
Capital Increase		
Marvin Duff's Investment, Jan. 1, 19—		**20,000**
Capital Increase for the Year		**$12,330**

Compare Marvin Duff's capital increase shown in the financial statement with his net profit shown in the profit and loss statement on page 265.

Make a financial statement for Problems 2, 3, and 4, pages 266–267.

PLANNING EXPENDITURES

A **budget** is an estimate of expected expenditures for a given period of time. In order that a budget shall be worth while, it is necessary that a careful record of expenditures be kept.

The purpose of a budget is threefold:

1. To try to set a limit on the amount that should be spent on indicated items.

2. To provide a means of knowing, by keeping a record of expenditures, how much more or less than the estimated amount is being spent.

3. To enable one to study the expenditures, with a view to cutting them down and thus making greater savings.

Each year the officials of a city, state, or nation prepare a budget of expected expenditures. Such a budget consists of a list of the expenses and the amounts which the officials know must be met and paid.

Among the items in such a budget are:

Salaries of officials	Education
Street lighting	Public playgrounds
Health department expenses	Interest on bonds
Public library fund	Fire department

Prepare a list of other items of expense that a city might have to meet.

An estimate is made of the amount of money required for each item of expense. The amount required is determined by the experience of the preceding year or years, and by expected new items of expense which the officials know must be met. Once the budget has been adopted, it is expected that expenditures for any item in excess of the budget allowance shall not be made. That is one of the reasons for preparing a budget.

Individuals and families should prepare a budget of the personal or family expenses, so that expenses may not exceed the income. Many persons do not know at the end of the year where their income has gone. Money is wasted because people do not set a limit on what they should spend for certain things.

Estimating Allowances for Expenses

Experience alone can tell how much to allow for each kind of expense.

Many figures on the subject of family expenses have been gathered by statisticians, who have prepared from those figures estimated average expenditures required for families of two, three, four, five, or more persons.

It must be understood that no two families have the same expenditures, and that a family's expenses will frequently vary from the averages stated below.

In general, it may be stated that for a family of four persons, having an income of from $100 to $200 a month, the following percentages are average:

Rent	20%	Education	10%
Food	25%	Recreation	10%
Clothing	15%	Benevolence	5%
Household expenses	10%	Savings	5%

Problems

1. Using the percentages stated above, prepare a budget for a family of four persons whose income is $150 a month. Tabulate the following indicated actual expenditures, month by month. If any month's total expenditure is less than the income for the month, it should be remembered that some other month's expenses may be more than the income for that month. Certain expenditures, as clothing, recreation, etc., are not uniform throughout the year. It is a good plan to set aside uniformly for savings 5% of the income per month until the end of the year. Then any amount left over and not spent should be added to the savings account.

Expenses Month by Month

(Consider rent uniformly $30 a month throughout the year.)

January. Food, $32.50; clothing, $25; household expenses, $6; education, $5; recreation, $3; benevolence, $10.

February. Food, $31.60; clothing, $7.50; household expenses, $5; education, $5; recreation, $4; benevolence, $5.

March. Food, $35.10; clothing, $7.75; household expenses, $8.50; education, $12.50; recreation, $5.25; benevolence, $6.30.

April. Food, $39; clothing, $41.50; household expenses, $12.60; education, $9.50; recreation, $25.60; benevolence, $8.50.

May. Food, $29.50; clothing, $17.50; household expenses, $15.10; education, $25; recreation, $2.50; benevolence, $7.50.

June. Food, $27.50; clothing, $11.75; household expenses, $2; education, $1.50; recreation, $3.50; benevolence, $6.

July. Food, $28.75; clothing, $9.75; household expenses, nothing; education, nothing; recreation, $9.50; benevolence, $5.30.

August. Food, $31.20; clothing, nothing; household expenses, $2.75; education, nothing; recreation, $65.60; benevolence, $4.20.

September. Food, $33.30; clothing, $67.25; household expenses, $11.30; education, $47.50; recreation, $1.50; benevolence, $8.30.

October. Food, $39.50; clothing, $27.80; household expenses, $22.50; education, $21.20; recreation, $2.30; benevolence, $11.50.

November. Food, $38.40; clothing, $27.50; household expenses, $7.80; education, $9.30; recreation, $12.50; benevolence, $5.15.

December. Food, $44.80; clothing, $36.50; household expenses, $16.80; education, $17.50; recreation, $41.85; benevolence, $16.70.

Rule and use a form like the one shown on page 272.

After you have tabulated the items for each month, find:

(*a*) The total spent each month.

(*b*) The total spent for each item for the year.

(*c*) The amount by which each item cost more or less for the year than the estimated cost as indicated in the budget.

(*d*) The amount by which the savings could be increased.

MONTHLY BUDGET

Monthly Income $150

Expenses	Budget	Monthly Expenditures												
		Jan.	Feb.	Mar.	Apr.	May	June	July	Aug.	Sept.	Oct.	Nov.	Dec.	Totals
Rent														
Food														
Clothing														
Household expenses														
Education														
Recreation														
Benevolence														
Savings														
Totals														

2. A bookkeeper's salary was $125 a month. He prepared a budget as follows: board and room, 35% of his wages; clothing, 7%; laundry, 5%; medical and dental service, 4%; recreation, including vacation, 10%; self-improvement, 5%; benevolence, 5%; miscellaneous expenditures, 9%; and savings, 20%. He kept a careful record of all expenditures, with the following result: board and room cost $479.50; clothing, $96.50; laundry, $78.75; medical and dental care, $15; recreation, $168.50; self-improvement, $68; benevolence, $92; miscellaneous expenditures, $102.75. Set up a budget form like that in Problem 1, and show how much more or less he was able to save than he planned to save.

COMPOUND INTEREST AND SAVINGS BANKS

COMPOUND INTEREST

Compound interest is interest on the principal plus unpaid interest.

Interest on a debt is generally due and payable at regular intervals of time, as every three months, every six months, or every year, according to agreement.

Compound-Interest Tables. Insurance companies, investment companies, and corporations setting up sinking funds all use compound interest tables to save labor and time.

AMOUNTS OF $1 AT COMPOUND INTEREST

YEAR	2%	2½%	3%	4%	4½%	5%	6%
1	1.0200	1.0250	1.0300	1.0400	1.0450	1.0500	1.0600
2	1.0404	1.0506	1.0609	1.0816	1.0920	1.1025	1.1236
3	1.0612	1.0769	1.0927	1.1249	1.1412	1.1576	1.1910
4	1.0824	1.1038	1.1255	1.1699	1.1925	1.2155	1.2625
5	1.1041	1.1314	1.1593	1.2167	1.2462	1.2763	1.3382
6	1.1262	1.1597	1.1941	1.2653	1.3023	1.3401	1.4185
7	1.1487	1.1887	1.2299	1.3159	1.3609	1.4071	1.5036
8	1.1717	1.2184	1.2668	1.3686	1.4221	1.4775	1.5938
9	1.1951	1.2489	1.3048	1.4233	1.4861	1.5513	1.6895
10	1.2190	1.2801	1.3439	1.4802	1.5530	1.6289	1.7908
11	1.2434	1.3121	1.3842	1.5395	1.6229	1.7103	1.8983
12	1.2682	1.3449	1.4258	1.6010	1.6959	1.7959	2.0122
13	1.2936	1.3785	1.4685	1.6651	1.7722	1.8856	2.1329
14	1.3195	1.4130	1.5126	1.7317	1.8519	1.9799	2.2609
15	1.3459	1.4483	1.5580	1.8009	1.9353	2.0789	2.3966
16	1.3728	1.4845	1.6047	1.8730	2.0224	2.1829	2.5404
17	1.4002	1.5216	1.6528	1.9479	2.1134	2.2920	2.6928
18	1.4282	1.5597	1.7024	2.0258	2.2085	2.4066	2.8543
19	1.4568	1.5987	1.7535	2.1068	2.3079	2.5270	3.0256
20	1.4859	1.6386	1.8061	2.1911	2.4117	2.6533	3.2071
21	1.5157	1.6796	1.8603	2.2788	2.5202	2.7860	3.3996
22	1.5460	1.7216	1.9161	2.3699	2.6337	2.9253	3.6035
23	1.5769	1.7646	1.9736	2.4647	2.7522	3.0715	3.8197
24	1.6084	1.8087	2.0328	2.5633	2.8760	3.2251	4.0489
25	1.6406	1.8539	2.0938	2.6658	3.0054	3.3864	4.2919

If the interest is not paid when due, it may be added to the principal and draw interest just as the principal draws interest.

Illustration. Find the compound interest on \$800 at 3% for 3 years.

3% of \$800 = \$24, interest for 1 year
\$800 + \$24 = \$824, amount at end of 1 year
3% of \$824 = \$24.72, interest for second year
\$824 + \$24.72 = \$848.72, amount at end of 2 years
3% of \$848.72 = \$25.46, interest for third year
\$848.72 + \$25.46 = \$874.18, amount at end of 3 years
\$874.18 − \$800 = \$74.18, compound interest for 3 years

Illustration. Using the table, find the amount of \$750 for 20 yr. at 5%.

In the column headed 5% and on the line with 20 yr. at the left, the amount of \$1 for 20 yr. at 5% is shown to be \$2.6533.

Then the amount of \$750 for 20 yr. at 5% = 750 × \$2.6533, or \$1989.98.

Problems

Find the compound amount of

1. \$1200 for 4 yr. at 5%

2. \$1500 for 5 yr. at 6%

3. \$2500 for 4 yr. at 8%

4. \$2000 for 4 yr. at 4%

5. \$3000 for 3 yr. at 4%, compounded semiannually.

6. Mr. Moore invested \$3000 for his son John on John's fifth birthday. The investment paid 4% interest, compounded semiannually. What amount will John have to his credit at the age of 17, when he is ready for college?

HINT. Using the table, find the amount of \$1 for twice the time at half the rate; that is, for 24 yr. at 2%.

7. Compare the simple interest with the compound interest on \$5000 for 15 yr. at 4%.

8. Find the amount of \$2500 for 5 yr. at 8%, payable quarterly.

HINT. Using the table, find the amount of \$1 for 4 times the time at $\frac{1}{4}$ the rate; that is, for 20 yr. at 2%.

9. Find the amount of $7500 for 25 years at 6% compound interest.

10. What will be the interest on $4000 at 4%, compound interest, in 15 yr. 3 mo. 20 da.?

HINT. Using the table, find the compound amount for 15 yr. at 4%. Then find the simple interest on that amount for 3 mo. 20 da. and add to it the amount for 15 yr.

SAVINGS BANKS

Savings banks perform three very important services:

(1) They provide a place where wage earners and people of small means may put their money for safekeeping.

(2) They pay compound interest on deposits of $1 or more.

(3) They lend money to those in need of funds, upon proper security.

The rate of interest paid by savings banks ranges from 2% to $2\frac{1}{2}$%, depending on varying conditions.

Each savings bank determines the rate of interest it will pay and formulates rules governing the affairs of the bank, such as the dates when interest will be paid or credited to the depositor's account, the date at which interest on deposits shall begin, the number of days' notice (if any) required to be given by a depositor when he wishes to withdraw money, etc. The rules vary in different banks as to the time interest begins to accrue on deposits, and at what dates interest is added to the depositors' accounts. In some savings banks interest begins to accrue at the date of deposit and is added to the depositor's account on the first day of January, April, July, and October; in other savings banks interest on deposits begins to accrue on the first day of the month following date of deposit. Another rule in some banks is that interest may not be drawn till the fifteenth day of the month in which it is credited to the account.

Illustration. The following is a transcript of an account furnished by a large savings bank. The interest rate is 2%, compounded quarterly. Interest begins to accrue on the date of deposit.

Date	Withdrawal	Deposit	Balance
1940			
Jan. 1		500.00	500.00
April 1		2.50	502.50
July 1	100		402.50
July 1		2.51	405.01
Aug. 11		150.00	555.01
Oct. 1		2.43	557.44
Nov. 30	200		357.44
Dec. 1	100		257.44
1941			
Jan. 1		1.28	258.72

At 2% per annum, the rate for 3 months is $\frac{1}{2}$%. $\frac{1}{2}$% of \$500 is \$2.50, the interest to be added on April 1. The withdrawal of \$100 on July 1 leaves a balance of \$402.50. The interest, however, is reckoned on \$502 because the entire amount of \$502.50 was on deposit for the entire interest period, from April 1 to July 1. $\frac{1}{2}$% of \$502 is \$2.51, making a balance of \$405.01. The additional deposit of \$150 on August 11 increases the balance to \$555.01. The interest due on October 1 is found as follows:

$\frac{1}{2}$% of \$405	=	\$2.02
The interest on \$150 at 2% for 1 mo. and 20 days	=	.41
The total interest	=	\$2.43

Adding this interest to the amount on deposit gives \$557.44. The withdrawals of \$200 on Nov. 30 and \$100 on Dec. 1 leave a balance of \$257.44, on which interest accrues to January 1, 1941. $\frac{1}{2}$% of \$257 = \$1.28, which gives a balance of \$258.72 on January 1, 1941.

Problems

1. Allowing interest at 2% per annum from the date of deposit, compounding quarterly, and adding interest on the first day of January, April, July, and October of each year, find the balance of the following accounts on the last date given in the list of entries:

a.

Date	Withdrawal	Deposit	Balance
1940			
Jan. 2*		400	
Apr. 1	100		
June 1		200	
July 1	50		
Oct. 3		150	
1941			
Jan. 2	100		
July 1		200	

* Deposits made on or before the 3d of January, April, July, or October draw interest from the first day of the respective months.

b.

Date	Withdrawal	Deposit	Balance
1940			
July 1		300	
1941			
Jan. 2		200	
April 1	100		
Oct. 2		300	
1942			
Jan. 2	75		
July 1		150	

2. Howard Hendy opened a savings bank account in the Peoples Savings Bank by depositing $150 therein on March 16, 1940. Deposits and withdrawals after that date were as follows: June 10, 1940, he deposited $75; on Oct. 15, 1940, he withdrew $15; on Feb. 20, 1941, he deposited $100; on Aug. 1, 1941, he withdrew $50; and on Dec. 1, 1941, he deposited $200. The Peoples Savings Bank paid interest at $2\frac{1}{2}\%$, compounded semiannually. Interest was added to the account Jan. 1 and July 1 of each year. Interest began to

accrue on deposits on the first day of the month following date of deposit unless the deposit was made on the first day of the month, in which case interest began on the date of deposit. The withdrawal of any amount canceled the interest on the amount withdrawn for the entire interest period. Find the amount on deposit on Jan. 1, 1942.

3. Arthur E. Emerson has an account in the Champion Savings Bank. He made the following deposits: Nov. 30, 1940, \$300; Jan. 2, 1941, \$200; June 29, 1941, \$100; Oct. 1, 1941, \$200. On April 30, 1941, he drew out \$150 and on Dec. 14, 1941, he drew out \$50. Interest at $2\frac{1}{2}\%$ was added July 1 and Jan. 1. Find his balance on July 1, 1942.

ACCURATE INTEREST

Accurate Interest is found by using 365 da. (366 da. in leap year) for a year. Time between two dates must be reckoned as the exact number of days. (For a discussion of exact time, see page 206.)

There are two methods of finding accurate interest:

1. By the cancellation method.
2. By first finding ordinary interest (as shown on pages 93–103) and deducting $\frac{1}{73}$ of the result.

By the "ordinary" interest method a year is considered to have 360 da. By the accurate method a year has 365 da. The difference of 5 da. is equivalent to $\frac{5}{365}$ yr., or $\frac{1}{73}$ yr. Hence to change ordinary interest to accurate interest, deduct $\frac{1}{73}$ from the ordinary interest.

Illustration. **Method No. 1.** Find the accurate interest on \$4500 at 5% from May 15 to Aug. 1.

From May 15 to Aug. 1 is 78 da.
(16 da. + 30 da. + 31 da. + 1 da. = 78 da.)

$$i = prt$$

$$\overset{45}{\cancel{\$4500}} \times \frac{\overset{1}{\cancel{5}}}{\underset{1}{\cancel{100}}} \times \frac{78}{\underset{73}{\cancel{365}}} = \frac{\$3510}{73} = \$48.08, \text{ accurate interest}$$

Illustration. **Method No. 2.** Find the accurate interest on $3750 at 6% from Mar. 10 to Oct. 16.

From Mar. 10 to Oct. 16 is 220 da.
(21 da. + 30 da. + 31 da. + 30 da. + 31 da. + 31 da. + 30 da. + 16 da. = 220 da.)

$37	50	= interest for 60 da.
$112	50	= interest for 180 da.
18	75	= interest for 30 da.
6	25	= interest for 10 da.
$137	50	= interest for 220 da.

$\frac{1}{73}$ of $137.50 = $1.88

$137.50 − $1.88 = $135.62, accurate interest

Problems

Find the accurate interest on

1. $4400 at 5% from May 1 to June 29
2. $3800 at 6% from Apr. 15 to July 27
3. $7500 at 4% from Mar. 10 to Sept. 1
4. $6400 at 4½% from Feb. 8 to Mar. 30
5. $5600 at 7% from Jan. 1 to Apr. 1
6. $8750 at 5% from June 30 to Oct. 10
7. $1500 at 4% from Aug. 1 to Dec. 20
8. $2500 at 5% from May 11 to July 21
9. $3750 at 6% from Jan. 15 to Mar. 16
10. $6800 at 8% from May 1 to Oct. 15

Fractional Periods. *Accurate interest* is reckoned on United States Treasury Notes for *fractional periods*, both by the Government and by bankers dealing in the Notes.

The United States Government issues United States Treasury Bonds and United States Treasury Notes. The chief difference is that the Notes are issued for short periods of time, usually not more than 5 years, while the Bonds may be for much longer periods of time. Among the Bonds there are those bearing the following names: U. S. Treasury Bonds; Federal Farm Mortgage Corporation Bonds; Home Owners' Loan Corporation Bonds; and Federal Home Loan Bank Bonds, etc. Some of the notes are called Commodity Credit Corporation Notes; Reconstruction Finance Corporation Notes; U. S. Housing Authority Notes.

On the Bonds, for fractional periods, the interest is reckoned on a 360-day basis, that is, each month is considered to have 30 days. On the Notes, however, accurate interest is reckoned. Each half year is considered an interest period, and the interest calculated for a fractional period is reckoned on a half yearly basis.

Illustration. On June 21 a man purchased \$10,000 of U. S. Commodity Credit Corporation Notes bearing interest at $1\frac{5}{8}\%$ interest. The interest dates were Feb. 1 and Aug. 1. Find the interest accumulation since Feb. 1.

The interest on \$10,000 at $1\frac{5}{8}\%$ for $\frac{1}{2}$ year = \$81.25
The exact number of days from Feb. 1 to Aug. 1 = 181 days
The exact number of days from Feb. 1 to June 21 = 140 days
The accumulated interest is $\frac{140}{181}$ of \$81.25 = \$62.85.

Had these Notes been purchased on Oct. 15, the number of days from Aug. 1 to Feb. 1 would then have to be used as the number of days in the half year. From Aug. 1 to Feb. 1 = 184 days; from Aug. 1 to Oct. 15 = 75 days. The accumulated interest to Oct. 15 would be $\frac{75}{184}$ of \$81.25 = \$33.12.

Problems

In a similar manner, find the interest on each of the following:

	Name and Face Value of the Notes	Interest Dates	Date of Purchase	Interest Rate
1.	\$5000 U. S. Housing Authority Notes	Feb. 1–Aug. 1	March 15	$1\frac{3}{8}\%$
2.	\$3000 Reconstruction Finance Corporation Notes	Jan. 1–July 1	Nov. 20	1%
3.	\$7500 Commodity Credit Corporation Notes	May 1–Nov. 1	Mar. 1	1%

PRESENT WORTH AND TRUE DISCOUNT

How much is the interest on \$1 at 6% for 60 days? for 120 days? for 6 months? for 1 year?

What is the amount of \$1 at 6% for 60 days? for 120 days? for 6 months? for 1 year?

If \$1 at 6% in 1 year amounts to \$1.06, what is the amount of \$100 at 6% for 1 year?

$$100 \times \$1.06 = \$106, \text{ amount}$$

From an interest standpoint, what is the \$100 called? What is the \$6 called?

If a person owes \$100 now, how much will the debt amount to in 1 year at 6% interest?

Now think of the reverse operation. Thus, if a man owes \$106 due in 1 year, how much money would be required to pay the debt now, allowing interest at 6%?

As shown above, the amount of \$1 at 6% for 1 year amounts to \$1.06.

Therefore, since $100 \times \$1.06 = \$106$, it follows that
$\$106 \div 1.06 = \$100$, the sum required to pay now.

In this exercise, \$100 is called the present worth, and \$6 (the difference between \$106 and \$100) is called the true discount.

A distinction must be made between *bank discount* and *true discount* and between the *proceeds* of a note and the *present worth* of a note.

Bank discount is the interest on the *maturity value* of a note.

True discount is the interest on the *present value* of a note or a debt.

The **proceeds** of a note is the difference between the maturity value and the bank discount.

The **present worth** of a note or a debt is the sum that with interest will amount to the maturity value of the debt.

To find the present worth of a note or a debt, divide the maturity value of the note or debt by the amount of $1 for the given time at the given rate.

Illustration. A note for $1000 is due in 60 da. Find (*a*) the bank discount at 6%; (*b*) the true discount at 6%.

(*a*) Bank discount = interest on $1000 for 60 da. = $10

(First find the *present worth*, then the *true discount*.)

(*b*) Interest on $1 for 60 da.	=	$.01
Amount of $1 for 60 da.	=	$1.01
Present worth = $1000 ÷ 1.01	=	$990.10
True discount = $1000 − $990.10	=	$9.90

To show that the true discount is the interest on the present worth of the note, find the interest on the present worth and add it to the present worth to see if you get the maturity value. Check as follows:

Present worth	=	$990.10
Interest on $990.10 for 60 da. at 6%	=	9.90
Maturity value	=	$1000.00

Problems

Find the present worth and the true discount for each of the following notes:

1. $1500 for 60 da. at 6%

2. $1650 for 90 da. at 6%

3. $1800 for 4 mo. at 6%

4. $2000 for 3 mo. at 6%

5. What sum of money must be set aside at 5% interest on March 1 of one year to amount to $2625 on March 1 of the next year?

6. Find the difference between the bank discount and the true discount on a debt of $15,000 due in 90 da. at 6%.

7. Mr. Andrews owes Jones and Company $1875, due in 4 mo. Jones and Company ask Mr. Andrews for a 4-month note which, with interest at 6%, will amount to the debt at maturity. Find the face of the note.

8. A merchant's cash price on a given article is $175 and his price on 90 days' credit is $185. At 6% interest, how much better for the buyer is the cash price?

SAVINGS AND LOAN ASSOCIATIONS

Nature of a Savings and Loan Association

A **savings and loan association** may be organized under either State or Federal law. Associations organized under State law are called by various names, some of which are *building and loan associations, savings and loan associations, co-operative banks,* and *homestead associations.*

These organizations are frequently considered under the common name of *savings and loan associations.* Under the provisions of the Home Owners' Loan Act of 1933, the Federal Home Loan Bank Board will issue a charter to qualified associations that wish the benefits and privileges of such incorporation. Such associations are known as Federal Savings and Loan Associations. The federal associations are governed by a uniform charter and are responsible to the Government for the proper conduct of their business. Savings of members are insured up to $5000 by the Federal Savings and Loan Insurance Corporation.

A savings and loan association, whether operating under state or federal law, has two purposes:

1. To promote thrift by providing a convenient and safe method for people to save and invest money.
2. To provide for the sound and economical financing of homes.

How to Join a Savings and Loan Association

The general plan of operating a state or federal savings and loan association is very much the same. It is quite common in the state associations for a person wishing to join an association to subscribe for a given number of shares at $100 per share, or multiple thereof. In some associations these shares are designated as **savings shares, installment shares,** and **income shares.**

Savings shares represent shares purchased by a person who does not wish, or is not able, to pay a definite amount each month, but will pay what he can at various intervals.

Installment shares represent shares purchased with the understanding that the purchaser will make regular monthly payments of $1 a share.

Dividends are also payable on the value of the savings shares and the installment shares.

Income shares represent shares fully paid for in advance and on which the purchaser will receive regular dividends.

In the *federal associations* a person who pays in a lump sum of $100 or multiple thereof is said to have an "investment share account." All other share accounts shall be known as savings share accounts. Payments upon share accounts shall be called share payments. Such payments are entered in share account books. Investment share accounts may be represented by membership certificates instead of by an account book.

To encourage prompt and regular payments into the account, the federal associations offer a bonus of one half of 1% additional bonus dividend if the regular payments are continued until the savings amount to one hundred times the original payment. This is called the "short term bonus plan."

A similar plan, called the **long term bonus plan,** carries a 1% additional bonus dividend if the regular payments continue till the amount of the account equals two hundred times the original payment.

The additional bonus dividend under either plan is credited to the member in a separate reserve account on the books of the association, and is added to the member's account when the account reaches either one hundred times, or two hundred times, the original payment. If a member wishes to withdraw his savings before the term is completed, he loses the accumulated bonus dividend credited to his account.

Borrowing from a Savings and Loan Association

A person who wishes to buy or build a home may borrow from a savings and loan association for that purpose. To do this he gives the association a first mortgage on the home to be purchased or to be built. The association will then require the borrower to pay off the loan by paying the association 1% of the amount of the loan each month.

Assume you borrow $3000 from a savings and loan association. The association will require you to make a monthly payment of 1% of $3000, or $30. If the interest rate is 6%, the interest on $3000 for 1 month is $15. Your first monthly payment would then be divided into two parts — $15 to pay the interest on the loan and $15 to pay on account of the mortgage. The balance due on the mortgage would be $2985. The second monthly payment of $30 would be divided into two parts as follows: First, to pay the interest on $2985 for 1 month. The interest would be $14.93. Second, the balance of the payment, $15.07 ($30 – $14.93 = $15.07), to apply on the mortgage.

A schedule of payments similar to the following, is kept with the account.

SCHEDULE OF PAYMENTS ON A LOAN OF $3000

DATES	MONTHLY PAYMENTS	INTEREST	TO APPLY ON LOAN	BALANCE DUE
September 1, 19—				$3000.00
October 1, 19—	$30	$15	$15	2985.00
November 1, 19—	30	14.93	15.07	2969.93
December 1, 19—	30	14.85	15.15	2954.78
January 1, 19—	30	14.77	15.23	2939.55
February 1, 19—	30	14.70	15.30	2924.25

Copy the schedule of payments shown above, and make the entries for the next six months.

If there is a savings and loan association, or a building and loan association in your neighborhood, find out how a loan similar to the foregoing explanation is handled. Prepare a schedule of payments for six months to illustrate the plan.

Sources of Profit in a Savings and Loan Association

There are two chief sources of profit in a savings and loan association:

1. Interest on loans
2. Rentals from properties on which the association has been forced to foreclose mortgages

Dividends are voted semiannually by the board of directors. After expenses are paid and reserves to the bonus account, to the guaranty fund, to the undivided profits account, etc., are set aside, the board of directors declare the dividend to be paid to the shareholders, from the remainder of the net earnings of the association for the six months' period.

Regulations governing state associations vary. Classes interested should consult their local association for the rules governing them.

In associations in which shares are sold, it is expected that the regular monthly payments will be made generally at the rate of $1 per share.

When dividends are declared, the dividend is added to the amount paid in on the shares so that the "present" or "book" value of the shares is constantly increasing. When the amounts paid in plus the dividends equal the par value of the share the share is said to mature, or become fully paid. The owner of the shares may then withdraw his money, or he may leave it with the association as **income** shares, in which case he will receive a dividend when it is declared by the directors.

The dividend rate on *income shares* is frequently less than the dividend paid on *installment shares*.

Withdrawing Shares from a Savings and Loan Association

Should a shareholder wish to withdraw his shares before they mature, he may do so, but generally he may not be entitled to all the earnings on his shares to date. In one association, the following schedule of withdrawal values is in force:

Shares Running From	Per Cent of Dividends Paid
1 to 5 years	60%
5 to 6 years	65%
6 to 7 years	70%
7 to 8 years	75%
8 to 9 years	80%
9 to 10 years	90%
After 10 years	100%

In that same association the table of installment shares showed, in part, the following facts:

Series Number	Number of Shares	Number of Months Payments Have Been Made	Present Value per Share	Withdrawal Value per Share
56	277	141	$197.72	$?
58	386	129	174.93	$?
64	407	93	114.71	$?
72	60	63	72.98	$?
90	223	9	9.27	$?

Illustration. Find the withdrawal value of a share in series 64.

Payments have been made for 93 months, hence $93 have been paid in.

93 months is between 7 and 8 years, hence 75% of dividends will be returned if shares are withdrawn.

$114.71 − $93 = $21.71, total dividends
75% of $21.71 = $16.28, amount of dividends that may be withdrawn
$93 + $16.28 = $109.28, withdrawal value of 1 share

Problems

1–4. Find the withdrawal value of one share in each of the other series listed above.

5. A man has 25 shares ($200 a share) fully paid for, which he is leaving with his association as income shares. He has subscribed for 20 additional shares on which he has been paying dues for 5 years at the rate of $1 per share per month. His dividend on the income shares is equal to a rate of $3\frac{1}{2}$% per annum. The dividend credited to his installment shares is equal to an annual rate of 5% of his total payments to date plus previously credited dividends, both of which amount to $67.21 per share. Find (*a*) the amount of the dividend check paid on the income shares; (*b*) the book value of one share of his new series.

USING THE INTEREST FORMULAS

Finding the Missing Factor

$3 \times 5 \times ? = 90$	$7 \times ? \times 4 = 56$	$9 \times 3 \times ? = 81$
$4 \times 3 \times ? = 72$	$? \times 5 \times 3 = 75$	$4 \times ? \times 7 = 84$
$5 \times ? \times 4 = 40$	$? \times 6 \times 2 = 60$	$? \times 6 \times 8 = 96$
$6 \times ? \times 3 = 54$	$7 \times ? \times 3 = 42$	$8 \times 3 \times ? = 120$

It is a fundamental law of arithmetic that **the product of two (or more) factors divided by all the factors but one, gives a quotient equal to that one factor.**

Thus, $$3 \times 4 \times 5 = 60$$

Hence, $$\frac{60}{3 \times 5} = 4$$

or, $$\frac{60}{3 \times 4} = 5$$

It is the same way, in the *interest formula*

$$i = prt$$

In this formula ***i*** represents *interest*, ***p*** represents *principal*, ***r*** represents *rate*, and ***t*** represents *time* (expressed in years).

The formula, ***i = prt*** or ***i = p × r × t*** means, therefore, that **interest equals principal × rate × time.**

The chief practical value of the formula is to find either *interest, principal, rate,* or *time* when the other three elements are known.

Thus, $$p = \frac{i}{r \times t}$$

$$r = \frac{i}{p \times t}$$

and, $$t = \frac{i}{p \times r}$$

Using the formula it is easy to find the principal, the rate, or the time, if the other factors are known.

Illustration. Find the sum of money that will earn $48 in 80 da. at 6%.

Since the principal is the unknown factor, use the formula

$$p = \frac{i}{r \times t}, \text{ or as usually expressed, } \frac{i}{rt}$$

$$\text{Hence, } p = \frac{\$48}{.06 \times \frac{80}{360}} = \frac{\$48}{\frac{4.8}{360}} = \frac{\$48 \times 360}{4.8} = \$3600$$

Therefore, the principal sum is $3600.

Problems

Find the missing factor in each of the following:

	Principal	*Rate*	*Time*	*Interest*
1.	$4000	?	60 da.	$ 30
2.	?	5%	90 da.	$ 25
3.	$7500	4%	?	$ 75
4.	$3000	7%	?	$105
5.	?	$4\frac{1}{2}$%	3 mo.	$ 45
6.	$8500	?	90 da.	$170

7. What sum of money at 5% interest will earn $108 in interest in 108 days?

8. A young man was credited with $15 interest at his savings bank. If the savings bank paid interest at the rate of $2\frac{1}{2}$%, and interest was credited quarterly, find the amount of the young man's savings prior to the crediting of the interest.

9. A young man's father left him a sum of money to be paid to him on his 21st birthday. Until that date he was to receive the income from the funds which were invested at $4\frac{1}{2}$%. If he received a monthly payment of $281.25, find the sum of money left him.

Illustration. At what rate of interest will \$4200 earn \$28 in 48 days?

Since the rate is the unknown factor, use the formula

$$r = \frac{i}{pt}$$

$$\text{Hence, } r = \frac{\$28}{\$4200 \times \frac{48}{360}} = \frac{\$28 \times 360}{\$4200 \times 48} = \frac{\$28}{\$560} = .05 = 5\%$$

Therefore, the rate is 5%.

Problems

1. If the interest paid on a loan of \$1500 for 72 days was \$22.50, what was the annual rate of interest?

2. A man paid in interest and bonus the sum of \$37.50 for a loan of \$1200 for 3 months. The interest and bonus payment was equal to what rate of interest on the amount borrowed?

Illustration. In what time will \$5000 earn \$150 interest at 4%?

Since the time is the unknown factor, use the formula

$$t = \frac{i}{pr}$$

$$\text{Hence, } t = \frac{\$150}{\$5000 \times .04} = \frac{\$150}{\$200} = .75$$

Therefore, the time is .75 of a year, that is, 9 months.

Problems

1. In how many days will \$5000 earn \$25 interest at 5%?

2. Mr. Austin paid Mr. Borden \$2537.50 for a loan of \$2500 and interest. If the rate of interest was 4%, for what length of time was the loan made?

Illustration. On an invoice the terms are 3/10, N/60. The cash discount is equivalent to what rate of interest per annum on the gross amount of the invoice?

On each dollar of the invoice there is a discount of \$.03. Hence the principal is \$1, and the interest is \$.03. Since the term of credit is 60 days, and the discount period expires in 10 days, the time is the difference, or 50 days. The unknown factor is the rate.

Use the formula $$r = \frac{i}{pt}$$

Hence, $$r = \frac{\$.03}{\$1 \times \frac{50}{360}} = \frac{\$.03 \times 360}{\$50} = \frac{\$10.80}{\$50} = .216 = 21.6\%$$

That is, the cash discount is equivalent to 21.6% interest on the gross amount of the bill.

If we reckon the rate of interest on the net amount of the invoice, the solution is:

$$r = \frac{\$.03}{\$.97 \times \frac{50}{360}} = \frac{\$.03 \times 360}{\$.97 \times 50} = \frac{\$10.80}{\$48.50} = .22268 = 22\tfrac{1}{4}\%$$

The principal is \$.97 because \$.97 pays for \$1 in the face of the invoice.

Problems

1. The cash discount on an invoice whose terms are 2/10, N/30 is equivalent to what rate of interest per annum (*a*) on the gross amount of the invoice; (*b*) on the net amount of the invoice?

2. An invoice of \$428.75, dated August 4, terms 3/10, N/30, was paid August 14. The cash discount was equal to what rate of interest per annum on the net amount of the bill?

3. From an interest standpoint which is better for the buyer, terms of 2/10, N/30, or 4/10, N/60?

Find the rate of interest on the gross amount of the invoice equivalent to the cash discount on each of the following invoices:

Amount of Invoice	*Terms*
4. \$391.54	3/10, N/60
5. \$717.75	5/10, N/90
6. \$811.90	4/10, N/60

BUYING ON THE INSTALLMENT PLAN

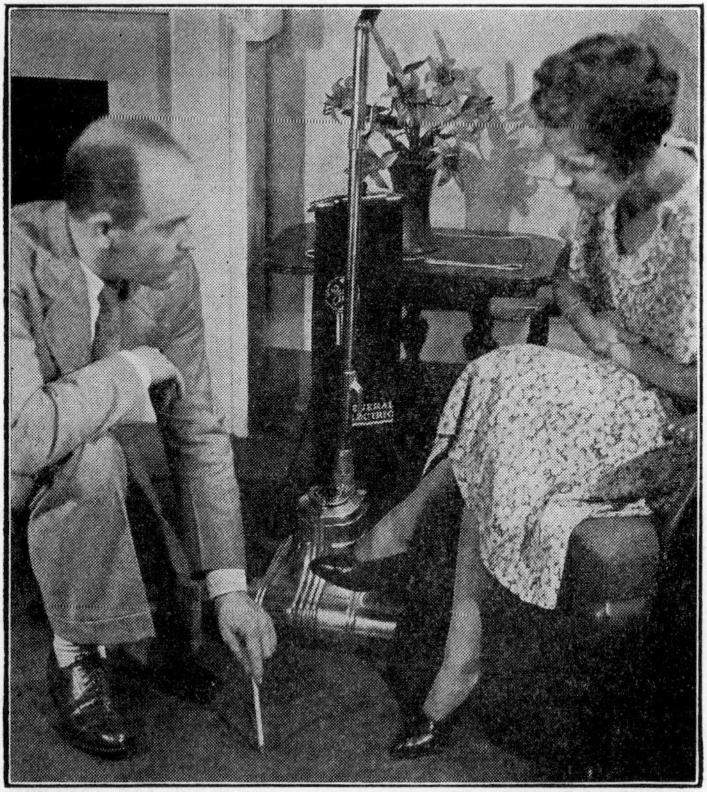

Courtesy General Electric Co.

A salesman can demonstrate the vacuum cleaner and persuade you to buy it, but you should know how to calculate the payments.

"No Money Down, and Only 10 Cents a Day." "Take a Year to Pay." "Your Credit Is Good." These and many other similar phrases are familiar in the advertisements of the present day. The invitations to make purchases on "easy terms" are very alluring to the man or woman of small means.

They make purchases look so easy that many people buy all kinds of things on the installment plan. On the other hand, many people would find it difficult or inconvenient to buy if they could not buy on the installment plan.

Installment buying is a plan whereby the purchaser makes a small first payment, called a *down payment,* and agrees to pay the balance of the purchase price in regular, equal weekly or monthly payments. This plan enables the person of small means to buy a needed article, and pay for it out of his earnings week by week, or month by month.

Before buying on the installment plan a prospective purchaser should first estimate how much more than the cash price he will have to pay if he buys on the installment plan and whether the article is worth the extra price; and second, whether he will be able to make the payments when they become due.

It is important that payments be made promptly when they are due, because in the contract to sell on the installment plan, there is generally a provision that if the payments are not made when they are due, the seller may demand and obtain the return of the merchandise sold. The seller has the right to demand the return of the merchandise because the contract states that the ownership of the goods sold is with the seller until the last payment is made.

The Installment Price Is Greater Than the Cash Price

Illustration. Mrs. Blake wishes to buy a new electric flat iron. The electric company offers her a new flat iron for $4.25 cash, or for $.75 down, and $1 a month for four months, the extra dollar each month to be added to the monthly electric bill. How much extra does Mrs. Blake pay? The extra cost is equivalent to what rate of interest?

The down payment	=	$.75
4 monthly payments of $1	=	$4.00
The total cost	=	$4.75
The cash price	=	$4.25
The extra cost	=	$.50

Finding the Rate of Interest on Deferred Payments

Mrs. Blake pays an extra $.50 for the privilege of delaying a payment of

	$1 for 1 month
	$1 for 2 months
	$1 for 3 months
	$1 for 4 months
a total of	$1 for 10 months

In other words, the $.50 is equivalent to the interest on $1 for 10 months.

Using the formula $r = \frac{i}{pt}$

$$r = \frac{\$.50}{\$1 \times \frac{10}{12}} = .60 = 60\%, \text{ rate of interest.}$$

That is, Mrs. Blake would be paying 60% interest on the deferred payments.

Problems

1. A coal company offered Barnes 8 tons of coal for $114 cash, or for $25 down, and 5 monthly payments of $19 each. How much more would the coal cost on the installment plan than for cash?

2. Bowen can buy a radio for $36.50 cash, or for $5 down, and 35 weekly payments of $1 each. How much more than the cash price does the radio cost by the weekly payment plan?

3. Marjorie wanted to take music lessons. Her mother bought a piano on the easy payment plan by paying $25 down, and $15 each month for 15 months. The cash price of the piano was $220. How much more than the cash price did Marjorie's mother pay by the installment plan?

4. A boy wanted a bicycle which could be bought for $27.50 cash. Not having that much money, he agreed to buy the bicycle if he could pay $3 down, and $2 a week for 14 weeks. The dealer agreed to these terms. How much more than the cash price did he pay for the bicycle?

5. Mrs. Holmes had been paying a laundress $2.50 weekly to do her washing. She decided to buy a washing machine and do her own washing. She bought a washer (cash price $48) by paying $9.50 down, and $2 a week for 23 weeks. *a.* How much more than the cash price did she pay for the washer? *b.* In how many weeks will Mrs. Holmes save an amount equal to the dealer's charge for credit? *c.* In how many weeks will she save an amount equal to the cost of the washer?

6. Mr. Ruiz bought a used car, agreeing to pay $10 a month, which was all the money he could spare after paying his living expenses. What do you think of the wisdom of his purchase?

7. A new car is priced at $1120. Lathrop is offered $320 as a trade in value for his old car. Not having $800 cash to pay for the new car, he agrees to pay $60 a month for 15 months. The extra charge was equal to what rate of interest on the deferred payments?

8. In the window of a furniture store is a living-room set priced as follows: "Cash price, $175; or $25 down, and 10 monthly payments of $16.80 each." What rate of interest per annum does a buyer pay on the deferred payments if he buys on the installment plan?

9. An electric refrigerator costing $282 cash may be purchased for $50 down, and 12 monthly payments of $21. Find the rate of interest paid on deferred payments by one who does not pay cash.

10. A young man wished to buy a diamond ring. The ring he wanted could be bought for $168 cash, or for a first payment of $21 plus 11 monthly payments of $15 each. If he bought the ring on the easy payment plan, what rate of interest did he pay on the deferred payments?

11. Bates has a savings bank account on which he receives $2\frac{1}{2}\%$ interest compounded semiannually, interest dates being April 1 and October 1. On April 1 he bought a used car for $25 down, and agreed to pay $25 a month for 5 months. He preferred to buy on the installment plan because he did not wish to draw money from his savings. He could have bought the car for $130 cash. The easy payment plan was equivalent to what rate of interest per annum on the deferred payments? How much interest would he have lost at the savings bank if he had drawn the $105 necessary to pay cash for the car?

12. If Bates in Problem 11 had drawn the money from the bank and paid cash for the car, and had deposited the $25 monthly in the bank instead of making payments on the car, how much more (or less) money would he have had in the bank October 1 than he had by making monthly payments on the car?

Interest begins to accrue on a deposit in the savings bank from the first of the month, if deposited before the 5th of the month.

INTEREST ON UNPAID BALANCES

A problem somewhat similar to buying on the installment plan is that in which a person borrows a sum of money and agrees to pay it back in equal, weekly or monthly payments, plus interest.

In problems of this kind interest is charged not on the whole loan for the entire time of the loan, but only on the unpaid portion of the loan. Each payment consists of two parts. One part of the payment pays the interest due, and the balance of the payment is applied to the loan. This is the plan used by personal finance companies. In most states personal finance companies are licensed by the state. They are limited as to the rate of interest they may charge. The rates vary in different states. In some states the maximum rate is 3% a month. At 3% a month, what is the annual rate? What is the annual rate if the monthly rate is 2%? $2\frac{1}{2}$%? $1\frac{1}{2}$%?

Illustration. A loan company offers to loan you $60 to be repaid in 6 equal, monthly payments, plus interest, for a total interest charge of $5.25. What is the monthly rate of interest charged?

You have the use of the entire amount of the loan ($60) for 1 month; at the end of the month you pay the interest due and $10 on the loan. For the second month you have the use of $50, when you pay the interest then due on \$50, and \$10 on the loan, and so on, until the loan is entirely paid. In all, interest is charged as follows:

On \$60 for 1 month
\$50 for 1 month
\$40 for 1 month
\$30 for 1 month
\$20 for 1 month
\$10 for 1 month
Total \$210 for 1 month

To find the rate of interest paid, use the formula $r = \frac{i}{pt}$.

$$r = \frac{\$5.25}{\$210 \times 1^*} = .025 = 2\tfrac{1}{2}\%, \text{ monthly rate.}$$

Problems

1. Using the monthly rate, find the total monthly payments on the loan. See illustration above.

Months	Monthly Balance of Loan	Monthly Payment on Principal	Monthly Interest	Total Monthly Payment
First . . .	\$60	\$10	\$1.50	\$11.50
Second . . .	50	10	1.25	11.25
Third . . .	40	10	1.00	11.00
Fourth . . .	30	10	.75	10.75
Fifth . . .	20	10	.50	10.50
Sixth . . .	10	10	.25	10.25
Totals . .		\$60	\$5.25	\$65.25

2. A young man borrowed \$75 from a personal finance company, agreeing to repay the loan in 5 equal monthly payments, plus interest on unpaid balances. The total interest cost was \$6.75. What monthly rate of interest did he pay? Set up a schedule of payments to show the amounts paid monthly on the loan and interest.

3. A stenographer borrowed from a loan broker \$120, and repaid it in 8 equal monthly payments, plus interest. The total interest charge was \$10.80. Find the monthly rate, and set up a schedule to show the total amount paid monthly.

* The time period is 1 month in this problem (not 1 year).

4. A coal dealer sells coal at $12.50 a ton for cash, or for $13 on one month's credit. What annual rate of interest does a purchaser pay, who buys on credit?

5. A man borrowed $100 and agreed to pay it back in 8 monthly payments of principal, plus interest on unpaid balances. The total amount paid was $109. What was the annual rate of interest paid?

6. A laboring man borrowed $30 from a broker who was operating illegally. The laboring man was charged $2 twice a month, and each time renewed the note for $30. What annual rate of interest was he paying?

7. A piano listed at $400 could be bought for cash for 10% less than the list price. On the deferred payment plan the purchaser was required to pay $100 down, and pay the balance in 30 equal, monthly payments on the principal, plus $\frac{1}{2}$% interest on unpaid balances. How much more would the piano cost on the deferred payment plan than for cash?

8. A. N. Story, a taxi driver, borrowed $240 from a credit union, promising to repay the principal in 12 equal, monthly payments of principal, plus 1% a month on unpaid balances. *a.* How much did the loan cost him in interest? *b.* The interest paid was equal to what annual rate?

9. Mr. and Mrs. Harry Edwards, to set up housekeeping, bought their furniture on the installment plan as follows: On a total purchase of $600, they paid $100 down and agreed to pay the balance in 10 equal, monthly payments, plus interest at $\frac{1}{2}$% a month on unpaid balances, plus $2.50 a month for finance charges. The total interest and finance charges are equivalent to what rate of interest per annum on the deferred payments?

10. Leon Brophy, an electrical worker, borrowed $360, giving a chattel mortgage on his household furniture, as security. He repaid the loan in 12 monthly payments of principal plus $1\frac{1}{2}$% interest on monthly balances, and a finance charge of $2 a month. The total interest and finance charge are equal to what monthly rate of interest on the deferred payments?

PARTIAL PAYMENTS

United States Rule

When part of the amount of a note is paid before the note is due, such payment is called a **partial payment**.

Payments, with the date of each payment, are recorded on the back of the note.

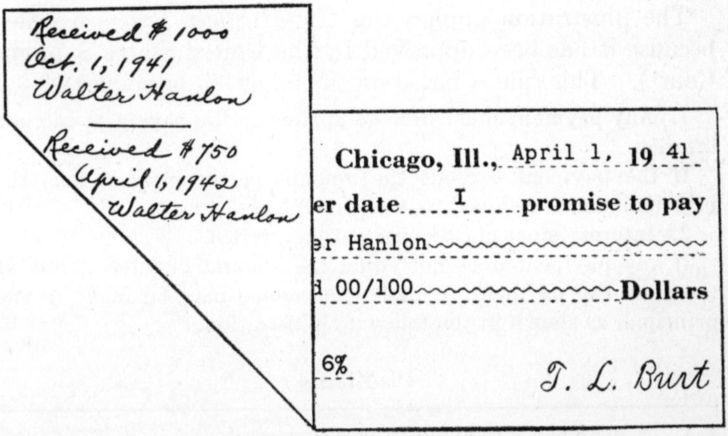

Illustration. Find the amount due on the note above at maturity.

The amount of this note is $2500; the interest rate is 6%; the time is 2 yr., hence the note is due April 1, 1943.

Dates	Time	Payments		Interest		Balance to Apply on Principal		Principal	
Note, 4-1-41								2500	00
First payment, 10-1-41	6 mo.	1000	00	75	00	925	00	1575	00
Second payment, 4-1-42	6 mo.	750	00	47	25	702	75	872	25
Maturity, 4-1-43 . .	1 yr.			52	34			924	59

The amount due at maturity is $924.59.

When the first payment of $1000 was made on Oct. 1, 1941, 6 mo. had elapsed since the date of the note. The interest on $2500 for 6 mo. is $75. After the interest was paid, $925 was left to apply on the face of the note, leaving $1575 due.

The time from Oct. 1, 1941, to Apr. 1, 1942, the date of the second payment, is 6 mo. The interest on $1575 for 6 mo. is $47.25. The payment of $750 was first applied to the interest, leaving $702.75 to apply to the principal. The principal was then reduced to $872.25.

No more payments were made until the date of maturity, Apr. 1, 1943. Adding the interest on $872.25 for 1 yr. gives $924.59 as the final amount due.

The illustration applies the *United States Rule* (so called because it has been approved by the United States Supreme Court). This rule is based on the following principles:

1. **Any payment must first be applied to the paying of accrued interest.**

If the payment exceeds the amount of the interest due, the principal sum is reduced by the amount of the excess.

2. **Interest must not be charged on interest.**

If any payment does not equal the amount of interest due at the time the payment is made, no change may be made in the principal, as shown in the following illustration.

Problems

1. A note for $3000, with interest at 6%, was to run 3 yr. from Feb. 1, 1941. On June 10, 1942, a payment of $200 was made; and on Dec. 1, 1943, $1800 was paid. Find the amount due at maturity.

Dates	Time	Payments		Interest		Balance to Apply on Principal		Principal	
Note, 2–1–41 . .								3000	00
1st pay't, 6–10–42	1 yr. 4 mo. 9 da.	200	00	244	50				
2d pay't, 12–1–43	1 yr. 5 mo. 21 da.	1800	00	265	50				
		2000	00	510	00	1490	00	1510	00
Maturity, 2–1–44	2 mo.			15	10			1525	10

The amount due at maturity is $1525.10.

2. Find the amount due at maturity on each of the following notes, partial payments having been made as indicated:

Date of Note	Face of Note	Time	Rate of Interest	Payments	
June 1, 1940	$1800	2 yr.	6%	March 1, 1941	$500
				August 1, 1941	$400
Oct. 1, 1940	$4500	18 mo.	5%	August 1, 1941	$175
				Dec. 1, 1941	$2500
Dec. 1, 1940	$3000	3 yr.	6%	June 1, 1941	$90
				Dec. 1, 1941	$1090
				June 1, 1942	$1000

Merchants' Rule

The *Merchants' Rule* for finding the balance due on interest-bearing notes on which partial payments have been made is frequently used if the time of the note is less than 1 yr. It is based on the following principles:

1. The face of the note draws interest from its date to the date of maturity.

2. Each payment draws interest from the date it is made to the date of maturity of the note.

Illustration. A note for $1750 was made Aug. 10, 1941. It was to run 10 mo., with interest at 6%. Payments were made as follows: Dec. 1, 1941, $250; April 15, 1942, $500. Find the amount due at maturity.

Date	Face	Time	Interest	Dates	Payments	Time	Interest
Aug. 10, 1941	1750	10 mo.	87 50	Dec. 1, 1941	250	6 mo. 9 da.	7 88
				Apr. 15, 1942	500	1 mo. 25 da.	4 58
	1750		87 50		750		12 46

$1750 + $87.50 = $1837.50, amount of note
$750 + $12.46 = $762.46, amount of payments
$1837.50 − $762.46 = $1075.04, balance due

The interest on $1750 for 10 mo. is $87.50, making the amount due on the note at maturity, if no payments had been made, $1837.50.

The first payment, made Dec. 1, not only cancels $250 on the face of the note, but cancels interest on $250 for the remainder of the time. From Dec. 1 to June 10, the date of maturity, is 6 mo. 9 da. The interest on $250 for 6 mo. 9 da. is $7.88.

The second payment of $500, made on April 15, cancels $500 on the face of the note and interest on $500 till June 10, a period of 1 mo. 25 da. The interest on $500 for 1 mo. 25 da. is $4.58.

Deducting the sum of the payments and the interest thereon from the amount of the note leaves $1075.04, the balance due at maturity.

Problems

1. Find, by the Merchants' Rule, the balance due at maturity on each of the following notes:

Date of Note	Face of Note	Time	Rate of Interest	Payments	
March 1, 1940	$1175	9 mo.	6%	July 1, 1940	$300
				Sept. 30, 1940	$500
July 10, 1940	$2000	11 mo.	6%	Oct. 14, 1940	$750
				Feb. 1, 1941	$500
Jan. 9, 1940	$1200	10 mo.	6%	April 10, 1940	$250
				June 15, 1940	$375
				Sept. 30, 1940	$400

Use the Merchants' Rule in the following problems:

2. A note for $1275, dated March 1, 1940, was to run 9 mo. with interest at 6%. On July 10, 1940, a payment of $300 was made, and on Sept. 15, 1940, $500. Find the balance due at maturity.

3. Henry F. George gave John C. Harrison a note for $2500, dated July 10, 1940, due in 11 mo. with interest at 6%. On Oct. 24, 1940, Mr. George paid $950. On Feb. 15, 1941, he paid $500.

(*a*) Write the note.
(*b*) Write the endorsements.
(*c*) Find the amount due at maturity.

PARTNERSHIP

When one person carries on a business alone or with the help of paid employees, his interest in the business is that of a **sole proprietor.** *He alone is responsible for the conduct of the business, is entitled to the net profit, and is responsible for debts and losses.*

When two or more persons agree to conduct a business by combining either their money or their services or both, they form a **partnership.** Generally each partner agrees to be responsible for conducting or directing some particular part of the work.

Dividing the Profits (or Losses)

Profits are shared according to agreement; **losses** are chargeable against all the partners. If a partner is exempted by complying with a special provision of law, he is known as a **limited partner** and such a partnership is called a **limited partnership.** The presence of a limited partner in a firm is indicated in the name, thus: Allerton and Company, Ltd.

If one or more of the partners are unable to contribute their share toward losses, the other partner or partners may be called on to pay all the losses over and above the assets of the firm.

Illustration. Three men agreed to do business together and to share profits or losses equally. At the end of a year their books showed a gross profit of \$24,250. The expenses of running the business were \$8050. How much was each partner's share of the net profit?

$$\$24{,}250 - \$8050 = \$16{,}200, \text{ net profit}$$
$$\$16{,}200 \div 3 = \$5400, \text{ share of each partner}$$

Illustration. A and B were partners. A invested \$9000 and B invested \$15,000 in the business. It was agreed that each partner should receive 6% interest on his investment. A was to have a salary of \$3000 and B, of \$4000. After interest and salaries were paid, the remainder of the net profit was to be divided equally. The gross profit for the year was $27,560. Running expenses were $10,120. How much did each partner receive?

$27,560 – $10,120 = $17,440, net business profit
6% of $9000 = $540, interest due A
6% of $15,000 = $900, interest due B
$3000 + $540 = $3540, salary and interest of A
$4000 + $900 = $4900, salary and interest of B
$17,440 – ($3540 + $4900) = $9000, amount to be divided equally
$9000 ÷ 2 = $4500, each partner's share
$3540 + $4500 = $8040, amount A received
$4900 + $4500 = $9400, amount B received

Problems

1. Adams, Anderson, and Atwell were partners in a grocery business. Adams and Anderson each invested $7500 and Atwell invested $5000. Each was to receive interest at 6% on his investment, after which the net profit was to be shared equally. The first year the gross profits were $19,495 and expenses were $3960. Find each partner's share of the net profit.

2. X, Y, and Z were partners, sharing gains and losses according to their investment. X invested $9000; Y, $12,000; and Z, $15,000. If their net profit was $15,000, how much was each partner's share?

3. Peterson and Wetzel shared profits in proportion to their investments. Peterson's investment was $7500 and Wetzel's was $5000. Their books at the end of the year showed gains and losses as follows: profit on sales, $11,375; loss on interest, $240; loss on expenses, $2590; profit on commission, $398.50. Find the net profit and determine each partner's share.

4. A, B, and C formed a partnership. A invested $3500; B, $5000; and C, $5500. They agreed to share gains and losses equally. At the end of a year their debts were all paid and they had assets amounting to $11,300. What was each partner's present worth at the close of the year?

5. Frasier, Koch, and Ward were equal partners in a manufacturing business, each having invested $8000. Their agreement provided that Frasier should have a salary of $250 a month, Koch $225 a month, and Ward $200 a month. After salaries were paid, the remaining net profit was to be divided equally. At the end of their first year of business, they had assets and liabilities as follows: Cash, $11,500; merchandise, $16,800; raw materials on hand, $5500; notes receivable (notes due from others), $4500; machinery, $7500; notes payable (notes due others), $7600; unpaid bills, $5200.

(*a*) What was each partner's share of the net profit?

(*b*) Including his salary, how much did each partner receive?

The **net profit** is the difference between the investment at the beginning and the net worth at the end of the year. The **net worth** at the end of the year is the difference between the total assets and the total liabilities. **Assets** are property owned plus what others owe the firm. **Liabilities** are what the firm owes to others.

6. At the beginning of the year T. J. Flanagan and K. E. Mooney had assets amounting to $32,500 and liabilities of $7250. At the end of the year their assets amounted to $49,250 and their liabilities to $8400. Mr. Flanagan received a salary of $250 a month and Mr. Mooney, of $225 a month. Of the net profit, after salaries were paid, Mr. Flanagan received $\frac{5}{9}$ and Mr. Mooney, $\frac{4}{9}$. Find each partner's income (including his salary) for the year.

Methods of Distributing Profits (or Losses)

Good business practice requires that the agreement should be written out in full, when two or more persons enter into a partnership agreement. In this way misunderstandings and disagreements as to what was agreed on will be avoided. Unless profits and losses are to be shared equally, the share of profits or losses to be credited or charged to each partner should be plainly stated.

Among the ways of distributing profits and losses are the following:

1. Equally among the partners
2. According to investment
3. According to average investment
4. According to an agreed ratio, as for three partners (25%, 35%, and 40%)

One partner's time and service to the company may be worth more to the business than that of another partner. In such case, each partner may be paid a salary in proportion to the value of his services to the company, after which the profits are divided equally, or in accordance with some other agreed ratio.

If the amounts invested in the business by the partners are unequal, each partner may receive interest on his investment (as well as salary for his services) after which the net profit may be divided according to agreement.

Illustration. Green and King agreed to enter into a partnership and share profits and losses according to average investment. Green invested \$10,000 on January 1, and \$2500 on April 1. King invested \$12,500 on January 1, and withdrew \$3500 on July 1. Their gross profit for the year was \$21,500, and their operating expenses were \$5210. Find each partner's share of the net profit.

Green invested	\$10,000 for 3 months	=	\$30,000 for 1 month
	\$12,500 for 9 months	=	112,500 for 1 month
	A total of		\$142,500 for 1 month
King invested	\$12,500 for 6 months	=	\$75,000 for 1 month
	\$9,000 for 6 months	=	54,000 for 1 month
	A total of		\$129,000 for 1 month

\$142,500 + \$129,000 = \$271,500, firm's average investment for 1 month

\$21,500 − \$5210 = \$16,290, net profit for the year

$\frac{142,500}{271,500} \times \$16,290 = \$8550$, Green's share of the profit

$\frac{129,000}{271,500} \times \$16,290 = \$7740$, King's share of the profit

Check: \$8550 + \$7740 = \$16,290, net profit

Problems

1. Hendy and Porter became partners on April 1, investing $15,000 each. On Aug. 1, Hendy withdrew $3000, and Porter invested an additional $2000. On Dec. 1, Hendy withdrew another $1000. It was agreed that Hendy should have a salary of $200 a month, and Porter, $175 a month. At the end of the first year of business, their books showed a gross trading profit of $19,750, and operating expenses, including salaries of the partners, of $9310. Including the salaries, find the total amount each partner received from the business, if they shared profits according to average investments.

2. On July 1, Arnott, Burt, and Cady invested $10,000, $12,500, and $15,000 respectively, in a partnership, under an agreement as follows: Arnott is to receive a salary of $1800, Burt, $1500, and Cady, $1200. Each partner is to receive interest at 5% on his investment. After salaries and interest are paid the remaining net earnings are to be distributed in proportion to investment. At the end of 1 year their gross earnings are $31,265, and their operating expenses (exclusive of partners' salaries and interest on their investments) are $6140. Assuming each partner returns his interest and salary to the business to increase the capital, find each partner's net worth at the close of the year.

3. A and B began a partnership with an investment of $13,500, of which A furnished 60% and B, 40%. They agreed to share profits and losses in proportion to their investments. At the end of one year their total assets were $17,500 and their liabilities were $25,000. Find each partner's net loss.

INVESTMENTS

The term **investment** conveys the idea of putting money to work where it will earn something for its owner. In this sense putting money in a savings bank is an investment, though it is not generally so called.

Investments have many forms. One person buys a house and rents it to tenants, another engages in the business of buying and selling merchandise, another buys stocks, another buys bonds, and so on.

Thousands of people lose money every year by putting it into unsafe investments.

The first thing to consider in every investment should be safety of the money invested. A small interest return coupled with safety of principal is far better than the promise of big returns with danger to principal.

Many modern business enterprises require large investment of capital. Any one person rarely has sufficient funds to capitalize a large business.

To form a partnership with sufficient capital would require a number of people who were interested in the business and could invest both time and money in it. A principle of law makes any partner (with certain exceptions) personally liable for the debts of the entire firm. As a result large partnerships are not common.

The more common form of business organization is known as a **corporation.**

Because stocks and bonds are such common forms of investment, some of the principles underlying these investments are here considered.

STOCKS

To avoid personal liability for debts of a business and to secure large sums of money for business enterprises, a number of persons may agree to put their money together and form a corporation for conducting business.

A **corporation** is an association of persons having an existence (or *entity*) separate and distinct from the persons forming the corporation, for the purpose of carrying on a business or an enterprise according to regulations contained in an agreement with the state. This agreement is called a **charter.**

The money or other property invested in a corporation is called its **capital stock.** The capital stock is divided into **shares** of an agreed value (from $1 or less to $100 a share). Each investor, called a **stockholder,** has as many shares as his investment pays for.

Suppose A, B, C, D, E, and F agree to invest $50,000 in an ice-manufacturing plant. They invest as follows:

A invests $10,000	D invests $10,000
B invests $10,000	E invests $5,000
C invests $10,000	F invests $5,000

They apply to the state for a **charter** giving them the right to manufacture and sell ice in their city. They ask that the company be called The People's Ice Company.

The state grants them a charter and provides that their capital stock shall consist of 500 shares valued at $100 each.

A, B, C, and D then have each invested $10,000 in 100 shares of ice stock, and E and F have each invested $5000 in 50 shares of stock.

Each stockholder (that is, each owner of stock) receives a paper called a **stock certificate** which states how many shares of stock he owns.

Certain stockholders are elected as **directors** to manage the business.

If the company prospers, it makes a **profit.** If the directors vote to divide the *profits* or part of the profits among the stockholders, such an apportionment is called a **dividend.** The *dividend* voted by the directors is expressed as a given number of cents or dollars per share.

The Investment

Illustration. A owns 100 shares of stock in the People's Ice Company and E owns 50 shares. The directors of the

Company vote a dividend of $5 a share. How much of a dividend will A and E each receive?

Since A owns 100 shares, he receives a dividend of 100 × $5, or $500. Since E owns 50 shares, he receives 50 × $5, or $250, and so on.

If the company is prosperous, other people may wish to buy some of the stock. Also some of the stockholders may wish to sell their stock.

Problems

1. Suppose G offers to give C $105 a share for 50 shares of his stock. If C accepts G's offer, how much does G pay C for the 50 shares?

2. How much profit does C make by selling 50 shares of his stock at $105 a share?

3. How much is G's investment?

The value of a single share of the stock ($100), as stated in the charter, is called its par value.

When G buys 50 shares of stock from C at $105 a share, the stock is sold *above par*. If he bought it at $98 a share, it would be sold *below par*.

4. D offered to sell 25 shares of his stock at $107 a share. If H bought 25 shares at this price, how much did he pay for it?

5. How much profit did D make?

6. Did D sell his stock above or below par? how much above or below?

7. At the end of the second year the directors of The People's Ice Company voted a dividend of $5 a share. Prepare a list of the stockholders (A, B, C, D, E, F, G, and H), showing how many shares of stock each now owns, the amount he paid for his stock, and the amount of the dividend he receives at the end of the year.

8. A offers to sell 25 shares of his stock at $110 a share and B offers to sell 50 shares of his stock at $110 a share. If H buys the stock offered by both A and B, how much does he pay each man for the stock?

Owing to the introduction of electric refrigerators into the homes of the people, the ice company's third year of business was much poorer than formerly. The directors decided not to pay a dividend that year.

9. Fearing losses, some of the stockholders offered to sell their stock at par. At what price was that?

10. As they did not find anyone who would buy the stock at par, they offered to sell it at $90 a share. How much below par was that?

11. H bought 25 shares from A at $90 a share; he also bought 25 shares from D and 50 shares from E at the same price. How much did the stock cost him?

12. How many stockholders are there now? How many shares of stock does each one own?

Finding the Rate of Income on Investment

Illustration. At the end of the first year of business the ice company paid each stockholder a $5 dividend on each share of stock he owned. What rate of income was this for the stockholders who had paid $100 a share for their stock?

The question, in equation form, is

$$?\% \text{ of } \$100 = \$5$$
$$\$5 \div \$100 = .05 = 5\%, \text{ rate of income}$$

Hence each stockholder who had paid $100 a share for his stock had a 5% investment, or a 5% income on his investment.

At the end of the second year a $5 dividend was again paid on each share of stock. During the second year G had bought 50 shares of stock at $105 a share. Find G's rate of income on his investment.

THE STOCK EXCHANGE

Throughout the country there are many corporations. Some of them are small and have very few shares of stock. Others are large with a very large number of shares of stock. In the large corporations the stock is owned by thousands of people. Among the stockholders there are always some who, for one reason or another, wish to sell their stock. There are also those who wish to buy stock; these persons buy their stock at places where stock is for sale. Such a place is called a stock **exchange.** In the same way and for the same reason a housewife who wishes to buy sugar, coffee, or flour does not go to the person who grows or manufactures these items. She instead buys them at a store where these articles are for sale.

A *stock exchange* is formed, under legal regulations, by a group of men who make a business of buying and selling stocks. These men are known as **stockbrokers.** A stockholder, or a corporation, wishing to sell stock places an order to sell the stock with a stockbroker.

One point of difference between the sale of stock and the sale of groceries (or other every-day commodities) is that the grocer first buys the groceries he sells. He then sells what he owns. The stockbroker generally sells what belongs to some one else. The broker may, of course, buy stock for his own account and then sell it, but the usual practice is to act as an agent for some one else.

For his services in selling stock the broker charges a fee called **brokerage.** The rate of brokerage depends on the selling price of the stock.

Following are the *rates of brokerage* charged for buying and selling stocks on the New York Stock Exchange:

Selling Price per Share	Minimum Commission Rate per Share
From $\frac{1}{4}$ of \$1 to $\frac{15}{32}$ of \$1	1.5¢ per share
From $\frac{1}{2}$ of \$1 to $\frac{31}{32}$ of \$1	3.0¢ per share
From \$1 to \$1$\frac{7}{8}$	5.0¢ per share
From \$2 to \$2$\frac{7}{8}$	6.0¢ per share
From \$3 to \$3$\frac{7}{8}$	7.0¢ per share
From \$4 to \$4$\frac{7}{8}$	8.0¢ per share
From \$5 to \$5$\frac{7}{8}$	9.0¢ per share
From \$6 to \$6$\frac{7}{8}$	10.0¢ per share
From \$7 to \$7$\frac{7}{8}$	11.0¢ per share
From \$8 to \$8$\frac{7}{8}$	12.0¢ per share
From \$9 to \$9$\frac{7}{8}$	13.0¢ per share
From \$10 to \$19$\frac{7}{8}$	14.0¢ per share
From \$20 to \$29$\frac{7}{8}$	15.0¢ per share
From \$30 to \$39$\frac{7}{8}$	16.0¢ per share
From \$40 to \$49$\frac{7}{8}$	17.0¢ per share
From \$50 to \$59$\frac{7}{8}$	18.0¢ per share
From \$60 to \$69$\frac{7}{8}$	19.0¢ per share
From \$70 to \$79$\frac{7}{8}$	20.0¢ per share
From \$80 to \$89$\frac{7}{8}$	21.0¢ per share
From \$90 to \$99$\frac{7}{8}$	22.0¢ per share
For each additional \$10 or fraction thereof	1.0¢ additional

Stock quotations in the United States are in dollars per share. Thus, "stock bought at $95\frac{1}{2}$," means "stock bought at $95.50 a share."

The seller of stocks has to pay a Federal tax as follows:

On the stock of no-par value the tax is
- $.04 per share if the selling price is under $20 per share.
- $.05 per share if the selling price is $20, or above, per share.

On stock having a par value the Federal tax is
- $.04 per share for each $100 of par value, or fraction thereof, if the selling price is under $20 a share.
- $.05 per share for each $100 of par value, or fraction thereof, if the selling price is $20 or more.

A sales, or transfer, tax is levied on stock sales in the following states, and at the rates indicated:

On Stock of No-par Value the Tax per Share Is,	On Stock Having a Par Value the Tax per Share Is,
New York $.03 if sale price is under $20	$.03 if sale price is under $20
$.04 if sale price is $20 or above	$.04 if sale price is $20 or above
Florida $.10	$.10 per $100 of face value or fraction thereof
Massachusetts $.02	$.02 per $100 of face value or fraction thereof
Pennsylvania $.02	$.02 per $100 of face value or fraction thereof
S. Carolina $.04	$.04 per $100 of face value

The chief stock exchange in the United States is the New York Stock Exchange in New York City. On this exchange large numbers of shares of stock are bought and sold by the members of the exchange, for their clients. It is not uncommon for several million shares to be sold in one day.

Daily reports are made through the newspapers of the number of shares of each kind of stock sold, and the price at which it was sold. Prices of stocks are changing constantly. The report on the price of a single stock generally gives the opening or first price of the day, the high price, the low price, and the last or closing price, of the day.

Following is a partial list of the stocks dealt in on the New York Stock Exchange, showing the *first, high, low,* and *last prices,* with the *net change in the last price* as compared with the *closing price of the preceding day.*

PRICES ON THE NEW YORK STOCK EXCHANGE

	FIRST	HIGH	LOW	LAST	NET CHANGE	SHARES SOLD
American Can	$83\frac{1}{2}$	85	$83\frac{1}{2}$	85	$+1\frac{1}{8}$	800
American Tel. & Tel. . .	150	150	148	$149\frac{3}{4}$	$-\frac{1}{4}$	6,100
Atch. Topeka & S. F. . .	$24\frac{5}{8}$	26	$24\frac{5}{8}$	26	$+1\frac{3}{8}$	4,200
Bethlehem Steel	$53\frac{5}{8}$	$55\frac{5}{8}$	$53\frac{1}{4}$	$55\frac{5}{8}$	$+3\frac{1}{8}$	16,100
Bon Ami	$105\frac{1}{4}$	$105\frac{1}{4}$	105	105	$-\frac{3}{8}$	30
Chrysler Corporation . .	$56\frac{1}{2}$	$58\frac{3}{8}$	$56\frac{1}{2}$	$58\frac{3}{8}$	$+2\frac{1}{4}$	25,200
Consolidated Edison . . .	$27\frac{1}{2}$	$28\frac{3}{8}$	$27\frac{1}{2}$	$28\frac{1}{8}$	$+\frac{3}{8}$	9,900
Douglas Aircraft	60	$61\frac{1}{2}$	60	$61\frac{1}{2}$	$+1\frac{7}{8}$	3,300
Eastern Air Lines	$12\frac{1}{2}$	$13\frac{1}{4}$	$12\frac{1}{2}$	$13\frac{1}{4}$	$+\frac{5}{8}$	1,300
Firestone Tire & Rubber .	$17\frac{5}{8}$	$18\frac{3}{4}$	$17\frac{5}{8}$	$18\frac{1}{2}$	$-\frac{3}{8}$	1,900
International Bus. Mach. .	$159\frac{1}{2}$	$160\frac{1}{8}$	$159\frac{1}{4}$	160	—	900
Northern Pacific	$7\frac{1}{8}$	8	$7\frac{1}{8}$	$7\frac{7}{8}$	$+\frac{1}{2}$	8,200
Radio Corporation of Am. .	$5\frac{1}{4}$	$5\frac{3}{4}$	$5\frac{1}{4}$	$5\frac{3}{4}$	$+\frac{1}{4}$	24,400
Sears Roebuck	$60\frac{1}{4}$	64	$60\frac{1}{4}$	$63\frac{1}{2}$	$+1\frac{7}{8}$	3,900
U. S. Steel	$45\frac{1}{8}$	$46\frac{7}{8}$	$44\frac{7}{8}$	$46\frac{5}{8}$	$+1\frac{1}{2}$	23,600

Buying Stock through a Broker

Illustration. Mr. Adams bought through a broker 80 shares of Bethlehem Steel at the first price quoted above. How much did the stock cost him? See page 312 for brokerage rates.

$$
\begin{aligned}
80 \times \$53.625 &= \$4290\text{, cost of stock} \\
80 \times \$.18 &= \underline{\quad 14.40}\text{, brokerage} \\
& \$4304.40\text{, total cost}
\end{aligned}
$$

Problems

In the following problems in stocks the prices are to be taken from the quoted prices on this page, unless otherwise indicated. Brokerage is to be reckoned on both *purchases* and *sales.* Using the *low price,* find the cost of the following:

1. 75 shares of American Can
2. 150 shares of U. S. Steel

3. 40 shares of Eastern Air Lines
4. 60 shares of Bon Ami
5. 175 shares of Atch. Topeka and S. F.
6. 250 shares of Firestone Tire and Rubber
7. 50 shares of American Tel. and Tel.
8. 125 shares of Sears Roebuck
9. 200 shares of Radio Corporation of America

Finding the Proceeds of a Sale

Illustration. Mr. Hubbell sold 200 shares of American Can at the high price. Allowing for both Federal and New York State tax, find the proceeds of the sale.

$$200 \times \$85 = \$17{,}000\text{, selling price}$$
$$200 \times \$.21 = \$42\text{, brokerage}$$
$$200 \times \$.05 = \$10\text{, Federal tax}$$
$$200 \times \$.04 = \$8\text{, New York State tax}$$

$$\$42 + \$10 + \$8 = \$60\text{, total charges}$$
$$\$17{,}000 - \$60 = \$16{,}940\text{, proceeds of sale}$$

Problems

Use the *high price* in each of the following problems. Allowing for Federal and State taxes as indicated in each problem, find the proceeds of the following sales of stock:

	Sales of Stock	*Tax to Be Charged*	
1.	150 shares of Bethlehem Steel	Federal	
2.	200 shares Chrysler Corporation	Federal	Pennsylvania
3.	75 shares of Consolidated Edison	Federal	Massachusetts
4.	125 shares of Douglas Aircraft	Federal	Florida
5.	50 shares of Northern Pacific	Federal	S. Carolina
6.	90 shares of U. S. Steel	Federal	New York

7. Herman Huston bought 100 shares of Sears Roebuck at the low price and sold it at the high price. Allowing brokerage both ways and for the Federal tax, find his net profit.

Finding the Number of Shares Bought

Illustration. Mr. Lucey invested \$4618.90 in Firestone Tire and Rubber stock at $17\frac{5}{8}$, plus brokerage. How many shares did he buy?

$$\$17.625 + \$.14 = \$17.765, \text{ total cost of 1 share}$$
$$\$4618.90 \div \$17.765 = 260, \text{ number of shares}$$

Using the last price quoted on page 314, and including brokerage, find how many shares of stock can be bought in each of the following cases:

Problems

Amount Invested	*Kind of Stock*
1. \$7501	American Tel. & Tel.
2. \$17,889.10	Bon Ami
3. \$7254.65	Bethlehem Steel
4. \$12,296.55	Chrysler Corporation
5. \$11,104.20	Douglas Aircraft
6. \$2628	Radio Corporation of America
7. \$3034.30	Northern Pacific
8. \$6786	Consolidated Edison
9. \$4686.50	Eastern Air Lines

BONDS

A manufacturing company has a capital stock of \$150,000, divided into 1500 shares of \$100 each. To increase the size of its factory, the company needs \$50,000 more money than it has on hand. The company arranges with an investment banker for a loan of \$50,000 for 5 yr.

Instead of giving the banker an ordinary promissory note, the company issues bonds for the loan.

For practical purposes, a **bond** may be thought of as a promissory note, although it is written in more formal language and in greater detail than a note.

A bond is generally made payable to bearer, that is, to the person who has possession of it.

Bonds are issued in different denominations, such as $50 (U. S. "Baby Bonds"), $100, $500, $1000, etc.; the $500 and $1000 denominations are probably the most usual amounts.

Each bond contains a promise to pay to the bearer, at its maturity, the full face value of the bond, and to pay (generally semiannually) the interest on the bond at a fixed rate.

There are two general classes of bonds, **coupon and registered.**

Coupon bonds have interest coupons attached. The coupons are made payable to bearer and are dated at regular intervals (usually semiannually) and are in effect negotiable notes promising to pay the interest on the bond as it becomes due. Thus, a coupon bond having 20 years to run would have attached 40 coupons numbered from 1 to 40, and dated in order every six months from the date of the bond. As each interest date occurs, the coupon bearing that date is cut from the sheet of coupons and cashed or deposited in the bank, as the bond holder desires.

Coupons are made payable to bearer. They may, therefore, be sold, or transferred from one person to another, without any formality other than delivery.

Registered bonds take their name from the fact that the name of the owner of the bond is registered with an agent of the maker of the bond. On "fully registered" (registered as to both principal and interest) bonds, interest is paid by check or draft to the registered owner of the bond. It is important, therefore, that in the transfer of registered bonds the name of the new owner be registered with the agent of the maker of the bonds.

Some registered bonds are "registered as to principal only." Such bonds carry interest coupons, the same as coupon bonds.

One advantage of registered bonds over coupon bonds is that if a registered bond is lost or stolen, the rightful owner is enabled to prove ownership by the fact of registry. A disadvantage is that ownership of registered bonds is not so conveniently transferred from one person to another.

State one advantage and one disadvantage of the coupon bond as compared with the registered bond.

Stocks and Bonds Compared

Stocks	*Bonds*
1. Owner is part owner of the corporation.	1. Owner is a creditor of the corporation.
2. Owner generally has a vote in the election of directors.	2. Owner generally has no vote.
3. Dividends are not due till declared by the directors.	3. Interest is due and payable regularly.
4. Dividends depend on earning power of the corporation.	4. Interest rate is fixed.
5. Purchased many times for speculation.	5. Purchased, generally, for investment.

Because of the facts stated in the foregoing comparison of stocks and bonds, bonds are generally considered a safer investment than stocks. Interest is paid on bonds before dividends are paid on stock. In case a corporation with bonds outstanding fails in business, the assets of the corporation are used to repay the money borrowed on bonds before the stockholders are paid anything on their stock. On the other hand, if a corporation is prosperous, the dividend rate may be increased above the rate of interest on the bonds. The relative merits of stocks and bonds as an investment must depend on the particular stocks and bonds under consideration.

Unless otherwise indicated, the term *bond* in this text will denote a $1000 bond.

Bonds are quoted in the market in terms of *per cent.* A quotation of "90" means that the bond is selling at 90% of its face value. That is, a bond selling at "90" would cost 90% of $1000, or $900, while a bond selling at "108" would cost 108% of $1000, or $1080.

In buying a bond, the buyer has to pay the seller the interest the bond has earned since interest was last paid.

The Investment

Illustration. **Coupons.** Mr. Healey owns a $1000 bond paying 6% interest. The coupons are dated Feb. 1 and Aug. 1 of each year the bond has to run. How much is each coupon worth?

Since the interest is paid every 6 mo., each coupon calls for the payment of one-half year's interest on \$1000 at 6%, which is \$30.

As the coupons become due, Mr. Healey cuts them off and cashes them or deposits them in his bank.

Illustration. **The Bond.** If Mr. Healey sells the bond on June 1 to Mr. Edison at 102, how much must Mr. Edison pay for the bond?

Mr. Edison must pay 102% of \$1000, the face value of the bond, and in addition he must pay the interest that has been earned on the bond from Feb. 1 to June 1.

$$1.02 \times \$1000 = \$1020, \text{ cost of bond}$$
$$\text{From Feb. 1 to June 1} = 4 \text{ mo.}$$
$$\text{Interest for 4 mo. at 6\% on } \$1000 = \$20$$
$$\$1020 + \$20 = \$1040$$

Therefore Mr. Edison must pay Mr. Healey \$1040 for the bond and the interest to June 1.

NOTE. In reckoning interest on bonds, count 30 days to the month.

Problems

Find the cost, including interest, of the following bonds:

1. \$1000 Warren Steel 5% bond at 103, interest dates Jan. 1 and July 1; date of purchase, Aug. 1.

2. Three \$1000 United Telephone 5% bonds at 109, interest dates June 1 and Dec. 1; date of purchase, Feb. 1.

3. Five \$1000 Mason Ward Company 4% bonds at $87\frac{1}{2}$, interest dates June 1 and Dec. 1; date of purchase, Sept. 16.

If bonds are bought or sold through a broker, a charge of \$2.50 per \$1000 bond is made as commission or **brokerage.**

4. Find the cost of ten \$1000 Premier Corporation 5% bonds at $102\frac{1}{2}$, interest dates April 1 and Oct. 1, if the date of purchase was July 21 and brokerage was \$2.50 per bond.

5. Three \$1000 Western Rubber 5% bonds at $83\frac{3}{4}$, interest dates Jan. 1 and July 1, were purchased May 16. If brokerage was \$2.50 per bond, find the total cost.

Finding the Rate on a Bond Investment

Reckoning the rate of income on an investment in bonds is a technical solution too advanced for this text. Rough estimates of the rate of income are sometimes made by dividing the interest on the bond by the cost of the bond.

Illustration. What is the approximate rate of income on an investment in a 6% bond bought at 96?

$$6\% \text{ of } \$1000 = \$60, \text{ interest}$$
$$\$60 \div \$960 = .06\tfrac{1}{4}, = 6\tfrac{1}{4}\%, \text{ rate of income}$$

NOTE. The $6\frac{1}{4}\%$ rate of income would be very nearly correct if the bond had 50 yr. or more to run. If it had but 5 yr. to run, the income rate would be very nearly 7%. If it had 10 yr. to run, the income rate would be a little more than $6\frac{1}{2}\%$.

Problems

---

1. Mr. Edwards invested $15,000 in Eureka Manufacturing Company 5% bonds at $74\frac{3}{4}$, brokerage $2.50 per bond. How many bonds did he buy? What was his annual income from the bonds? What was the approximate rate of income on his investment?

2. A man had $25,000 to invest in bonds. On May 25 he bought through a broker Western Rubber Company 5% bonds at 97. The interest dates were May 1 and Nov. 1.

(*a*) How many bonds did he buy?

(*b*) How much money did he have left over?

(*c*) How much interest did he receive annually?

(*d*) What was the approximate rate of income on his investment?

HINT. First find the total cost of each bond.

3. What is the approximate rate per cent of income on $4\frac{1}{2}\%$ bonds, bought at 94?

Comprehensive Test on Investments

1. An investor purchased stock as follows. During the first year he had the stock he received dividends as indicated. Find (*a*) the total cost of the stock; (*b*) the total dividends received; and (*c*) the rate per cent of income on his entire investment.

Number of Shares	*Price*	*Brokerage per Share*	*Dividend per Share*
50 shares Am Can	85	\$.21	\$4
25 shares Am Tel & Tel	$148\frac{1}{2}$	\$.27	\$9
40 shares Douglas Aircraft	$60\frac{1}{2}$	\$.19	\$3

2. Mr. Waters had \$10,000 with which he wished to purchase as many shares as he could of U. S. Steel. The price of U. S. Steel was $46\frac{5}{8}$, and brokerage was \$.17 a share. (*a*) How many shares of stock could he buy? (*b*) How much money did he have left?

3. If Sears Roebuck stock pays \$3 a share and the price of the stock is 64, plus brokerage of \$.19 a share, find the cost of stock enough to pay annual dividends of \$750.

4. Find the cost, including interest, of 25 bonds paying $4\frac{1}{2}\%$ interest, at $102\frac{1}{2}$, and brokerage of \$2.50 per bond. The bonds were bought on March 21, and the interest dates are Jan. 1 and July 1.

5. A man owned \$150,000 of Great Northern Railway bonds, and received \$3375 as the semi-annual interest on them. What annual rate of interest did the bonds pay?

6. A bond paying $5\frac{1}{2}\%$ interest cost \$880. Find the approximate rate of interest on the investment received by the purchaser.

7. Which is the better investment, stock paying \$4 dividends and bought at 88, or stock paying \$6 dividends and bought at 125?

EXCHANGE BETWEEN COUNTRIES

The principles underlying foreign exchange are very similar to those governing domestic exchange.

While gold and silver are shipped from one country to another at times to settle international debts, and to adjust balances in the great international banking houses, payment for purchases abroad (that is, for imported merchandise) is made chiefly by means of the bill of exchange.

A **bill of exchange** is merely another name for a foreign draft. The term **cheque** is also used for a foreign draft.

A **foreign draft** is a draft drawn in one country on a bank or company in another country.

Settlement of foreign debts is also made by **cable transfer.** A cable transfer is a cabled order to pay to a designated person or firm a certain sum of money. In principle it is similar to a domestic telegraph money order. (See page 137.)

Foreign drafts may be made payable in terms of United States dollars, or in terms of the monetary units of other countries. If a draft is made payable in terms of foreign money, it is necessary to calculate the cost of the foreign draft in United States dollars, at the prevailing rate of exchange.

In times of disturbed economic and political conditions, such as prevailed in 1938, 1939, and 1940, in Europe and Asia, many foreign concerns asked American importers to make payment to them (the foreign concerns) in dollar exchange — that is, by making the draft payable in United States dollars. This was done because it was believed abroad that United States dollars were (temporarily, at least) a more stable currency than the currencies of their own countries. To illustrate, an exporter in Paris, France, requests an American debtor to pay him $1000 in U. S. dollars. If the price of francs has decreased by the time the draft reaches him, he can get more francs than he otherwise would; but if the price of francs has increased, he will get fewer francs for the draft. The request is made by the foreign exporter when he thinks the price of his own currency will decrease.

The real value of foreign money in terms of dollars depends upon the amount of gold in the foreign coins. The Treasury Department of the United States issues a quarterly statement showing the values of foreign coins, in terms of United States dollars. A partial list of such coins and their values, contained in a recent report, follows:

VALUES OF FOREIGN COINS

COUNTRY	MONETARY UNIT	VALUE IN U. S. DOLLARS
Argentine Republic	Peso	$1.6335
Belgium	Belga	.1695
Canada	Dollar	1.6931
Cuba	Peso	1.0000
France	Franc	No value given
Germany	Reichsmark	.4033
Great Britain	Pound Sterling	8.2397
Ireland	Pound	8.2397
Italy	Lira	.0526
Japan	Yen	.8440
Sweden	Krone	.4537
Turkey	Piaster	.0744

Due to varying economic conditions in the nations of the world, and to the fact that gold is not at present a circulating medium of exchange, the values of foreign coins, as expressed in the daily rates of exchange, depend very largely on the law of supply and demand.

Thus, the United States exports goods to Italy and imports goods from Italy. If the exports and imports are equal, the goods shipped to Italy balance, or pay for, the goods imported from Italy. That is, there is no balance of trade, and in neither country is there an excess demand for foreign exchange. On the other hand, if the exports from the United States to Italy greatly exceed the imports from Italy, there will be a greater demand in Italy for drafts to pay for goods purchased from the United States than there is in the United States to pay for goods purchased in Italy. This condition tends to increase the value of dollars, or, what is the equivalent situation, it decreases the market value of the lira. Hence, the rates of exchange quoted in the daily market reports seldom are equal to the values of the coins as reported by the Treasury Department. Following are a few market rates recently quoted:

MARKET RATES

COUNTRY	MONETARY UNIT	MARKET QUOTATION
Argentine Republic	Peso	\$.2335
Belgium	Belga	.1683½
France	Franc	.0264⅞
Germany	Reichsmark	.4021
Great Britain	Pound Sterling	4.68⅛
Italy	Lira	.0526¼
Japan	Yen	.2727
Sweden	Krone	.2413

Pupils should learn to consult the newspapers and find in them the current rates of exchange.

Illustration. Find the value of £238 14*s.* at \$4.68½.

14*s.* = £.7 (14*s.* ÷ 20*s.* = .7)
£238 14*s.* = £238.7
238.7 × \$4.68½ = \$1118.31, value.

Illustration. How large a draft on Great Britain can be bought for \$4119.85 at 4.67¾?

\$4119.85 ÷ \$4.6775 = 880.7803, number of pounds
.7803 × 20*s.* = 15.606*s.*
.606 × 12*d.* = 7.272*d.*
.272 × 4 far. = 1.088 far.

Hence the amount of the draft is £880 15*s.* 7*d.* 1 far.

The decimal of a pound — .7803 — is changed to shillings by multiplying the number of shillings in a pound — 20 — by .7803, which gives 15.606 shillings. Likewise the decimal of a shilling — .606 — is changed to pence by multiplying the number of pence in a shilling — 12 — by .606, which gives 7.272 pence, and so on to farthings.

Problems

Using the market rates of exchange quoted on the preceding page, find the value in United States money of the following amounts of foreign money:

1. 4500 lire	**4.** £375	**7.** 7500 lire
2. 2750 yen	**5.** 4150 kronor	**8.** 6250 reichsmarks
3. 3275 belgas	**6.** 4376 yen	**9.** 3750 pesos

Find the face value of drafts on London (that is, in pounds sterling) that can be bought for:

10. \$1500 at \$4.72½	**12.** \$1875 at \$4.68¾
11. \$545.50 at \$4.69½	**13.** \$637.75 at \$4.77½

Use the market rates on page 324 for the following problems:

14. How many yen can be bought for \$2110?

15. A bill of exchange on London cost \$19,507.49. Find its face value.

16. A merchant paid \$473.85 for a draft on Argentine Republic. For how many pesos was the draft drawn?

17. How large a draft on Stockholm, Sweden, can be bought for \$8167.50?

18. Find the cost in dollars for a draft on London for £750.

19. An American woman bought in Paris a dress for which she paid 4000 francs. If she had exchanged her American money into francs at the rate of \$.0275 per franc, how much was the equivalent dollar cost of the dress? If a similar dress would cost \$225 in the United States, how much did she save by buying the dress in Paris? When she returned to America, if she paid a duty of 65% of the purchase price, how much money (if any) did she save by the purchase?

NOTE. Merchandise, not exceeding \$100 in value, purchased abroad, may be brought into the United States free of duty, if it is brought in for personal use.

UNITED STATES CUSTOMS

In the United States, wages are higher and living conditions are better than in any other country. To help in maintaining this position among the nations of the world, the United States government charges a protective tariff, or duty, on certain kinds of imported merchandise.

Charging a duty on imported merchandise does two things.

1. It helps to keep the wages of the American laborer high by preventing other nations, where labor is cheap, from selling merchandise in the United States for less than it can be manufactured here where wages are high.

2. The money paid in duties helps to pay the expenses of the government.

Hence, it is that the tariff is spoken of as a **protective tariff**, or a **tariff for revenue.**

The Tariff Act gives two lists of imported merchandise: (1) A **dutiable list of articles,** on which duties are required to be paid and (2) a **free list,** on which no duty is charged. Among the items on the *free list* are the following: bananas, broken bells, gold and silver bullion, uncut diamonds, grindstones, ice, crude India rubber, Paris green, silk cocoons, wood charcoal, etc.

Duties are of two kinds, **ad valorem duties** and **specific duties.**

Ad valorem means "according to value." An *ad valorem duty* is expressed as a per cent of the invoice value of the merchandise imported.

A *specific duty* is a fixed charge per unit of measure of the imported article, as $.44 a pound, or $.25 a yard, etc.

On some imported articles only an *ad valorem duty* is charged, on some articles only a *specific duty* is charged, and on some articles both kinds of duty are charged.

The following is a partial list of articles on which an ad valorem duty, a specific duty, or both, are charged, according to the Tariff Act of 1930:

Articles	Ad Valorem Duty	Specific Duty
Apples		\$.25 a bushel
Bicycles (not including tires) . .	30%	
Bicycle tires	10%	
Butter		\$.14 per pound
Carpets (chiefly cotton)	35%	
Carpets (cork)	35%	
Cheese		\$.07 per pound, but not less than 35% ad valorem
Cherries (in natural state) . .		\$.02 per pound
Cherries (Maraschino)	40%	\$.09½ per pound
Chickens (live)		\$.08 per pound
Eggs		\$.10 per dozen
Electric light bulbs	30%	
Fish glue	25%	\$.02 per pound
Fountain pens	40%	\$.72 per dozen
Grapefruit	25%	
Hay		\$5 per ton of 2000 lb.
Honey		\$.03 per pound
Lawn mowers	30%	
Oats		\$.16 per bu. of 32 lb.
Rugs (valued at not more than \$.40 per sq. ft.) . . .	40%	
(valued at more than \$.40 a sq. ft.)	60%	
Safety razors (valued at \$4 or more per dozen)	30%	\$.45 each
Silk handkerchiefs (hemmed) . .	60%	
Skates (ice and roller)	20%	
Sugar		\$.01725 per pound
Washing machines (electric) . .	35%	

All imported merchandise must be reported at a port of entry, and the duty paid by the importer, before the importer can receive his merchandise.

The invoices of imported merchandise are made out in the terms of the coinage of the country from which they are imported. It is necessary, therefore, to calculate the value of the goods in terms of United States money before the duty is paid. This calculation is made at the custom house.

In calculating the value of foreign money in terms of United States money, the law provides that the calculation "shall be made at the values proclaimed by the Secretary of the Treasury — for the quarter in which the merchandise was exported," unless "the value so proclaimed varies by 5 per centum or more from a value measured by the buying rate in the New York Market at noon on the day of exportation," in which case the calculation "shall be made at a value measured by such buying rate."

Ad valorem duties are not computed on fractions of a dollar. \$.50 or more is counted as a dollar; less than \$.50 is rejected.

Generally *specific duties* are not reckoned on fractions of a unit. Fractions of units equal to, or greater than one half, are counted as whole units. Otherwise they are rejected.

Illustration. How much is the duty on 3 dozen bicycles valued at \$15 each, and 3 dozen sets of tires valued at \$2.25 per tire?

$3 \times 12 \times \$15 = \$540$, value of the bicycles.
$3 \times 12 \times 2 \times \$2.25 = \$162$, value of the tires.
30% of $\$540 = \$162$, duty on the bicycles.
10% of $\$162 = \$16.20$, duty on the tires.
$\$162 + \$16.20 = \$178.20$, total duty.

Illustration. A stationer imported 5 dozen fountain pens valued at \$18.50 per dozen. How much duty did he pay?

$5 \times \$18.50 = \$92.50$, value of the fountain pens.
40% of $\$93 = \$37.20$, ad valorem duty.
$5 \times \$.72 = \$3.60$, specific duty.
$\$37.20 + \$3.60 = \$40.80$, total duty.

Problems

---

1. On what value would the *ad valorem duty* be charged on importations valued at \$345.60? \$534.25? \$657.90? \$290.45?

2. On what quantities would specific duties be charged on the following: $547\frac{1}{4}$ tons? $856\frac{3}{4}$ yd.? $8542\frac{3}{4}$ lb.?

For rates of duty see page 327.

3. A produce dealer at Port Huron, Mich., bought from a farmer in Canada, 75 tons of hay at \$9.50 a ton. Including duty, how much did the hay cost him?

4. A wholesale fruit dealer imported grapefruit valued at $1154.60. How much duty did he pay?

5. A firm in Buffalo, N. Y., bought from a cheese factory in Ontario, Canada, 1500 lb. of cheese at $.22 a pound. Find the total cost of the cheese.

6. A merchant imported 20 dozen safety razors, invoiced at $5.50 a dozen. Including duty, how much was paid for them?

Find the duty on each of the following importations:

7. Electric light bulbs worth $275.

8. Honey weighing 1800 lb.

9. Lawn mowers invoiced at $962.50.

10. 120 dozen eggs valued at $.22 a dozen.

11. Fish glue weighing 48 lb., and valued at $.75 a pound.

12. 250 chickens weighing 2 lb. each.

13. 24 Wilton rugs 12′ × 15′, invoiced at $2.50 per square yard.

14. 12 Wilton rugs 12′ × 15′, invoiced at $4.50 per square yard.

15. 2500 bushels of apples.

16. 1200 square yards of cork carpet at $2.50 a square yard.

17. 20 tons (2000 lb. a ton) of sugar.

WORKMEN'S COMPENSATION INSURANCE

Provisions of Compensation Insurance

Because of the many accidents in industry and the consequent loss of wages by workers and the resulting hardship to their dependents, nearly all the states of the United States require an employer either to carry workmen's compensation insurance or show that he himself is able to provide for his employees the benefits provided for them under the law.

Workmen's compensation insurance provides that an employee who, in the regular course of his employment, is injured and thereby rendered unable to work for a time shall be paid a stipulated amount, varying from one half to two thirds of his earnings, in lieu of wages, while incapacitated. If medical care is required, the law provides that, in general, the worker shall be entitled to such care in addition to the partial wage payment.

If an injury results in death to the worker, insurance payments are made to his dependents for varying periods of time, determined by the state laws.

An **employee** is one who is employed and is paid a wage or a salary. Thus, a carpenter, a chauffeur, or a clerical worker who is hired and paid a daily, weekly, or monthly wage comes under the law and is protected. A carpenter who does work by the job, as building a garage or a house for an agreed amount, is not protected by the law; but if in the prosecution of his work he hires other carpenters to work for him by the day, he himself becomes an employer and is required to take out compensation insurance for the protection of those whom he employs.

Rates of premium in compensation insurance vary widely, depending on the hazards involved in the work. The table on page 331 gives a brief list of premium rates based on $100 of pay roll.

PREMIUM RATES ON WORKMEN'S COMPENSATION INSURANCE

CLASSIFICATION OF OPERATION	RATES PER $100 OF PAY ROLL	LOSS AND EXPENSE CONSTANT
Masonry (Includes bricklaying) . . .	$10.31	$43
Carpentry	$9.53	$43
Concrete Construction — Concrete Blocks	$10.31	$43
Cement Work — Sidewalks, Cellar Floors or Driveways, not Street or Road paving or surfacing	$5.85	$43
Concrete Construction — including Building of Forms, etc.	$12.03	
Concrete Constructions — Bridges, Culverts, etc.	$14.76	$43
Electrical wiring	$3.54	$43
Excavations — Cellars, Basements . .	$10.77	$43
Iron and Steel Erection — Private Residences	$25.95	$43
Painting, Paper Hanging, etc. . . .	$9.99	$43
Plumbing	$4.51	$43
Tile, Stone or Mosaic Work	$3.38	$43
Watchmen	$7.10	$43

NOTE. To the premium computed on the basis of pay roll, there is added a policy fee called "Loss and Expense Constant." This is added only once to the policy, not for each type of work.

Illustration. A contractor in erecting a small business block pays wages as follows: excavation, $350; basement floors, $125; masonry, $900; plumbing, $200. At the rates quoted above, find the premium paid by the contractor for compensation insurance.

Excavation	3.50 × $10.77 =	$37.70
Cement Floors	1.25 × 5.85 =	7.31
Masonry	9.00 × 10.31 =	92.79
Plumbing	2.00 × 4.51 =	9.02
		$146.82
Loss and Expense Constant	=	43.00
Total Premium		$189.82

Only one policy would be issued in the problem illustrated. The several kinds of work would be listed as shown.

Problems

1. A contractor on a given job pays wages as follows:

Bricklayers	$778	Tile and mosaic work	$192.50
Carpenters	$584	Watchman	$212.50
Electric wiring	$281		

Find the cost of his compensation insurance.

2. In building a concrete highway, a contractor engaged 42 men an average of 63 da. each at $4.50 a day to work on the roadway and 25 men an average of 15 da. each at $5.25 a day to work on bridge and culvert construction. How much did compensation insurance cost him?

3. Mr. Harrison engaged a painter at $5.50 a day to paint his house. The painter worked 14 da. and used 16 gal. of paint at $4.00 a gallon. How much did it cost Mr. Harrison to have his house painted, if he included compensation insurance?

4. A workman offered to hang the paper, paint all woodwork, and furnish all materials required for papering and painting the interior of a new house for $290; or he would perform all labor at $6 a day if materials were furnished. The owner of the house decided to buy the materials and hire the workman by the day. He bought 22 gal. of paint at $3.75 per gallon, 30 double rolls of paper at $.75 a double roll, and size, paste, etc. for $5.75. Including compensation insurance, did the owner save or lose money by hiring the workman by the day, if it took the workman 25 da. to do the work?

5. The workman in Problem 4 fell from a ladder while he was painting and broke his arm and was unable to work for 6 wk. How much insurance did he receive if he was paid 50% of his wages while he was incapacitated?

6. In Problem 5, how much did the owner of the house save by taking out compensation insurance instead of taking the risk himself?

FEDERAL SOCIAL SECURITY

The Purpose of the Act

The Federal Social Security Act was originally enacted August, 1935. It was amended August, 1939. The prime purpose of the Act is to provide "safeguards against the major misfortunes of life." Among the more important benefits provided for in the Act are the following:

1. Old Age and Survivors' Insurance
2. Grants to the States for Old-Age Assistance
3. Grants to the States for Unemployment Compensation Administration

OLD AGE AND SURVIVORS' INSURANCE

The Social Security Act provides a benefit payment to retired workers who are 65 years of age and over, and supplementary benefits to aged wives and dependent children of such annuitants. It also provides survivor benefits for widows and orphaned children.

Among the classes of workers who are not covered by the Act are the following: farm laborers, domestic servants, school teachers, public employees, workers in religious and charitable organizations, etc.

To provide funds from which the monthly benefit payments are payable, each employer and each employee in covered employment must pay to the Federal Government taxes as follows:

From 1937 to 1942 inclusive	1% of total wages paid
From 1943 to 1945 inclusive	2% of total wages paid
From 1946 to 1948 inclusive	$2\frac{1}{2}$% of total wages paid
From 1949 and thereafter	3% of total wages paid

Wages in excess of $3000 earned from one or more employer may not be counted.

The employer is required by law to deduct from the wages of his employees the amount of tax each employee has to pay, and to forward it with a like amount paid by himself to the Government.

Monthly benefit payments began January 2, 1940.

Qualifications for Monthly Benefits

For monthly benefits a worker must qualify as follows:

(1) **Be 65 years of age, or over, and retire from active labor.** A worker may continue working after he has retired and is receiving his monthly benefits, provided his wages do not exceed $15 a month.

A worker need not stop work at age 65 if he wishes to continue working. If at age 65 he is not eligible to receive monthly benefit payments, he may become eligible by working after he is 65. Benefit payments do not begin, however, until the worker retires.

(2) **Be fully insured.**

The term "covered wages" means wages earned in employment covered, or allowed, by the Social Security Act.

The term "quarter," or "calendar quarter," means a three-months' period; the quarters end March 31, June 30, September 30, and December 31.

To be *fully insured* a worker must have "quarters of coverage" (quarters in which he earned not less than $50 a quarter in covered employment) equal to half the number of quarters after 1936 (or his 21st birthday if it is later than 1936) and before the quarter in which he became 65, or died; but in no case less than 6 quarters. When a worker has 40 quarters of coverage he is fully insured regardless of employment thereafter.

Illustration 1. **Fully Insured.** A worker became 65 years of age in January, 1940. During the years 1937, 1938, and 1939, he was employed not less than 6 quarters and received not less than $50 in wages each quarter. He is fully insured and eligible to receive monthly benefits the rest of his life.

Illustration 2. **Fully Insured.** A worker earning $125 a month from 1937 to 1947 inclusive, is then incapacitated and unable to work again. He becomes 65 years of age in 1965. This worker is "fully insured" because he has 40 quarters of coverage.

Illustration 3. **Not Fully Insured.** A worker is steadily employed at $150 a month from 1937 to 1945 inclusive and is then taken ill and is not again able to work. He becomes 65 years of age in 1956. This worker is not fully insured because he was not employed one half of the quarters from 1937 to 1956, nor has he 40 quarters of coverage.

(3) **A worker may be currently insured.**

To be **currently insured** a worker must have had not less than 6 quarters of coverage in the three years preceding the quarter in which he died.

Illustration 1. **Currently Insured.** A worker has been regularly employed at $100 a month for two years. He then becomes idle for one year and dies. He is "currently insured" because he has six quarters of coverage during the three years prior to his death.

Illustration 2. **Not Currently Insured.** A man is employed for 3 years at $150 a month. He then is out of work for a period of 2 years, when he is re-instated in his former position. One year later he dies. He is not "currently insured" because he did not have 6 quarters of coverage in the 3 years prior to his death.

Determining Monthly Benefit Payments

The monthly benefit payment is based on the average monthly wage of the worker. The average monthly wage is found by dividing the total wages from covered employment by the number of months in which the worker could have earned such wages — *i.e.,* 3 times the number of quarters from the time he began work after 1936 and before the quarter in which he became eligible to receive the benefits.

The monthly benefit is determined as follows:

(1) 40% of the first \$50 of the average monthly wages, plus
(2) 10% of the next \$200 of average monthly wages, plus
(3) 1% of the sum of the items in 1 and 2 for each year in which he earned not less than \$200 in covered wages.

Supplementary Benefits

In addition to the monthly benefit payment a retired worker receives, he may also receive **supplementary benefits** as follows:

(1) For his wife at age 65 or over — $\frac{1}{2}$ his monthly benefit (unless the wife has in her own right a monthly benefit equal to or greater than this supplement).

(2) For each unmarried child under 16 years of age (18 years if attending school) — $\frac{1}{2}$ his monthly benefit. (But in no case may the total benefits paid exceed twice the worker's primary benefit.)

Illustration. **Fully Insured.** A man employed at \$200 a month from January 1, 1937 to June 30, 1950, is then forced to stop work due to injuries received. He becomes 65 years of age on January 17, 1957. He is "fully insured" because he has 40 quarters of coverage.

His average monthly wage is found as follows: From January 1, 1937 to June 30, 1950 is 54 quarters, or 162 months. His total wages are $162 \times \$200 = \$32{,}400$.

The total time from January 1, 1939 to December 31, 1956 (the quarter before he became 65 years of age) is 20 years, or 240 months. The average wage is $\$32{,}400 \div 240 = \$135$.

His monthly benefit is calculated as follows:

$$\begin{aligned} 40\% \text{ of } \$50 &= \$20.00 \\ 10\% \text{ of } \$85 &= \$8.50 \\ 13\tfrac{1}{2} \times 1\% \text{ of } \$28.50 &= \underline{\$3.85} \\ \text{Total} &= \$32.35, \text{ called the primary benefit.} \end{aligned}$$

Illustration. If this man has a wife who is 65 years of age, there is a supplementary benefit equal to $\frac{1}{2}$ the husband's benefit.

If there is a dependent child under 16 years of age (18 years if attending school) there is also a supplementary benefit equal to $\frac{1}{2}$ of the father's primary benefit. Hence this worker at age 65, with a wife aged 65 or over, and one dependent child, would be eligible to receive benefits as follows:

His own benefit	$32.35
Benefit of aged wife	16.18
Benefit of dependent child	16.17
Total	$64.70

The benefit for the dependent child would cease when the child became 16 years of age (18 years if attending school).

If there were more than one dependent child the total benefit would not be more than $64.70 because the law limits the total benefit to twice the primary benefit paid to the worker.

Survivors' Benefits

In case a worker who is either "fully insured" or "currently insured" dies, the Act provides survivors' benefits as follows:

(1) A surviving widow 65 years old receives $\frac{3}{4}$ of the worker's benefit rate.

(2) A widow less than 65 years of age who has dependent children receives $\frac{3}{4}$ of the worker's benefit rate.

(3) For each unmarried dependent child under 16 years of age (18 years if attending school) the widow will receive $\frac{1}{2}$ the worker's benefit rate. (Except that in no case will the total amount received be more than double the worker's benefit rate.)

(4) Each dependent parent, over 65 years of age, of a deceased worker, if he leaves no widow or dependent children, is entitled to receive $\frac{1}{2}$ of the worker's monthly benefit rate.

Illustration. A man 43 years of age has been regularly employed at $175 a month from 1937 to 1946 inclusive. He then dies leaving a widow and two small children. The widow will receive a monthly benefit as follows:

The average wage is \$175 a month. The primary benefit is

40% of \$50	=	\$20, plus
10% of \$125	=	12.50, plus
10 × 1% of \$32.50	=	3.25
Total	=	\$35.75

The surviving widow is entitled to $\frac{3}{4}$ of \$35.75	=	\$26.81
Each surviving child is entitled to $\frac{1}{2}$ of \$35.75	=	35.75
The total monthly benefit	=	\$62.56

If there were three or more dependent children the total monthly benefit would not exceed \$71.50, because the law limits the total to twice the primary benefit.

In case a worker has not earned sufficient wages to entitle him to receive benefits equal to or greater than the following rates, then the following minimum rates apply:

Minimum Monthly Benefits

Single worker at retirement	\$10
Retired worker and 1 dependent	15
Retired worker and 2 or more dependents	20
Surviving widow 65 or over	10
Widow and 1 child	12.50
Widow and 2 children	17.50
Widow and 3 or more dependent children	20
One or 2 orphans	10
Three orphans	15
Four or more orphans	20
One or both dependent parents	10

Lump-sum Death Benefit. In case a worker dies and leaves no survivor entitled to receive monthly benefits, a lump sum not exceeding 6 times his monthly benefit rate will be paid to the worker's estate.

The Maximum Amount to a Retired Worker

The maximum amount payable to any retired worker and his dependents, or to all survivors, is the least of the following 3 amounts:

1. Twice the monthly benefit rate.
2. 80% of the average monthly wage.
3. \$85.

Illustration. At age 22 a man begins working at covered employment, receiving more than $200 a year. He continued to work till he was 70 years of age. During the 48 years of his employment his total wages amount to $158,400, or an average of $275 a month. At 70 years of age he retires. He has a wife 67 years old. His monthly benefit would be determined as follows:

40% of $50 =	$20
10% of $200 =	20
48 × 1% of $40 =	19.20
Total =	$59.20, primary benefit.

His wife would be entitled to ½ of $59.20, or $29.60, making a total of $88.80, but since $85 is the maximum benefit payable under any conditions, the monthly benefit would be $85 and not $88.80.

It should be noted that while the average wage is $275 per month, wages only to the amount of $250 per month are counted in determining the monthly benefit.

OLD-AGE ASSISTANCE

The Social Security Act provides that the Federal Government shall aid the States in furnishing "financial assistance to aged needy individuals." The individuals referred to in this section of the law are those who do not or cannot qualify for monthly old-age insurance benefits described on pages 333–338.

Under this plan the Federal Government will pay to each State "an amount which shall be used exclusively for old-age assistance, equal to one-half of the total sums expended" by the State for old-age assistance to needy individuals who are 65 years of age or older (except that in no case will the Government pay more than $20 a month toward the assistance granted to any needy individual) plus 5% of such amount, which shall be used solely for the purpose of administering the State plan.

UNEMPLOYMENT COMPENSATION ADMINISTRATION

The Social Security Act makes provision for the Federal Government to aid the states in the establishment and administration of unemployment compensation.

The laws under which the benefits are paid are state laws.

The plan of operation under the Federal Social Security Act is that the Government will assist the States in the administering of their unemployment compensation program. The law provides that $80,000,000 shall be appropriated annually to be used in aiding the States. Upon certification by the Social Security Board to the Secretary of the Treasury, the Secretary will pay to the State Agency in charge of administering the law, "such amounts as the Board determines to be necessary for the proper and efficient administration" of the law, in any State having an approved Unemployment Compensation Law.

To provide funds for assisting the States in their unemployment compensation programs, each employer of eight or more persons on each of twenty or more days in each of twenty or more weeks in a taxable year, shall pay an unemployment tax of 3% of the wages paid to his employees, except that he need not pay a tax on wages in excess of $3000 to any one employee in one year.

The States levy an unemployment tax on employers, and in some instances, on employees, to provide funds for unemployment compensation.

Against the Federal tax there may be credited the amount paid as a State unemployment tax, but the credit allowed may not exceed 90% of the Federal tax.

Illustration 1. If an employer's taxable pay roll for one year is $150,000, and both the State and Federal taxes are 3%, his unemployment compensation tax would be as follows:

State tax 3% of $150,000		= $4500
Federal tax 3% of $150,000	= $4500	
Less 90% of $4500 (Federal tax)	= 4050	
Net Federal tax		= 450
Total State and Federal tax		= $4950

Illustration 2. An employer has a taxable pay roll for $125,000 a year. The State tax is 3.7%, of which the employees pay 1% and the employer 2.7%. Find the total unemployment tax paid by the employer.

State tax paid by employer 2.7% of \$125,000	= \$3375
Federal tax 3% of \$125,000 = \$3750	
Less 90% of 3750 (Federal tax) = 3375	
Net Federal tax	= 375
Total State and Federal tax	= \$3750

In this instance it should be noted that the State tax is all deducted from the Federal tax, because it is just equal to 90% of the Federal tax.

Problems

1. An employee has worked steadily from January 1, 1937, to December 31, 1943. His wages were \$90 a month. How much has been deducted from his wages for social security?

2. An employer of 6 persons has paid wages averaging \$25 a week to each of his employees. Find the total amount paid to the Government for social security by both the employer and the employees for the years 1940 to 1946 inclusive.

3. A manufacturer employing 100 persons has a taxable payroll of \$12,500 a month. How much social security tax did he and his employees pay in 1942? In 1943?

4. If the employer in Problem 3 lived in a state in which the State tax for unemployment compensation was $2\frac{1}{2}$%, of which he pays $1\frac{1}{2}$% and his employees pay 1%, how much Federal and State unemployment compensation tax would he pay in 1943?

5. Find the monthly benefit payable to Mr. Haskins who has worked under covered employment from 1937 to 1950, inclusive, if he becomes 65 years of age in January 1951 and retires. His total wages were \$37,800.

6. A stenographer has worked regularly for 21 years, after 1936, and has earned wages amounting to \$32,760. Having become 65 years of age, she retired and received her monthly benefit payment. Find the monthly payment.

7. A bookkeeper has been regularly employed at \$2750 a year since January 1, 1937. His 65th birthday is March 10, 1957. If he continues working until his 65th birthday and then retires, find his monthly retirement allowance. If he had a wife 65 years of age, what total monthly payment will they both receive?

8. Mr. Arden, after 7 years of steady employment at $2150 a year, dies and leaves a widow and two children aged 4 and 7 years. Find the amount the widow will receive in survivor benefits.

9. A factory employee was steadily employed from January 1, 1937, for 12 years. He then was unemployed for 6 years, when he became 65 years of age and retired from active labor. His total wages were $16,200. Was he "fully insured"? If so, what total monthly benefit would he receive if his wife also was 65 years of age, and they had 2 dependent children?

10. A laboring man earning $50 a month in employment covered by the Social Security Act, died after 27 years of work. He left a widow and 3 dependent children. If the widow was 50 years of age, how much was the monthly survivors' benefit she received?

11. A married man having 2 children under 16 years of age has been employed for 10 years at $250 a month in work covered by the Social Security Act. If he then dies, how much will his widow receive in monthly benefits?

12. A young man, age 25 years on January 4, 1937, was receiving an annual salary of $1800. If he continues to work and receives an increase in salary of $300 a year at the expiration of each 5-year period, how much would be his retirement allowance per month when he retires at age 65, provided he has a wife who also is 65 years of age?

13. An employer has a pay roll of $22,500 a month. (No employee receives over $3000 a year.) The State unemployment compensation tax is $2\frac{3}{4}\%$, of which the employees pay 1% and the employer $1\frac{3}{4}\%$. Find (*a*) the amount of social security tax paid by both the employer and the employees for 1946.

(*b*) The State unemployment compensation tax paid by the employees for the year 1946.

(*c*) The State and Federal unemployment compensation tax paid by the employer in 1946.

WAGES AND PAY ROLLS

JUST A MINUTE!

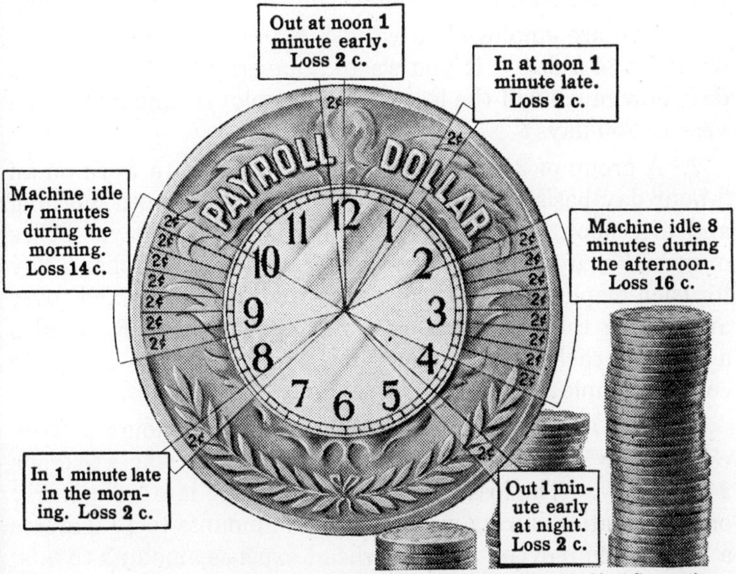
Out at noon 1 minute early. Loss 2 c.
In at noon 1 minute late. Loss 2 c.
Machine idle 7 minutes during the morning. Loss 14 c.
Machine idle 8 minutes during the afternoon. Loss 16 c.
In 1 minute late in the morning. Loss 2 c.
Out 1 minute early at night. Loss 2 c.
PAYROLL DOLLAR
2¢
12 1 2 3 4 5 6 7 8 9 10 11

Courtesy International Business Machines Corporation

How small, how short a time a minute is!

Did you ever stop to think how many of these little minutes you waste in a day? The illustration above gives a vivid picture of the value of every minute on a job.

The figures in the illustration are based on the following:

Hourly wage of employee	\$.60
Hourly overhead expense per employee	.60
A total hourly cost of	\$1.20, or \$.02 a minute.

By adding, the time lost as indicated in the illustration shows that for one employee a total of 19 minutes was lost in one day, for the reasons specified.

At \$.02 a minute the total loss for the day is \$.38.

On the basis of a 7-hour day, the loss of \$.38 is slightly more than 9% of the employee's wages. In the course of a year of 250 days the loss would be 250 × \$.38 = \$95.

Problems

Do a little figuring for yourself on the following problems:

1. You are employed to work 8 hours a day for 5 days a week for \$4 a day. If you waste an average of 12 minutes a day, how much will the loss to your employer amount to in a year of 250 days?

2. A group of 25 stenographers is employed to work on an 8-hour-day basis (with a 15-minute rest period both morning and afternoon). The average wage is \$3.50 a day. Office overhead chargeable to this group of workers is a dollar a day for each employee. If the average time lost or wasted (over and above the 15-minute rest periods) averages 6 minutes a day for each stenographer, how much does the lost time cost the employer in a year of 240 days?

3. In a factory employing 100 men for 40 hours a week (5 days of 8 hours each) for 250 days a year, the wages average \$4.50 a day. The loss of time due to coming late, going early or conversation during working hours, amounts to 10 minutes a day per employee. The overhead expense amounts to \$.50 a day per employee. Find the loss to the employer for the year. Give answer in nearest whole dollar.

FIGURING WAGE-TIME

Of the many sources of income, wages are the chief source to a great number of people. It is important, therefore, that a person should be able to reckon the amount of wages due him for his labor. In the days when job-time memoranda were recorded with a pencil, only "round-numbers" were set down. Now, however, in many offices and factories time is mechanically recorded and shows fractions of hours. In order to check a modern timecard one should be able to calculate fractions.

Problems

You receive 42¢ an hour for the time you work between 8 A.M. and 5 P.M. What are your wages for the time recorded on the card below? How much will you receive after your employer has deducted the old-age-benefit tax of 1%?

Days	In	Out	In	Out
Monday	8:00	12:00	1:00	5:00
Tuesday	8:30	12:00	1:00	4:30
Wednesday	8:00	12:00	1:00	5:00
Thursday	8:00	12:00	1:00	5:00
Friday	9:00	12:00	1:00	5:00

(*a*) On the basis of an 8-hour day, how much of your possible earnings did you lose because you came late to work, and went before 5 o'clock on one day? (*b*) What per cent of your possible earnings did you lose? (*c*) At this rate of loss, how much will your loss amount to in one year? (Reckon 50 weeks to the year — allowing 2 weeks for vacation.)

Percentage ÷ Base = Rate

That is, **Loss ÷ Possible Earnings = Rate of Loss**

Solve (*b*) above also by common fractions, by stating the question this way: What *part* of your possible earnings did you lose by coming late and going early?

OVERTIME

The wage-time of employees is generally figured by the hour or by the day. They usually receive their pay at the end of the week. An employee working on an hourly basis usually receives extra pay for working overtime. For example, if he works 1 hour overtime and is paid for $1\frac{1}{2}$ hours' work, he is said to receive **time and a half for overtime.**

Illustration. You are paid at the rate of $.44 an hour for 8 hours and receive time and a half for 2 hours overtime. How much are your earnings? How much would your employer deduct for the old-age-benefit tax?

$1\frac{1}{2} \times \$.44 = \$.66$ an hour for overtime
$8 \times \$.44 = \$3.52$, earnings for regular time
$2 \times \$.66 = \underline{1.32}$, earnings for overtime
$\$4.84$, total earnings
1% of $\$4.84 = \$.05$, deducted for old-age-benefit tax

Firms employing many persons on an hourly or daily time basis generally require each employee to punch his time of coming to work and going from work, on a card by means of a time-recording clock.

Courtesy International Business Machines Corporation

TIME-RECORDING CLOCK

The illustration shows an employee punching his card. Note that the time punched shows on the front of the clock.

The time of day, 8:18, as well as the day of the week are recorded on his card.

Two timecards are illustrated. At the top of each of these cards are recorded the total regular time and wage per hour, the total overtime and the rate per hour for overtime, and total earnings.

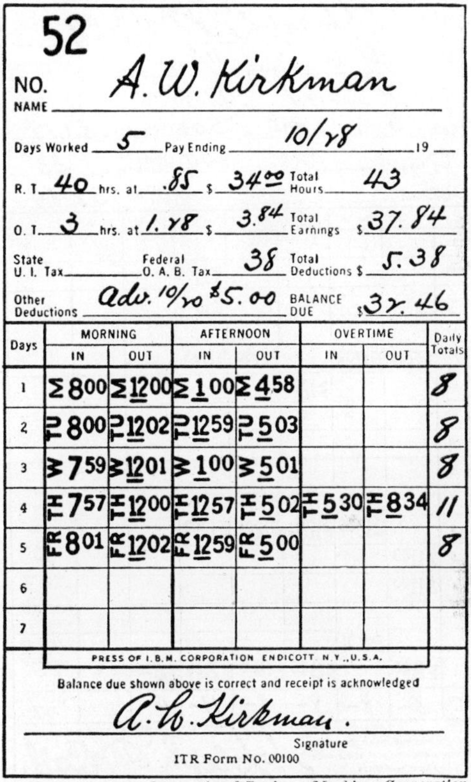

52

NO. NAME A. W. Kirkman

Days Worked 5 Pay Ending 10/28 19

R. T. 40 hrs. at .85 $ 34.00 Total Hours 43

O. T. 3 hrs. at 1.28 $ 3.84 Total Earnings $ 37.84

State U. I. Tax Federal O. A. B. Tax 38 Total Deductions $ 5.38

Other Deductions adv. 10/20 $5.00 BALANCE DUE $ 32.46

Days	MORNING IN	MORNING OUT	AFTERNOON IN	AFTERNOON OUT	OVERTIME IN	OVERTIME OUT	Daily Totals
1	M 800	M 1200	M 100	M 458			8
2	TU 800	TU 1202	TU 1259	TU 503			8
3	W 759	W 1201	W 100	W 501			8
4	TH 757	TH 1200	TH 1257	TH 502	TH 530	TH 834	11
5	FR 801	FR 1202	FR 1259	FR 500			8
6							
7							

PRESS OF I. B. M. CORPORATION ENDICOTT N. Y., U. S. A.

Balance due shown above is correct and receipt is acknowledged

A. W. Kirkman.

Signature

ITR Form No. 00100

International Business Machines Corporation

The old-age-benefit tax is also indicated and deducted from total earnings. The employee has signed the card, hence the card becomes a receipt for the payment of the wages. Card No. 632 illustrates an interesting method of indicating the time. The clock on which this card was punched records the hours from 12 o'clock midnight to the next midnight at 24 hours instead of two periods of 12 hours each. Note that the time of coming to work in the morning is recorded at the bottom of the card. Time OUT for lunch is recorded higher up on the card, and the time of leaving in the afternoon is recorded still higher on the card. It is stamped M 17^{31}, which means the time is Monday and is seventeen hours and 31 minutes after midnight, which on an ordinary

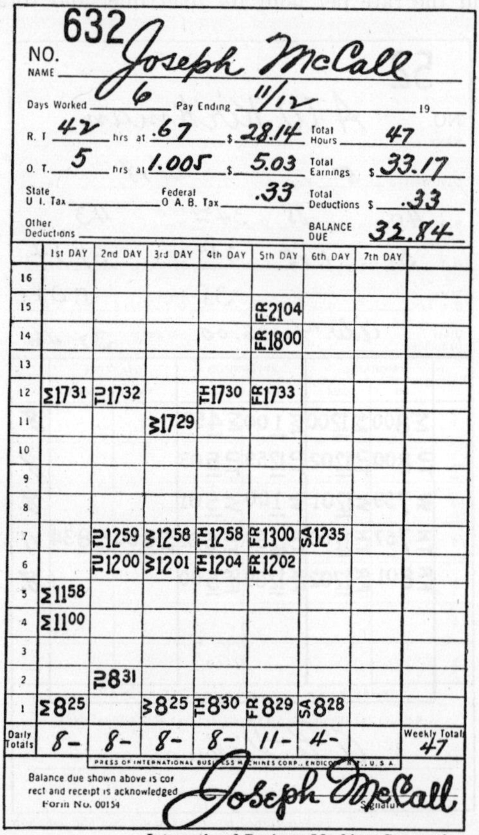

NO. 632
NAME Joseph McCall
Days Worked 6 Pay Ending 11/12 19__
R. T. 42 hrs at .67 $ 28.14 Total Hours 47
O. T. 5 hrs at 1.005 $ 5.03 Total Earnings $ 33.17
State U. I. Tax ______ Federal O. A. B. Tax .33 Total Deductions $ .33
Other Deductions ______ BALANCE DUE 32.84

	1st DAY	2nd DAY	3rd DAY	4th DAY	5th DAY	6th DAY	7th DAY	
16								
15					FR 21^{04}			
14					FR 18^{00}			
13								
12	M 17^{31}	TU 17^{32}		TH 17^{30}	FR 17^{33}			
11			W 17^{29}					
10								
9								
8								
7		TU 12^{59}	W 12^{58}	TH 12^{58}	FR 13^{00}	SA 12^{35}		
6		TU 12^{00}	W 12^{01}	TH 12^{04}	FR 12^{02}			
5	M 11^{58}							
4	M 11^{00}							
3								
2		TU 8^{31}						
1	M 8^{25}		W 8^{25}	TH 8^{30}	FR 8^{29}	SA 8^{28}		
Daily Totals	8-	8-	8-	8-	11-	4-		Weekly Total 47

PRESS OF INTERNATIONAL BUSINESS MACHINES CORP., ENDICOTT, N.Y., U.S.A.

Balance due shown above is correct and receipt is acknowledged
Form No. 00154
Joseph McCall
Signature

International Business Machines Corporation

clock would be 5 : 31 P.M. The total hours worked are written in at the bottom of the card, by the pay-roll clerk at the end of the week.

Problems

When solving the following problems deduct the old-age-benefit tax.

1. Including time and a half for overtime, what will be your earnings at $.52 an hour for the following timecard?

Days	Regular Time	Overtime	Days	Regular Time	Overtime
Monday	8 hr.	$1\frac{1}{4}$ hr.	Thursday	7 hr.	45 min.
Tuesday	8 hr.	$3\frac{3}{4}$ hr.	Friday	8 hr.	1 hr.
Wednesday	8 hr.	$1\frac{1}{2}$ hr.	Saturday	4 hr.	$2\frac{1}{2}$ hr.

2. Find the wages paid for the week to each of the employees below. The regular time was 7 hr. a day. Count any time over 7 hr. as *overtime at time and a half.*

Employees	Number of Hours Worked						Rate per Hour
	Mon.	Tues.	Wed.	Thur.	Fri.	Sat.	
1. Condon, George	7	8	8	5	4	4	$.42
2. Disbrow, Henry	8	7	9	4	5	4	$.42
3. Frasier, Martin	$6\frac{1}{2}$	7	8	7	4	3	$.48
4. Lannon, Joseph	5	7	8	8	8	—	$.52
5. Peters, James	6	6	7	7	$7\frac{1}{2}$	—	$.50
6. Ward, John	7	8	9	—	7	4	$.58

3. Copy the following form and fill in the missing columns. Allow *time and a half* for any time over 36 hr. in a week.

Employees	M.	T.	W.	T.	F.	S.	Reg. Time	Over-Time	Total time	Weekly Rate	Wages
1. Alden, Henry	7	7	8	7	8	4				$22 50	
2. Davis, Joseph	6	8	7	4	7	4				$24 00	
3. Green, Richard	7	7	7	8	9	4				$24 40	
4. Hughes, Ira	8	7	8	8	8	5				$22 50	
5. Koch, Bernard	7	7	7	4	7	4				$21 60	
6. Nash, Byron	8	8	7	7	8	4				$22 50	
7. Rogers, Berton	7	7	7	6	5	4				$24 00	
8. Simms, Addison	7	8	8	7	8	4				$27 00	

Piecework

When the earnings are based on the amount of work performed, the plan is generally known as **piecework.** A certain price is paid for each piece of work completed. As the worker becomes skilled and is able to complete more pieces of work in a day, he earns more per day. In many cases a higher price per piece is paid to a worker who can complete a larger number of pieces of work in a day.

1. Using the schedule of rates per piece shown at the right, find Harry Mack's daily wage if he completed 33 pieces of work a day. If in three months he improved in skill so that he could finish 43 pieces a day, by how much were his daily wages increased? What is the rate per cent of his increase in wages?

Pieces per Day	Rate per Piece
Up to 21	$.11
22 to 25	$.11½
26 to 29	$.12
30 to 33	$.12½
34 to 37	$.13
38 to 41	$.13½
42 to 45	$.14

Notice the increase in the rate per piece as the number of pieces each day increases.

2. Using the schedule of rates in Problem 1, find (*a*) the daily wage of each of the employees in the table below; (*b*) the weekly wage of each; and (*c*) the total wages for the week.

Employees	Number of Pieces						Daily Wage						Total for Week
	M.	T.	W.	Th.	F.	S.	M.	T.	W.	Th.	F.	S.	
Brennan, Alice	26	28	27	29	30	17							
Brown, Mary	22	24	25	24	25	14							
Carr, Edith	29	31	31	34	32	17							
Fuller, Ruth	32	33	35	31	36	20							
Miller, Sadie	33	33	34	35	36	20							
Nason, Jean	35	37	36	36	38	20							
Pratt, Irene	22	24	23	25	26	16							
Wilson, Belle	27	29	32	34	31	18							
Totals													

THE COIN MEMORANDUM

The employee usually receives his pay in the form of cash in an envelope, or by check. Employers pay at the end of a week, two weeks, or monthly. Before pay day the pay-roll clerk prepares a coin memorandum from the individual amounts due as recorded on the pay-roll record. From the coin memorandum the clerk can see at a glance just what denominations of money to insert into each employee's envelope. Occasionally errors occur in calculating the time, or the wage totals, or in counting the coins. Every employee should, therefore, work out his own timecard and count the contents of his pay envelope.

Problems

1. Prepare a coin memorandum similar to the following to show the kind and number of bills and coins required for each employee in Problem 2, page 349. Deduct the old-age-benefit tax from each employee's total earnings before entering the wages due and distributing the bills and coins. How much does the employer pay in wages? How much tax does he pay the Government for old-age-benefit?

Employees	Wages		$10	$5	$1	$.50	$.25	$.10	$.05	$.01
Condon, George	15	38	1	1			1	1		3
Disbrow, Henry										
Frasier, Martin										
Lannon, Joseph										
Peters, James										
Ward, John										
Totals										

2. Prepare a coin memorandum for the pay roll in Problem 3, page 349, showing the kind and number of bills and coins required. Deduct the old-age-benefit tax of 1% from each employee's earnings. What is the total amount of tax paid by both the employer and employee?

BONUSES AND WAGE COMMISSIONS

Retail salespeople frequently receive an hourly, daily, or weekly wage, and an additional bonus or commission for all sales above a specified amount. This extra pay may vary with different types of work in different stores; however, the principle is the same. The bonus may be a definite sum of cash for extra sales, or it may be a commission figured as a certain percentage of the extra sales.

It should be understood that bonuses and commissions of this type are not confined to storework. This practice is sometimes found in various offices and factories where piecework or unitwork is an element in figuring the earnings of employees.

Illustration. Your daily sales average \$150, and your rate of commission is 1% of all sales above \$125. How much is your commission?

\$150 − \$125 = \$25, sales on which commission is paid
1% of \$25 = \$.25, commission
Base × Rate = Percentage
That is, Sales × Rate of Commission = Commission

Percentage Drill

To change a rate per cent to an equivalent decimal omit the per cent sign (%) and move the decimal point two places to the left.

Illustration. Change 10%, 1%, and $1\frac{1}{2}$% to equivalent decimals.

By dropping the per cent sign and moving the decimal point two places to the left we have

$$10\% = .1;\ 1\% = .01;\ 1\tfrac{1}{2}\% = 1.5\% = .015$$

Note that when a fractional rate is changed, the fraction is first changed to a decimal before removing the per cent sign, thus, $\frac{3}{4}\% = .75\% = .0075$.

Mental Drill

Express the following per cents as equivalent decimals:

1. 2%	**3.** $12\frac{1}{2}$%	**5.** $\frac{1}{4}$%	**7.** 2.5%	**9.** $0.10\frac{1}{2}$%
2. $4\frac{1}{4}$%	**4.** $\frac{1}{2}$%	**6.** $3\frac{1}{3}$%	**8.** 0.5%	**10.** $0.16\frac{1}{2}$%

Problems

1. Your regular salary is $25 a week and you receive a commission of $2\frac{1}{2}\%$ on all sales above $1000. (*a*) How much are your weekly earnings if your weekly sales amount to $1588.75? (*b*) How much will you receive in your pay envelope? (*c*) What per cent of your total earnings is your commission?

In (*c*) what two quantities are compared? Which quantity becomes the dividend? Which, the divisor?

2. You have made the following daily sales. Find your total for each day; for the week.

Mon.	*Tues.*	*Wed.*	*Thurs.*	*Fri.*	*Sat.*
3.75	1.89	8.76	19.78	8.98	3.75
3.82	8.90	6.98	56.89	18.91	8.29
4.98	2.76	6.98	43.45	6.79	3.95
2.54	5.87	5.75	23.96	12.86	2.95
1.39	4.67	5.79	56.34	40.89	4.95
.08	3.84	6.87	23.74	.89	1.75
.98	2.65	5.98	74.76	1.76	.98
1.76	4.98	5.98	34.89	15.78	.65
9.59	5.98	4.54	23.09	2.96	2.85
5.85	6.85	3.78	56.78	1.78	3.20
1.39	3.87	5.54	43.29	6.58	2.40
7.45	4.76	3.45		2.86	14.85
2.35	9.43	2.34		29.68	1.98
2.97	3.65	9.65		4.62	.92
4.67	9.00	4.56		1.95	1.50
9.50	1.76	4.78		2.98	12.38
1.75	5.63	3.69		4.69	15.29
1.59	2.98	1.56		39.57	9.68
1.35	1.98	1.98		.89	7.20

a. Your commission is $\frac{1}{2}$ of 1% of sales and your daily wage is $4. How much money will you earn in each of the six days? *b.* If your commission is $1\frac{1}{2}\%$, what will your total earnings be for the week? How much should be in your pay envelope?

3. Find the total of your sales for each day; for the week.

Mon.	*Tues.*	*Wed.*	*Thurs.*	*Fri.*	*Sat.*
.89	.98	7.95	1.57	2.80	3.85
2.95	.98	1.98	.98	1.70	3.97
1.65	1.98	.98	.98	1.83	2.85
2.15	.89	.98	1.85	1.97	2.98
1.39	.68	1.98	1.75	1.92	2.98
2.85	7.85	2.95	.50	1.85	2.98
2.79	1.95	.75	2.59	1.93	1.75
3.95	2.18	1.65	2.89	.98	1.75
1.85	3.75	1.38	2.78	.98	1.89
1.93	2.65	2.85	2.85	.98	1.35
2.86	2.55	2.98	1.39	1.98	1.98
1.97	1.98	1.69	1.89	2.79	2.98
2.58	.89	1.89	1.75	2.89	3.95

a. Your commission is $\frac{1}{4}$ of 1% of sales and your daily wage is \$3. How much money will you earn in each of the six days? *b.* If your commission is $2\frac{3}{4}\%$, what will your total earnings be for the week? How much should be in your pay envelope?

4. You do not receive a regular wage, but you receive $2\frac{1}{2}\%$ commission on all sales, and an additional $1\frac{3}{4}\%$ commission on all sales above \$1000. (*a*) How much are your weekly earnings if your sales amount to \$1588.75? (*b*) Are the wage terms better in Problem 1 than Problem 4? Explain. (*c*) How much greater or less are your earnings in Problem 1 than in Problem 4? (*d*) What per cent greater or less? Select carefully the quantities to be compared and determine the dividend and divisor.

SINKING FUNDS AND DEPRECIATION

SINKING FUNDS

In financing large undertakings, as the erection of great buildings, building railways, or the formation of a large corporation, immediate funds are provided by borrowing the money and issuing bonds therefor. In essence, issuing a bond is giving a promissory note promising to repay the money borrowed to the lender or to whomever may have the bond at maturity. The bonds are payable in 5, 10, 20, or more years, as the case may be. Interest on the bonds is payable, usually semiannually, during the lifetime of the bonds. To provide for paying the bonds at maturity, each year or semiannually a sufficient sum of money is set aside which, with compound interest, will amount to the face value of the bonds. The sum thus set aside is called a **sinking fund.**

Sinking funds are generally thought of as applying to large amounts which are to be paid in the future. The principle of the sinking fund is, however, applicable to smaller undertakings. For instance, when a man buys a new automobile, he would find it easier to replace it several years later if he would set aside each year the amount of depreciation on the car; in bookkeeping or accounting this is usually called a *reserve for depreciation.* Business firms provide for the depreciation on their trucks by setting aside or reserving part of their net profits for that purpose. If every car owner would make provision annually for the replacement of his car when he wished to get a new one, he would find it easier to procure the new car. He would also realize what many car owners do not realize, namely what is the real annual cost of running a car.

In setting up a *sinking fund* it is essential to note that the first year's (or half year's) payment into the fund does not earn any interest during the first year (or half year) of the period of the debt to be paid. That is, if a corporation borrows $1,000,000 and issues 10-year bonds for it, the first payment into the sinking fund will not be made till the end of the first year (or first half year). Therefore, the compound interest table showing the amount of $1 paid annually into a sinking fund, shows $1 as the first amount.

TABLE SHOWING AMOUNT OF A SINKING FUND OF $1 AT THE END OF EACH PERIOD

n	$1\frac{1}{2}\%$	2%	$2\frac{1}{2}\%$	3%	4%	n
1	1.0000 0000	1.0000 0000	1.0000 0000	1.0000 0000	1.0000 0000	**1**
2	2.0150 0000	2.0200 0000	2.0250 0000	2.0300 0000	2.0400 0000	**2**
3	3.0452 2500	3.0604 0000	3.0756 2500	3.0909 0000	3.1216 0000	**3**
4	4.0909 0338	4.1216 0800	4.1525 1563	4.1836 2700	4.2464 6400	**4**
5	5.1522 6693	5.2040 4016	5.2563 2852	5.3091 3581	5.4163 2256	**5**
6	6.2295 5093	6.3081 2096	6.3877 3673	6.4684 0988	6.6329 7546	**6**
7	7.3229 9419	7.4342 8338	7.5474 3015	7.6624 6218	7.8992 9448	**7**
8	8.4328 3911	8.5829 6905	8.7361 1590	8.8923 3605	9.2142 2626	**8**
9	9.5593 3169	9.7546 2843	9.9545 1880	10.1591 0613	10.5827 9531	**9**
10	10.7027 2167	10.9497 2100	11.2033 8177	11.4638 7931	12.0061 0712	**10**
11	11.8632 6249	12.1687 1542	12.4834 6631	12.8077 9569	13.4863 5141	**11**
12	13.0412 1143	13.4120 8973	13.7955 5297	14.1920 2956	15.0258 0546	**12**
13	14.2368 2960	14.6803 3152	15.1404 4179	15.6177 9045	16.6268 3768	**13**
14	15.4503 8205	15.9739 3815	16.5189 5284	17.0863 2416	18.2919 1119	**14**
15	16.6821 3778	17.2934 1692	17.9319 2666	18.5989 1389	20.0235 8764	**15**
16	17.9323 6984	18.6392 8525	19.3802 2483	20.1568 8130	21.8245 3114	**16**
17	19.2013 5539	20.0120 7096	20.8647 3045	21.7615 8774	23.6975 1239	**17**
18	20.4893 7572	21.4123 1238	22.3863 4871	23.4144 3537	25.6454 1288	**18**
19	21.7967 1636	22.8405 5863	23.9460 0743	25.1168 6844	27.6712 2940	**19**
20	23.1236 6710	24.2973 6980	25.5446 5761	26.8703 7449	29.7780 7858	**20**
21	24.4705 2211	25.7833 1719	27.1832 7405	28.6764 8572	31.9692 0172	**21**
22	25.8375 7994	27.2989 8354	28.8628 5590	30.5367 8030	34.2479 6979	**22**
23	27.2251 4364	28.8449 6321	30.5844 2730	32.4528 8370	36.6178 8858	**23**
24	28.6335 2080	30.4218 6247	32.3490 3798	34.4264 7022	39.0826 0412	**24**
25	30.0630 2361	32.0302 9972	34.1577 6393	36.4592 6432	41.6459 0829	**25**
26	31.5139 6896	33.6709 0572	36.0117 0803	38.5530 4225	44.3117 4462	**26**
27	32.9866 7850	35.3443 2383	37.9120 0073	40.7096 3352	47.0842 1440	**27**
28	34.4814 7867	37.0512 1031	39.8598 0075	42.9309 2252	49.9675 8298	**28**
29	35.9987 0085	38.7922 3451	41.8562 9577	45.2188 5020	52.9662 8630	**29**
30	37.5386 8137	40.5680 7921	43.9027 0316	47.5754 1571	56.0849 3775	**30**

Illustration. For the erection of a new high school building a city borrowed $350,000 and issued bonds to mature in 20 years. To pay the bonds when they were due, the city set up a sinking fund earning 3%. Find the amount to be raised in taxes each year to provide for the sinking fund.

From the sinking fund table (page 356) in the 3% column at the line marked 20, we find $26.87037449 which is the amount of $1 invested each year for 20 years, at 3%.

Dividing $350,000 by 26.87037449 gives the annual contribution to the fund.

$350,000 ÷ 26.87037449 = $13,025.50, amount to be raised in taxes each year for the sinking fund.

Problems

1. To provide for the payment of a debt of $10,000 due in 15 years, a man invested at 4% annually at the end of each year, a sum sufficient, with compound interest accumulation, to make the payment. Find the annual investment.

2. To build a new highway a county borrowed $2,500,000 and gave county bonds due in 30 years. The county set up a sinking fund earning 4% to pay the bonds when due. How much was paid into the fund annually?

3. A department store has 6 delivery trucks costing $2500 each. It is known from past experience that at the end of four years the trucks will need to be exchanged for new ones. If the trade-in value of each truck at the end of 4 years is $500, find the sum the store must set aside annually at $2\frac{1}{2}$% compound interest, to replace the trucks.

4. A. B. Hartly bought a new car for pleasure driving, for $2250. He plans to use the car for 6 years before exchanging it for a new one. He estimates its value at the end of 6 years will be $300. From past experience he reckons his annual cost of driving the car each year will average as follows:

License plates, $17.50
Insurance, $55.00
Driving permits — 3 at $.50 each, $1.50
Gasoline, 750 gallons at $.18
Oil, 10 gallons at $.25 a quart

Lubrication 8 times a year at $1
Tires, average 2 a year at $14.50 each
Incidental repairs, new brake linings, grinding valves, etc., $25 a year

If he deposits in a savings bank semiannually at 3% enough money to provide, with the trade-in value of the old car, for the purchase of a new car for $2250, find to the nearest whole dollar the annual cost of owning and running a car.

5. A piece of machinery costs $13,500. It will last 8 years when its junk value will be $1000. The purchaser provides for replacing the machine at the end of 8 years by means of semiannual deposits in a sinking fund earning 3%. How much should be put into the fund each 6 months?

6. A family in the city had been riding in a taxicab when they wished to go about the city, and had ridden in buses when going out of the city. Their average monthly expenditures for that purpose were $37.50. They decided to buy a small car for family use. The cost of the car was $750. They were told they could exchange it at the end of 5 years and be allowed $100 toward the price of a new car. At the end of the five years they calculated the costs as follows:

Gasoline, average 900 gal. a year at $.19
Oil, average 12 gallons a year at $1 a gallon
Lubrication, 9 times a year at $1
Tires, 2 each year on the average, at $13.50
License plates, annual cost $14.50
Driver's permits, 2 at $.50 each year
Brakes relined twice during the 5 years at $12 a time
Valves ground twice during the 5 years at $12 a time
Incidental expenses for repairs, etc., $30 a year
Garage rent, $8 a month

If a fund was provided annually at 2% compound interest to amount to enough to cover the depreciation, at the end of five years, did it cost more or less, and how much, to use their own car than to pay taxi and bus fares?

7. A man erected a \$25,000 factory building on a plot of ground which he had rented for 20 years at \$2500 a year. Find the amount of earnings required annually to pay the rent, and annual payments into a sinking fund earning $2\frac{1}{2}\%$ to cover the cost of the building at the expiration of the lease on the land.

DEPRECIATION

The *straight-line method* of reckoning depreciation was explained on page 88.

Different kinds of property depreciate at different rates of speed; that is, some kinds of property, as automobiles and trucks, depreciate rather fast in the first year or two of their use, while buildings and furniture depreciate much more slowly, at first, and more rapidly after a number of years' use.

The chief factors to be taken into consideration in determining the amount of annual depreciation are:

1. Original cost of the property
2. The probable number of years the property may be used
3. The value of the property at the expiration of its period of usefulness. This latter value is generally called its junk, or scrap, value.

Of the various methods of reckoning depreciation, only two will be considered here. They are:

1. The fixed percentage on reducing balance method
2. The diminishing rate method

The Fixed Percentage on Reducing Balance Method

The mathematical calculation for finding the exact rate that should be charged by this method is too difficult for a text of this nature. Those who wish to use this method, and who cannot make the calculation to find the exact rate, must be guided by experience, and estimate a rate which experience shows is practically correct.

Illustration. A piece of machinery cost $800. It was estimated that it would last 5 years, and that the depreciation should be reckoned at 20% a year on the reduced value of the machinery. Find the annual amount of depreciation and the scrap value of machinery at the end of 5 years.

Solution:

20% of $800 = $160, depreciation the first year
$800 − $160 = $640, value at the end of the first year
20% of $640 = $128, depreciation the second year
$640 − $128 = $512, value at the end of the second year
20% of $512 = $102.40, depreciation the third year
$512 − $102.40 = $409.60, value at end of third year
20% of $409.60 = $81.92, depreciation the fourth year
$409.60 − $81.92 = $327.68, value at end of fourth year
20% of $327.68 = $65.54, depreciation the fifth year
$327.68 − $65.54 = $262.14, value at end of the fifth year

The value of the machinery at the end of any given year is generally spoken of as the **book value of the machinery**, because that is the value at which it is recorded on the books of the owner.

It should be borne in mind that the total depreciation at any given time plus the book value at the same time equals the original value of the machine.

Problems

Find the annual amount of depreciation and the book value year by year for each of the following:

	Original Cost	Number of Years of Service	Rate of Depreciation	Depreciation	Book Value
1.	$900	6	25%		
2.	$1200	5	20%		
3.	$375	7	$16\frac{2}{3}$%		

The Diminishing Rate Method

By this method the rate of depreciation grows less year by year.

Illustration. An electric motor cost $450. Its scrap value at the end of 4 years was estimated to be $100. Find, by the diminishing rate method, the amount to be charged off each year as depreciation.

Since the original cost was $450, and the scrap value was $100, the total amount of depreciation was $450 − $100 = $350. The life of the motor when installed was 4 years; at the end of the first year the life of the motor was 3 years; at the end of 2 years the life of the motor was 2 years, and at the end of 3 years, its life was 1 year.

Adding these periods of usefulness together, thus, 4 + 3 + 2 + 1 gives a sum of 10. The first year's depreciation then, is

$\frac{4}{10}$ of $350 = $140
The second year it is $\frac{3}{10}$ of $350 = $105
The third year it is $\frac{2}{10}$ of $350 = $70
The fourth year it is $\frac{1}{10}$ of $350 = $35
A total of $350

Problems

Find, by the diminishing rate method, the annual depreciation on each of the following; also state the book value each year.

	Original Cost	Number of Years of Service	Scrap Value	Depreciation	Book Value
1.	$1000	6	$160		
2.	$650	5	$125		
3.	$1250	7	$130		

POSTAL RATES

Mailable matter is divided into four classes.

First Class. Consists of letters and written and sealed matter.

Limit of weight, 70 pounds.

RATES: 3¢ an ounce or fraction thereof, except when addressed for local delivery, in which case the rate is 2¢ an ounce or fraction thereof; and 1¢ an ounce or fraction thereof at post offices where there is no local or rural delivery.

Government postal cards, 1¢ each.

Private mailing or post cards, 1¢ each.

AIR MAIL: 6¢ for each ounce or fraction of an ounce.

Second Class. Consists of newspapers, magazines, and other periodicals containing notice of second-class entry.

No limit of weight.

RATE: 1¢ for each 2 ounces or fraction thereof, or the fourth-class rate, whichever is lower.

Third Class. Consists of circulars and other miscellaneous printed matter and merchandise.

Limit of weight, 8 ounces.

RATE: $1\frac{1}{2}$¢ for each 2 ounces or fraction thereof.

Books consisting wholly of reading matter and containing no advertising matter, other than incidental announcements of books, may be mailed at $1\frac{1}{2}$ cents a pound.

Fourth Class (Parcel Post). Consists of any mailable matter not contained in the first or the second class.

Limit of weight, over 8 ounces, not over 70 pounds.

Limit of size, 100 inches in length and girth combined.

Parcel-post Rates

Zones	Limit of Distance	First Pound	Additional Pounds
Local	Local Delivery	7¢	1¢ for each 2 pounds
1 and 2	150 miles	8¢	1.1¢ for each pound
3	300 miles	9¢	2¢ for each pound
4	600 miles	10¢	3.5¢ for each pound
5	1000 miles	11¢	5.3¢ for each pound
6	1400 miles	12¢	7¢ for each pound
7	1800 miles	14¢	9¢ for each pound
8	over 1800 miles	15¢	11¢ for each pound

1. Make a table showing to which class of mail each of the following belongs:

(*a*) A basket of apples weighing 30 lb.
(*b*) A newspaper weighing 4 oz.
(*c*) A book weighing 6 oz.
(*d*) A catalogue weighing 14 oz.
(*e*) Four copies of a magazine in one parcel
(*f*) A parcel of merchandise weighing 2 lb., sealed against inspection
(*g*) A letter weighing $2\frac{1}{4}$ oz.
(*h*) A letter weighing $\frac{1}{4}$ oz.
(*i*) A package of garden seeds weighing 5 oz.
(*j*) A package of books weighing 8 lb.
(*k*) A 4-ounce magazine in a sealed envelope
(*l*) A typewritten unsealed letter

2. A mail-order clerk has the following items of mail to send out. Indicate the amount of postage for each item, the total for each group of items, and the total postage required on all.

(*a*) 150 letters weighing $\frac{3}{4}$ oz. each
(*b*) 300 circulars weighing $1\frac{1}{2}$ oz. each
(*c*) 36 parcels of merchandise, weighing $3\frac{1}{2}$ lb. each, to zone 4
(*d*) 28 parcels of merchandise, weighing $1\frac{1}{4}$ lb. each, to zone 3
(*e*) A package of newspapers, weighing 3 lb. to zone 2

(*f*) 200 letters for local delivery, weighing $\frac{3}{4}$ oz. each
(*g*) 150 catalogues of 48 pages each, weighing 3 oz. each
(*h*) 32 parcels of books, weighing $4\frac{1}{2}$ lb. each, to zone 6
(*i*) 20 parcels of merchandise, weighing $4\frac{1}{4}$ lb. each, to zone 5
(*j*) 15 parcels of merchandise, weighing $7\frac{1}{2}$ lb. each, to zone 4

3. A package containing 4 lb. of butter (gross weight, $4\frac{3}{4}$ lb.) is to be sent to a city in the fourth zone. Which is cheaper, to send it by parcel post or by express, if the express charge is 36¢?

4. May a package 27 in. by 22 in. by 14 in. be sent by parcel post?

5. The following parcels are to be sent as indicated. State which should be sent by parcel post and which by express. How much is saved by the cheaper method in each case?

(*a*) 10-pound parcel to fifth zone. Express charge is $.70.
(*b*) 50-pound parcel to fourth zone. Express charge is $1.57.
(*c*) 5-pound parcel to fourth zone. Express charge is $.35.

6. Find the total cost of sending a parcel weighing $34\frac{1}{2}$ lb. to the seventh zone.

PART THREE

NARRATIVES

NARRATIVES

Each narrative is divided into separate problems, yet it carries on in logical order a story of an actual enterprise or a business. The narratives provide practice in a considerable variety of problem solving, and the problems are of such a nature as to sustain an interest in the entire narrative. No attempt has been made to be exhaustive, or complete, with respect to details in the various lines of enterprise presented.

Technical data have been furnished by those engaged in the various types of work outlined. Both commodity and labor prices vary widely in different sections of the country so that fixed prices applicable to all sections are not possible. Local prices should be used by those wishing to make the narratives applicable to local conditions.

As the work of each narrative progresses, a complete record of all results should be kept by the student. Specific suggestions for the type of record to be kept will be found in each narrative.

NARRATIVE NO. 1

WHOLESALE MERCHANDISING

In this narrative will be found a large number of problems common to the everyday experience of any trading concern. It will furnish practice in topics such as cash discount, trade discount, bank discount, checking bills, keeping a bank record of all deposits and checks drawn, pay roll, lumber measure, filing, postage and stationery, parcel post, marking goods to sell at a desired price, insurance, commission, import duties, installment buying, the preparation of a balance sheet, and distribution of net profits. The problems of this narrative provide drill in applying fundamental principles to actual store problems.

Reference is made from time to time throughout the narrative to facts and conditions appearing earlier in the narrative.

The pupil will find it very much to his advantage, therefore, to keep a complete record of all results obtained in the problems as the work progresses; these results should be numbered according to the number of the problem and labeled sufficiently to enable the student to know what each result means.

Benson and Company conducts both a wholesale and a retail business. As an assistant in the office you are called on to solve various types of arithmetic problems as they arise in the business. You begin work August 1.

Ewing Galloway

Wholesale and retail merchandising require constant use of arithmetic as applied to many kinds of transactions.

August 1

1. On your first day you are handed a number of invoices from firms from whom Benson and Company has bought goods. The names of the firms, dates of the invoices, terms, and amounts of the several invoices are shown on page 369.

Prepare an accounts payable register like the illustration, enter the invoices, and complete the record. Show the amount of cash discount, the cash required to pay each bill, and the date of payment.

Firm	Date of Invoice	Terms	Amount of Invoice
The Northern Company .	July 22	3/10, 2/30, N/60	$1375.60
Gristow Brothers . . .	July 23	2/10, N/60	$1891.90
Gilmore's Refinery . .	July 27	3/10, N/60	$2275.80
Reeves and Reeves . .	July 29	2/15, N/30	$1694.70
Butler Brothers . . .	July 19	3/20, N/60	$3172.88
The Fisher Company . .	July 24	2/10, E. O. M.*	$947.86
Ray Furniture Company	July 28	5/10, 3/30, N/60	$7147.90

* "2/10, E. O. M." means 2% discount if paid within 10 days after the expiration of the month in which the purchase is made.

Accounts Payable Register

Name of Firm	Date of Invoice	Terms	Amt. of Invoice	Cash Discount	Cash Required	Date of Payment

Benson and Company's bank balance, as of August 1, is $1427.64, which is not enough to take advantage of the discounts offered by the different firms.

2. In order that Benson and Company may have cash on hand to meet the bills as the discount periods of the invoices expire, discount a 20-day note of $15,000, which the cashier asks you to draw up in favor of the National Bank. The rate of discount is 6%.

NOTE. It is to be assumed that Benson and Company is a partnership. One of the partners is acting as cashier and has been authorized to sign all checks, notes, etc., for the firm.

(*a*) Would it be legal and good business practice to draw the note payable to Benson and Company instead of the National Bank?

(*b*) If so, what would the cashier have to do before the note could be discounted?

(*c*) In drawing up this note, which expression would you use — "I promise to pay to the order of," etc., or "we promise to pay to the order of," etc.?

(*d*) What is the difference in the method of finding the discount on this note and the discount on the invoices on the preceding page?

(*e*) After depositing the proceeds of the note in the bank, what is the balance to the credit of Benson and Company?

NOTE. At this point begin a cash account to show the original cash balance in the bank, and record all deposits and payments, to enable you at any time to report the bank balance.

(*f*) When the note comes due in 20 days, how much must Benson and Company pay the bank?

3. Checks on the National Bank were written to pay the invoices due today and tomorrow (Aug. 1 and 2). Enter the amounts in the cash account.

August 2

The following orders were received in the morning mail. The billing clerk has prepared the invoices, using the prices listed on page 371. The terms on all invoices will be 2/10, N/30.

4. Order from Baker Brothers, City.

20 chests Japan tea 80# (80 lb. to a chest)
30 half-chests Orange Pekoe 40#
12 cartons Bokar Coffee, vacuum tins 24's (24 1-lb. tins to a carton)
16 cases Ivory Soap 100's (100 cakes to a case)
10 bags granulated sugar 100# (100 lb. to a bag)

5. Order from Lettieri Brothers, 88 N. Adams St., Philadelphia, Pa.

12 bags Rio coffee beans 120# (120 lb. to a bag)
8 cartons Whitehouse Coffee 24's
12 cartons granulated sugar 12-5's (12 5-lb. pkg. to a carton)
6 gross Palm Olive Soap

6. Order from D. Albrecht and Company, 1115 Allen St., Pittsburgh, Pa.

20 cartons Circle Coffee 24's
20 packages of Lipton's Tea ¼'s (24 to a package)
20 cases O. K. Soap 60's
20 cases Big Ben Soap 60's

7. Order from S. Simons and Sons, City.

36 cases P. & G. Naphtha Soap 80's
30 cases Lux Toilet Soap 50's
100 bags granulated sugar 25#
40 bags granulated sugar 100#
20 cartons Confectioners' sugar 24's
20 chests Japan Tea 80#
40 cartons Circle Coffee 24's

The amounts of the several invoices, as determined by the billing clerk are as follows: Baker Brothers, $710.33; Lettieri Brothers, $291; Albrecht and Company, $206.40; S. Simons and Sons, $1041.73. Check the calculations before the invoices are sent out to see if there is any error in them. If an error is found, note of it should be made, and the bookkeeper and the billing clerk notified.

PRICE LIST

TEA		COFFEE	
Japan	22½¢	Rio	13¢
Lipton's (¼)	11¢	Bokar (tins)	18½¢
Orange Pekoe	14½¢	Circle	14½¢
		Whitehouse	17½¢

SOAP		SUGAR	
O. K., case	$2.10	Granulated, 100# bags	$.04⅝
Big Ben, case	$2.10	Granulated, 25# bags	$.04⅝
P. & G. Naphtha, case	$3.00	Granulated, carts. 12–5's	$.04¾
Ivory, case	$4.80	Confectioners'	$.05½
Palm Olive, gross	$6.00		
Lux Toilet, case	$3.25		

August 4

8. An order from Harding and Son, Cleveland, Ohio, was received in the morning mail, for the following:

18 Rockers	at $47.50
18 Day Beds	at $33.75
24 I. X. L. Radios	at $62.50
36 Electric Coffee Percolators	at $11.75
Less $33\frac{1}{3}$% and 10%	

The billing clerk has prepared the invoice showing a net amount of $2031.30. Check his figures to insure accuracy.

9. A check was sent to pay Gilmore's Refinery for the invoice of July 27. Enter it in the Cash Account.

August 6

Checks were received for invoices as follows:

	Customers	*Amount of Invoice*	*Checks*
10.	Randall and Reeves	$1328.90 less 3%	$1289.03
11.	Butler and Butler	$2492.50 less 2%	$2424.65
12.	Griswold and Son	$915.25 less 2%	$896.94
13.	Hammond and Company	$3246.80 less 3%	$3149.40

Check the discount deductions to see if the checks are for the right amount. If any error is found, present the right solution, showing the correct amount for which the check should have been written. What should be done to rectify an error, if there is an error?

Deposit the checks received. Enter the amount of the deposit in the Cash Account.

14. A check was mailed to Butler Brothers for the invoice of July 19.

15. A check was sent to The Ray Furniture Company for the invoice of July 28.

16. The time sheet for part of the office and warehouse employees, on a weekly basis, is as follows. Pro rata deductions are made for any loss of time with time and a half for overtime. Wages are based on an 8-hour day.

	S	M	T	W	T	F	*Total Time*	*Rate*
A. James, Bookkeeper	0	8	8	8	4	8		$4.50
L. Tyler, Stenographer	4	8	9	4	$8\frac{1}{2}$	8		3.50
F. Dexter, Billing Clerk . . .	4	8	4	8	0	8		4.00
G. Drew, Receiving Clerk . . .	4	9	8	9	8	4		3.35
S. Simons, Stock Clerk	4	8	8	8	4	8		3.40
R. Reed, Shipping Clerk . . .	4	8	8	8	4	10		3.90
B. Barton, Assist. Shipping Clerk	4	8	8	4	9	10		3.10
Yourself, Office Assistant . . .	4	9	9	10	8	4		5.75

Prepare the pay roll by finding, first, the wages earned by each employee (deduct the old-age tax), second, the total wages, and third, the bills and coins required for each pay envelope. For the coin memorandum use a form like the following: How may you check the accuracy of your currency memorandum?

CURRENCY MEMORANDUM

NAMES	WAGES	$20	$10	$5	$1	$.50	$.25	$.10	$.05	$.01
Totals										

August 8

The following invoices of incoming merchandise have been handed you with instructions to prepare a selling-price mark for each item. The marked price must be such as to allow a trade discount of 20% to customers, 17% of net selling price for overhead expenses, 5% of net selling price for bad debts, and 8% of net selling price for profit. (Mark each item in nearest $.05.)

17. JABLONOWER MANUFACTURING COMPANY

Cleveland, Ohio

Terms: 3/10, N/60

24 Flat Top Desks	#476F	$45	1080			
18 Roll Top Desks	#476R	57.50	1035			
36 Filing Cabinets	#324	37.50	1350			
48 Swivel Chairs	#274S	27.50	1320			
30 Radio Cabinets	#98X	65	1950			
			6735			
Less 25% and 20%			2694			
					4041	

NOTE. The cash discount of 3% has no bearing on the selling marked price. It has no bearing on this problem.

18. NATIONAL POTTERY WORKS

Louisville, Ky.

Terms: 5/10, 2/30, N/60

36 doz. Dinner Plates	#10	$ 8.75	315			
18 doz. Bread and Butter Plates	#7	6.35	114	30		
15 doz. Breakfast Plates	#8	7.50	112	50		
30 doz. Teacups and Saucers	#16	9.80	294			
8 doz. Platters	#18	11.50	92			
			927	80		
Less 20% and 10%			259	78		
					668	02

19. The following cash sales were made to city merchants. A cash discount of 2% was allowed on each sale. Find the net amount received for the cash sales.

The Cash Grocery	$750.62
The Better Grocers	$632.60
The Northside Grocery	$431.98
Self-Service Stores	$513.27
Henry and Henry	$821.19

Deposit the cash received. Enter the amount of the deposit in the Cash Account and find bank balance.

August 9

20. In the Stationery Department, six new tiers of shelves, six shelves to a tier, are to be built. The shelves are to be 1 foot deep, 4 feet long, with 11 inches of clear space between the shelves. The shelves are to be of spruce lumber 1 inch thick. The upright pieces are of the same material as the shelves. A board is placed over the top tier of shelves, as shown in the illustration. The bottom shelf is to be 1 foot from the floor. The shelves are supported by iron braces — 2 braces at each end of each shelf. Each brace requires 4 screws. Find:

(*a*) the quantity of lumber required for the shelves, uprights, etc.;

(*b*) the cost of the lumber at $55 per M board feet;

(*c*) the number of braces required, and their cost at 3 for 10¢;

(*d*) the number of screws required, and their cost at $.45 per gross.

August 10

21. A check, favor of The Fisher Company, was sent for their invoice of July 24. What is the cash balance at this point?

22. With the increase in shelf space it was decided to increase the maximum quantity of certain kinds of stock. The old maximum, the new maximum, the present quantity on hand, and the cost price of each item, are shown in the list, page 376.

(*a*) Find the quantity of each kind of stock required to bring each item up to the new maximum.

(*b*) The value of the entire stock at the new maximum quantity is what per cent greater than the value of the total stock at the old maximum quantity?

Items	Stock on Hand	Old Maximum	New Maximum	Price
Typewriter Paper . .	18 rm.	50 rm.	75 rm.	$.56 a rm.
Second Sheets	22 rm.	40 rm.	60 rm.	$.37 a rm.
Carbon Paper	11 bx.	30 bx.	40 bx.	$1.75 a bx.
Hammermill Bond . .	17 rm.	60 rm.	75 rm.	$.69 a rm.
Hammermill Envelopes .	17 M	40 M	50 M	$1.25 per M
Writing Fluid	6 gal.	15 gal.	20 gal.	$2.25 a gal.
Typewriter Ribbons . .	3 doz.	1 gr.	15 doz.	$2.75 a doz.
Mimeograph Paper . .	50 rm.	100 rm.	150 rm.	$.24 a rm.

August 12

23. Checks were received this morning for goods shipped to the following firms, August 2:

Baker Brothers	$696.12
Lettieri and Son	$285.18
D. Albrecht and Company . .	$220.27
S. Simons and Son	$1011.09

What is the total amount you should receive? If these receipts were deposited at once, what should be your bank balance?

24. The Company's office clerks have transferred certain records from the books to cards. Each card is to represent one customer's account. These cards are to be filed alphabetically. There are 19,200 cards. To provide filing space, new filing cabinets have to be ordered. The drawers are 18 inches deep. 8 inches of space in each drawer is to be left for new cards as new accounts are obtained. 80 cards, with guide cards, take up 1 inch of space. Reckoning 6 drawers to a cabinet, how many additional filing cabinets are required for the cards?

25. Referring to the preceding problem, find how many filing clerks will be required to alphabetize and file the cards in 4 days, if one clerk can handle an average of 800 cards a day.

26. The Company opens up 30 new accounts a day. There is, on the average, a loss of 10 old accounts a day. There are 680 old customers, on the average, making credit purchases daily. The cards of the old customers who have ceased to deal with the firm have to be removed from the "live" files and placed in a "dead" file. One file clerk can handle 40 cards an hour. How many file clerks working 6 hours a day are required to keep the files up to date?

27. Find the cost of the following new filing materials required for the new filing system:

25 M cards for customers' accounts	at $6.75	per M
12 C guide cards	at $5.50	per C
250 "Out" cards	at $1.25	per C
25 C folders	at $13.75	per M
5 C cross reference sheets	at $1.10	per C

28. The Company plans a mail advertising campaign to cover a period of 4 weeks. A series of four letters (one letter a week) is to be sent to each of the 19,200 customers. Stenciling and mimeographing are to be done by the regular office workers. Each letter is to be on a single sheet of paper. In estimating the quantity of material for the letters allow 480 sheets to a ream. (A ream of paper handled by the Company contains 500 sheets, but there is always some waste in mimeographing.) 75% of the customers live within the 2-cents postage zone. For the others, 3-cents postage is required for each letter.

Find:

(*a*) the number of reams of paper required for all the letters;

(*b*) the cost of postage for all the letters;

(*c*) the total cost of paper, envelopes, and postage. (Use prices stated under date of August 10, page 375.)

August 14

29. You sent a check to

(*a*) D. Albrecht and Company for the amount they overpaid on the 12th.

(*b*) Reeves and Reeves for their invoice of July 29.

30. Checks for invoices as follows have been received.

(*a*) Johnson and Johnson	$1391.75, less 2%	$1363.91
(*b*) Ames and Benson	$531.92, less 3%	$515.96

(*c*) Cutten Brothers	\$2276.87, less 3%	\$2208.56
(*d*) Craddock and Sons	\$3787.91, less 3%	\$3674.27
(*e*) Caputo Brothers	\$5492.86, less 5%	\$5208.22

Verify the discount deductions, to see if the checks are for the right amounts.

The amount of these checks has been deposited. What is your bank balance?

August 20

31. The Company's 20-day note of \$15,000 is due at the Bank tomorrow. For how much should a check be written to pay the National Bank?

32. A new office assistant has reckoned the selling prices on goods as shown in the following list. Check his figures for "net cost" and for "our marked price," and verify or correct his results.

Item	Gross Purchase Price	Trade Discount	Net Cost	Trade Discount to Our Customers	Allowance for Bad Debts	Overhead Expense	Profit on Sales	Our Marked Price
A	\$3.75	20%	\$3.00	10%	5%	$23\frac{1}{2}$%	9%	\$5.33
B	\$9.98	$16\frac{2}{3}$%	\$6.65	$12\frac{1}{2}$%	4%	18%	8%	\$10.69
C	\$12.00	20%	\$9.60	20%	3%	16%	9%	\$16.67
D	\$170.00	25%	\$127.50	$16\frac{2}{3}$%	4%	14%	7%	\$198.33
E	\$15.00	10%	\$13.50	20%	5%	19%	$8\frac{1}{2}$%	\$25.00
F	\$17.70	$16\frac{2}{3}$%	\$14.75	10%	$3\frac{1}{2}$%	$16\frac{1}{2}$%	10%	\$23.41
G	\$12.50	20%	\$10.00	None	2%	24%	$11\frac{1}{2}$%	\$16.00
H	\$16.20	$33\frac{1}{3}$%	\$10.80	25%	3%	19%	6%	\$20.00

Note. The variation in rates allowed for bad debts, overhead expenses, and for profits on sales, within the same business is due to the variation of such rates in different departments of the same business.

August 23

33. The special advertising campaign is already bringing results. The ten departments advertised show sales for the first week, as follows. The sales for the same week of last year are given for comparison.

Department	Sales This Year August 15–21	Sales Last Year August 14–20
Millinery	$5762.40	$4988.60
Coats and Dresses	$9485.90	$8792.25
Gloves	$4782.50	$3684.40
Shoes	$4927.50	$4428.90
Men's Clothing	$6937.60	$6678.20
Jewelry	$7428.60	$6947.85
Crockery	$2438.70	$2146.90
Sporting Goods	$6168.93	$4756.72
Auto Accessories	$2296.80	$1754.98
Haberdashery	$3187.50	$2647.84

Find (*a*) the increase in each department, and the total increase.

(*b*) The per cent of increase in each department and the per cent of total increase.

How may these results be checked for accuracy?

34. In Problem 33, if the net profit was $9\frac{1}{2}\%$ of sales, find the increase in net profit for the first week of the campaign, due to the increase in sales.

August 25

35. As a result of the advertising campaign, the following parcels, ordered by mail, are to be sent either by parcel post or by express, whichever is cheaper.

15 parcels weighing 10 lb. each to the 4th parcel post zone.
24 parcels weighing 50 lb. each to the 4th parcel post zone.
18 parcels weighing 50 lb. each to the 3rd parcel post zone.
6 parcels weighing 8 lb. each to the 5th parcel post zone.

(For parcel post rates, see page 363.)

Inquiry reveals that the express charges on the parcels mentioned would be as follows:

For each 10 lb. parcel, $.70.
For each 50 lb. parcel to the 4th zone, $1.57.
For each 50 lb. parcel to the 3rd zone, $1.47.
For each 8 lb. parcel to the 5th zone, $.70.

Determine which method of shipping is cheaper, and find the cost of shipping all the parcels.

August 26

36. One of the small warehouses burned last night. The damage to the building was $8000, and to the contents, $12,000. From records kept in the safe, it was learned that the value of the merchandise stored in the building was $27,500. The building was valued at $15,000. The stock was insured for $20,000, and the building for $9000. Both policies contained the 80% "co-insurance clause." Find the amount received from the insurance company.

August 27

37. Benson and Company has on hand the following promissory notes:

(*a*) A 3-months note, dated July 22, for $1750.
(*b*) A 60-day note, dated August 10, for $1425.50.
(*c*) A 2-months note, dated July 31, for $1190.75.

Have these notes discounted at the bank, and the proceeds placed to the credit of Benson and Company. Rate 6%.

38. The Company increases the amount of insurance on the main warehouse from $35,000 to $50,000, and on the contents from $60,000 to $80,000. The policies are each for five years. The rate on the building is $.96 per $100, and on the contents, $1.15 per $100. Find the annual increase in the cost of insurance. What is the per cent of increase?

39. There are two traveling salesmen — White and Larkin. White is guaranteed $40 a week, plus 5% commission on all sales over $1000 a week. Larkin receives a straight commission of 5% on all his sales. Each man is allowed $30 a week for traveling expenses. Sales made by each man for the last week of July and the first three weeks of August are:

For the Week	White	Larkin
July 25–30	$1275.25	$1215.38
August 1–6	$750.80	$1470.60
August 8–13	$1767.96	$1784.72
August 15–20	$1391.90	$1857.75
Totals	$5185.91	$6328.45

Prepare a statement showing the amount, including expense money, that should be sent to each salesman for the four-week period.

40. In the women's coat and suit department of the store are five salesladies. They are paid a certain wage per week plus a commission as follows: $\frac{3}{4}$% on all sales up to a given quota, and 3% on all sales above the quota. The wages paid, the quota, and the sales for one week, for each saleslady are as follows:

SALES REPORT FOR WEEK ENDED AUGUST 27

SALESLADY	WEEKLY WAGE	QUOTA	SALES FOR THE WEEK
Miss A	$13.50	$350	$475
Miss B	$14.50	$375	$512.50
Miss C	$15.00	$400	$587.60
Miss D	$16.00	$500	$608.25
Miss E	$17.50	$600	$856.40

Use a form like the following, and fill in the data for each saleslady, and complete the form to show the amount earned by each.

SALES-LADY	SALES	QUOTA	COM. ON QUOTA $\frac{3}{4}$%	SALES OVER QUOTA	COM. ON EXCESS 3%	WAGES PER WEEK	TOTAL EARNED

August 29

41. An invoice of woolen goods imported from London came this morning, and shows the following items:

750 lb. woolen yarn at $1.25
1200 pr., 200 lb., woolen hose at $.50 per pair
75 dozen, 1200 lb., woolen sweaters at $45 a dozen

Duties are as follows:

	Specific	*Ad Valorem*
Woolen yarn	$.40 a pound	35%
Woolen hose	$.50 a pound	50%
Woolen sweaters	$.50 a pound	50%

Prepare a statement showing the:

(*a*) import value of each item,
(*b*) specific duty on each item,
(*c*) ad valorem duty on each item,
(*d*) total cost of each item,
(*e*) total cost of all.

42. Using the facts given in Problem 41, find the selling price of the yarn per pound, of the hose per pair, and of each sweater, to make a gross profit of 25% of total cost.

43. In the house furnishing department, merchandise is sold on the installment plan. Mrs. Adams, a customer, calls and asks for an explanation of the installment plan of buying. You are asked to show her how the plan works, what the additional cost is, and why it costs more than selling for cash. She asks you to illustrate using the prices on a bedroom suite which sells for cash for $160, and on the installment plan for $25 down, and $25 monthly for six months. Show her how much more the total installment cost is than the cash price, and what rate of interest she would be paying on the deferred payments.

44. Another customer, Mrs. Mary Winter, called and wished to have you explain how she could purchase an electric refrigerator without paying the full price at once. The refrigerator she wished is priced at $225, or it could be bought for $25 down and the balance paid in 11 equal monthly installments of $20 each. Prepare a complete schedule of payments for Mrs. Winter, to show exactly what the total cost would be, and also show by solution what rate of interest she would be paying on the delayed payments.

September 1

45. Benson and Company is composed of three partners. They are A. W. Benson, whose share of the capital is $40,000;

L. B. Coady and S. B. Undine, whose share in the capital was $30,000 each. They have been in business since the first of the calendar year. Their capital on January 1 was $100,000. On this day (September 1) they plan to re-organize the company by admitting M. M. Munford who is ready to purchase for cash a one-fourth interest in the business. It is agreed that any profit to date shall be divided among the original partners in proportion to their investments, and that the cash paid in by Mr. Munford shall be divided among the original partners so as to make them all equal partners in the business.

From the bookkeeper you obtain the following list of assets and liabilities as of this date:

Cash on Hand	$28,750.60	
Notes Receivable	6,425.00	
Accounts Receivable	6,950.40	
Merchandise Stock on Hand	78,600.00	
Store Equipment	15,700.00	
Office Equipment	2,500.00	
Delivery Trucks, etc.	9,000.00	
Miscellaneous Supplies	3,000.00	
Real Estate	75,000.00	
Notes Payable		$6,500.00
Mortgage Payable		50,000.00
Accounts Payable		13,500.00

(*a*) Find the firm's net profit or loss to date.

(*b*) Show how the net profit or loss should be distributed among the three partners.

(*c*) How much must Mr. Munford pay and how much does each of the other three partners receive as his share?

NARRATIVE NO. 2

REAL ESTATE AND BUILDING

Philip D. Gendreau, N. Y.

In this narrative the pupil is brought into contact with a variety of problems and conditions connected with building a house and owning a home.

Beginning with the purchase of a plot of ground, and making payment therefor, the narrative presents such problems as excavating the basement, mixing concrete for the walls, reckoning the quantity and the cost of brick, lumber, tile, roofing materials, plumbing fixtures, supplies, etc. The matter of providing cash through a savings and loan association, and other finance charges form part of the narrative. Taxes, insurance, and general overhead expenses are reckoned and the total cost of owning one's own home form the concluding part of the narrative.

A detailed record of all results obtained by the student should be kept by him.

Acquiring the Land

1. James Andrews has agreed to buy from Peter Henshaw a plot of ground 60′ by 125′, on which he plans to erect a house. The purchase price is $20 a foot front, payable as follows: $400 is to be paid upon the delivery of the deed, and the balance in semiannual installments of $200 each, with interest at 6% on unpaid balances.

Find (*a*) how many semiannual payments are required; (*b*) the total cost, including interest, of the plot of ground.

2. Before Henshaw gave Andrews a deed for the plot of ground, he paid a balance of $750 with interest at 6%, due on a mortgage he had given on the property. Interest was reckoned from February 1 to June 21. Find the amount required to settle the mortgage.

Excavation Work (Cement)

3. Andrews engaged John Armand to excavate the basement for the house he plans to build. The basement is to be 6 ft. deep, 36 ft. long, and 32 ft. wide. The cost of excavation is to be $1.25 a cu. yd. for ordinary soil, and $5.00 a cu. yd. for rock. Upon completion it was found that 25% of the excavation was rock. Find the cost of digging the basement.

Concrete is made by mixing cement, sand, and gravel (or crushed stone) with water. The proportions of cement, sand, and gravel vary, depending on the purpose for which the concrete is to be used. The strength of the concrete depends upon the quantity of cement used. Concrete mixtures are expressed as 1–2–4, 1–2½–5, 1–3–5, etc.

A 1–2–4 mixture means that it is made of 1 part cement, 2 parts sand, and 4 parts gravel. The parts are by volume, not by weight. Since the cement and sand fill in the spaces between the coarse pieces of gravel, it takes more than a cubic yard of the several ingredients to make a cubic yard of concrete. In general, the quantities of cement, sand, and gravel required to make a cubic yard of concrete are about as follows:

Mixture	Quantities of Cement, Sand, and Gravel		
	Cement	Sand	Gravel
1–2–4	5½ bags	.4 cu. yd.	.8 cu. yd.
1–2½–5	4½ bags	.4 cu. yd.	.8 cu. yd.
1–3–5	4½ bags	.5 cu. yd.	.8 cu. yd.

28 bags of cement are equal to 1 cu. yd. 4 bags of cement are equal to 1 barrel.

To make 120 cu. yd. of 1–2–4 concrete requires

$120 \times 5\frac{1}{2}$ bags cement,	or	660 bags of cement
$120 \times .4$ cu. yd. of sand,	or	48 cu. yd. of sand
$120 \times .8$ cu. yd. of gravel,	or	96 cu. yd. of gravel

4. Find the quantity of cement, sand, and gravel required to make

5. 80 cu. yd. of 1–2$\frac{1}{2}$–5 concrete.

6. 110 cu. yd. of 1–3–5 concrete.

7. A concrete wall is 80 ft. long, 9 ft. high, and 1$\frac{1}{2}$ ft. thick. Find the required quantity of cement, sand, and gravel for a concrete mixture of 1–2$\frac{1}{2}$–5.

8. A street $\frac{1}{2}$ mile long and 50 ft. wide is to be paved with concrete 6 inches thick. Find the required quantity of cement, sand, and gravel for a concrete mixture of 1–2–4. (Reckon quantities to nearest cubic yard.)

9. The inside dimensions of a concrete basement wall are 27 ft. by 32 ft. The wall is 1 ft. thick and 7 ft. high. How much cement, sand, and gravel are required to build the wall with a concrete mixture of 1–2–4?

10. Referring to Problem 3, page 385, find the quantity of cement, sand, and gravel required for a 1–3–5 mixture of concrete for the basement walls, if the dimensions are outside dimensions, and the wall is to be 6$\frac{3}{4}$ ft. high and 1 ft. thick. (Reckon quantities in nearest whole bag or cubic yard.)

11. The basement floor, Problem 3, page 385, is to be made of a 1–3–5 mixture of concrete 3 inches deep. How much cement, sand, and gravel are required for the concrete? (In whole bags and cubic yards.)

12. Covering the rough concrete in the basement (see Problem 3) there is a surface coat of cement and sand. Each square (100 sq. ft. of surface) requires 4 bags of cement and .3 cu. yd. of sand.

Estimate the quantity of cement and sand required for the surface coat.

13. If cement costs \$.60 a bag, sand costs \$1.75 a cubic yard, and gravel costs \$1.50 a cubic yard, find the cost of the materials required for building the basement of the house referred to in Problem 3, page 385.

Brick Construction Work

Bricks are of various sizes. Common bricks are $8'' \times 4'' \times 2''$. The mortar in which bricks are laid has the effect of apparently increasing the size of each brick in a wall. In estimating the number of bricks to be used in a wall, it is customary to reckon 22 common bricks to a cubic foot of the wall.

Give quantity of brick in round hundreds.

14. How many common bricks are required for a wall 120 ft. long, 8 ft. high, and 1 ft. thick?

15. The Andrews' garage is to be constructed of brick on two sides and one end. Inside dimensions are 22′ by 12′. The walls are 1 ft. thick and 8 ft. high. There is a window in each side wall. The bricks saved in the window areas will be sufficient to provide the extra bricks required for the corners. How many common bricks are required for the garage?

16. A brick house is 22′ wide and 38′ long, outside measurements. Its walls are 27′ high and 1′ thick. There are 16 windows whose average area is 18 sq. ft. There are two doors each 7′ high and 3′ 6″ wide. Making proper allowances for the windows, doors, and for the corners, find the quantity of brick required for the walls. (Reckon in whole thousands.)

17. The house which Mr. Andrews plans to build is to be of brick. Outside dimensions are $32' \times 36'$. The walls are three bricks thick (1 foot) and are to be 18 ft. high. There are 18 windows whose average area is 20 sq. ft. and three doors averaging 24 sq. ft. each. Allowing for corners, windows, and doors, find how many bricks are required for the walls.

For laying each thousand bricks there are required additional materials as follows:

Cement	6 bags
Sand	.6 cu. yd.
Waterproof	12 lb.

18. Assuming the price of bricks to be \$11 per M, of cement, \$.65 a bag, of sand, \$2.40 a cubic yard, and waterproof, \$.10 a pound, find the cost of brick and other materials for laying 1000 bricks.

19. Using the information obtained in Problems 17 and 18, find the cost of the brick, and of each of the other materials required for the Andrews house described in Problem 17.

The labor cost of laying 1000 bricks varies with varying conditions of locality and wage levels. If a brick layer lays 1000 bricks in a day, the cost may be as follows:

Bricklayer, wages	\$8.00
Helper, wages	3.00
Foreman or other laborers	1.50
Total	\$12.50

Find the cost of laying the brick in Andrews' house.

20. A moving-picture theater is 110 ft. long, 60 ft. wide, and 40 ft. high. Its walls are three bricks (1 foot thick). Allowing 300 cu. ft. for doors, exits, etc., and making no allowance for the corners, find

(*a*) the number of bricks required;

(*b*) the cost of the brick and of each of the other materials required for laying the brick (Use prices and data given in Problems 17 and 18);

(*c*) the labor cost of laying the brick (Use data given in Problem 19); and

(*d*) the total cost of erecting the walls of the moving-picture theater, if the contractor added $12\frac{1}{2}\%$ of all the costs as his profit.

Lumber Construction Work

Lumber is measured by the board foot. A *board foot* is a piece of lumber containing 144 cu. in. (unless the lumber is less than 1 inch thick. Lumber less than 1 inch thick is reckoned as being 1 inch thick).

A piece of board $12'' \times 12'' \times 1''$ contains 1 board foot. A piece of scantling eighteen inches long (frequently called "2 by 4's") contains 1 board foot, because $(2 \times 4 \times 18)$ cu. in. = 144 cu. in.

21. Make a list of four other sizes of lumber each of which is equal to 1 board foot.

22. A piece of lumber is 6″ × 8″ × 18′. How many board feet are there in it?

23. A plank 2″ thick and 12″ wide is 16′ long. How many board feet are there in it?

24. For the house which Andrews is building, the carpenter has ordered lumber as follows:

4 pc. 3″ × 12″ × 18′ at \$60 per M
6 pc. 3″ × 12″ × 16′ at \$60 per M
80 pc. 2″ × 12″ × 18′ at \$55 per M
40 pc. 2″ × 10″ × 18′ at \$55 per M
144 pc. 2″ × 4″ × 9′ at \$45 per M
4800 board feet of sheathing at \$37.50 per M

(Sheathing is used as the first layer of a double floor, as flooring for the attic and for roof boards.)

Find:
(*a*) the quantity of lumber ordered;
(*b*) the cost of the lumber.

25. A separate order was placed for rafters. There were 52 rafters each 2″ × 10″ × 22′. They cost \$60 per M. Find their cost.

26. The roof extends 18″ over the ends of the house. The rafters are used full length. How many squares of roofing material are required? (A square is equal to 100 sq. ft.)

27. To provide sufficient cash to complete the payments for electric wiring, plumbing, installation of doors, windows, etc., Mr. Andrews arranges for a loan of \$4000, with interest at 6%, at a savings and loan association. The plan calls for a payment of 1% of the loan each month. Each payment of \$40 is divided into two parts. One part pays the interest on the loan and the other part is a payment on the loan. Continue the following schedule of payments to show how much Andrews will have paid on the mortgage at the end of one year.

Schedule Showing Payments on a Loan of $4000

Dates	Payment	Interest	Amount Paid on Principal	Balance
October 1, 19—				$4000
November 1, 19— . .	$40	$20	$20	3980
December 1, 19— . . .	40	19.90	20.10	3959.90
January 1, 19— . . .	40	19.80	20.20	3939.70
February 1, 19— . . .	40	19.70	20.30	3919.40
March 1, 19—	40	19.60	20.40	3899.00
April 1, 19—	40	19.50	20.50	3878.50

28. Lumber for the oak floors costs $75 per M. Inside measurements of the house are 30′ × 34′. Make no allowance for stairways and partitions, but allow $\frac{1}{4}$ for waste of the entire area of both floors. Find the cost of floor lumber.

29. Henry Doremus has been engaged to install an oil-heating plant for $900 cash, or for a cash payment of $100 and 12 monthly payments of $75 each. The additional cost on the installment plan is to cover interest and finance charges. Find to the nearest tenth per cent the rate of interest Andrews pays on the deferred payments.

30. Find the cost of plumbing materials, as follows:

1 porcelain bath tub		$45
2 porcelain toilets and flush traps	@ $19.50	
2 porcelain wash basins	@ 16.75	
1 porcelain kitchen sink		42
2 stationary laundry tubs	@ 15.60	
1 shower-stall outfit		11.75
1 60-gallon hot-water tank		13.75
140 ft. of soil pipe	@ .22	
60 ft. of $\frac{3}{4}$ in. copper tubing	@ $11.50 per C	
90 ft. $\frac{1}{2}$ in. copper tubing	@ 8.75 per C	
8 $\frac{3}{4}$-in. elbows	@ .20	
24 $\frac{1}{2}$-in. elbows	@ .14	
8 $\frac{3}{4}$-in. to $\frac{1}{2}$-in. T's	@ .28	
6 shut offs	@ .55	
Furnace connections		17

31. In the Andrews house are two bathrooms, each $6' \times 10'$. The floors are to be covered with tile at \$.65 a square foot. The walls are to be tiled to a height of $3'\,6''$ at a cost of \$.95 a square foot. Allowance must be made for a door $3'\,6''$ wide for each bathroom. Find the cost of the tile work.

32. When the house was finished it was assessed at \$6500. The tax rate was \$2.1235 per \$100. How much were the taxes?

33. Andrews had the property insured for \$7000 at \$.75 per \$100 for three years. Find the annual cost of insurance.

34. It is estimated that it will require 2200 gallons of oil at \$.06$\frac{3}{4}$ a gallon to heat the house for one year. Find the annual cost of heating.

35. Water rent is \$14 a year. If the house and lot have cost Andrews \$8700 (exclusive of the cost of the oil-heating plant), find the monthly cost of the fixed charges for the first year. Include interest at 4% on the cost price of \$8700.

NARRATIVE NO. 3

MANUFACTURING WALLPAPER

This narrative covers the essential operations in the cost and production of wallpaper. The facts in the narrative have been furnished by a large wallpaper mill.

Wallpaper is made from wood pulp. **Wood pulp** is made by grinding water-soaked wood on large stones somewhat similar to grindstones. The grinding process reduces the wood literally to a powder to which water is added when making the pulp.

Sulphide, alum, and size are mixed with the pulp to cause the wood particles (powder) to stick together when the water is drained off; the pulp is then run between hot rollers to dry and press the pulp into flat sheets of paper. As the sheets of paper come from the hot rollers they are wound into large rolls ready for the printing process.

The **printing process** consists of running the paper over a series of rollers on which are placed the designs to be printed on the wallpaper. Each different color, shade, or tint in the finished paper is printed on the paper from a separate roller. After the long sheets (hundreds of yards long) have been printed, the paper is cut into double-length rolls (48 feet each) and made into rolls for the market.

Courtesy International Paper Co.

In their course to the paper mill the logs frequently form log jams that must be broken up as seen in this picture.

The Southern Paper Company has a capital stock of $2,500,000, divided into 25,000 shares of the value of $100 each. The business of the company is to grind wood into pulp, manufacture wallpaper from it, print, cut, and roll the paper into rolls ready for the market, and market the product. The wood is bought by the cord.

A "roll" of 18-inch wallpaper is 8 yards long. Two rolls of paper are rolled together and are called a double roll.

You have been employed by the Company to assist in preparing cost and production records. You are to receive $35 a week for your week.

Company Business

1. It requires the services of 75 men to operate the grinding machines, handle the wood, repair the machines, and perform other duties pertaining to the making of wood pulp and converting it into paper. These men work in shifts, 40 hours a week, to keep the mill running 24 hours a day, six days a week. The hourly wages are as follows:

24 men average \$.85 an hour
13 men average \$.72 an hour
25 men average \$.54 an hour
13 men average \$.44 an hour

Find the weekly pay roll.

2. The company pays \$10.50 a cord for wood. The men grind an average of 22 cords of wood a day. Find the cost of wood required for one week's grinding.

3. One cord of wood makes 2100 pounds of wood pulp. How many tons of pulp are made in one week? (In nearest whole tons.)

In this wallpaper mill there are two separate departments — one, a department in which paper (hanging stock) is manufactured from wood and other materials, and the other, a printing department in which the hanging stock is printed and prepared for market. Their costs are kept entirely separate.

The Hanging-Stock Department

Hanging stock is the name given to wallpaper before it is printed with its various designs and patterns.

To make hanging stock there is mixed with the wood pulp three other materials — sulphide, alum, and size. Hanging stock, when dry, is 80% wood pulp and 20% of the three foregoing materials. In the drying process the wood pulp loses 8% of its weight. As a result in making hanging stock there has to be used more than 80% by weight of pulp.

In a ton of hanging stock, when dry, there is
80% of 2000 lb. = 1600 lb. of wood pulp, and
20% of 2000 lb. other materials = 400 lb., other materials.

Since 8% of the wood pulp has dried out, the 1600 lb. of dried wood pulp in a ton of hanging stock represents only 92% of the weight of the wood pulp before it is dried.

Hence, 1600 lb. ÷ .92 = 1739+ = 1740 lb. of wood pulp for 1 ton of hanging stock.

4. How many tons of hanging stock can be made from the quantity of wood pulp made in one week? (Reckon in nearest whole tons.)

5. Find the cost of labor for 1 ton of hanging stock.

6. Find the cost of wood pulp required to make one ton of hanging stock.

7. The quantity of other materials combined with wood pulp in one week to make hanging stock is as follows:

Sulphide	48,000 lb.
Alum	6,400 lb.
Size	9,600 lb.

What per cent, by weight, of the finished product is (*a*) sulphide? (*b*) alum? (*c*) size?

8. If sulphide costs $43 a ton, alum, $21 a ton, and size, $70.50 a ton, find the cost of these three items used in one week.

9. Find the cost of sulphide, alum, and size required to make 1 ton of hanging stock.

10. Overhead expenses, consisting of depreciation on plant and machinery, factory management, power (both steam and electric) supplies, fire protection, etc., cost $14.75 per ton of hanging stock. Find the total cost of 1 ton of hanging stock.

The Printing Department

11. The manufactured hanging stock is sold to the printing department at $55 a ton. Find the profit per ton on hanging stock sold to the printing department.

12. Ten printing machines are used in the printing department to print the wallpaper. To supervise this part of the work and operate the machines require the services of the following:

A superintendent at	$5000 a year
An assistant superintendent at	$2500 a year
A chemist at	$1800 a year
3 foremen at	$30 each per week
5 color mixers at	$1.10 per hour
A color mixer foreman at	$1.19 per hour
A foreman printer at	$1.19 per hour
A printer for each machine at	$1.10 per hour

(*a*) Find the weekly salary cost on an annual salary basis.

(*b*) Reckoning 40 hours per week, find the weekly-wage cost of the employees not on an annual salary basis.

13. To complete the operation of printing, caring for the machines, handling the large rolls of hanging stock, preparing the paper for market, etc., requires the services of 60 other employees averaging $.50 an hour, and 40 others at $.38 an hour. Find the weekly pay roll for these employees.

14. Each printing machine prints on the average 6000 rolls of paper a day. How many rolls of paper are printed in 6 days?

15. One ton of hanging stock makes 3800 rolls of paper. How many tons of hanging stock are required to keep the printing machines busy for 1 week? (In nearest whole tons.)

16. Find, for 100 rolls of paper, the cost of

(*a*) hanging stock at $55 a ton

(*b*) labor, including those on an annual salary basis.

17. To print one week's run of wallpaper requires other materials costing as follows:

Colors	$1044
Clay	$720
Size	$1656
Bronze	$1692
Mica	$468

Find the cost per 100 rolls (*a*) of each of these materials; (*b*) of all of these materials.

18. If overhead expenses amount to $1.02 per hundred rolls, find the total cost of 100 rolls of wallpaper.

19. If the company maintains the same rate of manufacture (as indicated in Problem 14) for 48 weeks of the year, and sells the paper at an average price of $7.50 per hundred rolls, how much is the gross manufacturing profit in the printing department for the year?

20. Under the term "sampling" comes the cost of buying wallpaper designs from artists, buying rolls to which the designs are transferred, making samples for the trade, etc. The average cost is $.50 per 100 rolls of paper manufactured. Find the cost of sampling for 1 year.

21. Selling expenses amount to an average of $.30 per 100 rolls. How much are the annual selling expenses?

22. Find for the printing department, the net profit for the year.

23. In the hanging-stock department of the mill more paper is made than is used in the printing department. The excess is sold to the Central Wallpaper Company at $55 a ton, *f. o. b.* factory. Reckoning on the basis of whole tons, and 48 weeks to the year, find the net profit per annum on the paper sold to the Central Wallpaper Company.

24. How much is the profit on the hanging stock sold to the printing department?

25. Find the net profit for the entire mill.

26. If the Company pays $7 a share on its stock, and puts the balance of the net profit into the surplus account, find
(*a*) the amount paid in dividends and
(*b*) the amount put into the surplus account.

NARRATIVE NO. 4

DAIRY FARMING

This narrative provides experience in reckoning and recording income and expenses incurred in running a farm.

The narrative is in no sense exhaustive. The transactions, owing to limitations of space, are not chronological throughout the year. Related transactions are treated together. For instance, the cost of care and feeding the cows and the record of income from milk production are grouped together, instead of being presented month by month, as they come, of necessity, on the farm.

The narrative suggests a simple method of keeping farm accounts, and provides experience in keeping such a record.

As the pupil proceeds with the work, he should keep a complete and accurate record of all results obtained. He should rule up a form like the one suggested on page 400, and as each item of cash is received or paid out, or each item

of cost or production is met with, it should be recorded in the proper place.

The Statement, page 398, presents the financial condition of L. K. Burton on March 31, 19—, after one year of farming.

This form of statement is called a **financial statement** or **balance sheet.** All the assets (things owned) are listed first, and all the liabilities (debts) are then listed and deducted from the total assets to find the *net capital* or *present worth* of the proprietor. The **net worth** or **present worth** of the proprietor represents what is left if all the liabilities were paid. Observe that by subtracting Burton's investment from his net capital at the end of a business year, the difference represents the capital increase (or profit) for the year.

L. K. BURTON
Financial Statement
As of March 31, 19—

Assets		
Cash	$ 754.32	
Notes Receivable	150.00	
Accounts Receivable	75.00	
1 Truck	450.00	
1 Tractor	700.00	
Miscellaneous Tools	1100.00	
Land (75 Acres)	3750.00	
2 Horses	175.00	
12 Cows	940.00	
4 Pigs	40.00	
50 Chickens	25.00	
Total Assets		$8159.32
Liabilities		
Notes Payable	$200.00	
Taxes (Unpaid)	50.00	
Accounts Payable	180.00	
Total Liabilities		430.00
Net Worth, March 31, 19—		$7729.32
Capital Increase		
Burton's Investment, April 1, 19—		7000.00
Capital Increase		$729.32

With the recent farm legislation enacted by the government it is becoming more and more necessary for farmers to keep careful and accurate records of farm costs and income.

The following series of problems is designed to help in formulating a method of keeping such a record.

Every result obtained should be recorded and kept throughout the entire series of problems, otherwise it will be difficult to make the final conclusion called for at the end of the series of problems.

Owing to limitations of space it is impossible to give dates and individual transactions throughout the year. Of necessity, totals and summaries must be used.

1. On April 1, 19— L. R. Moody made a list of his assets and liabilities, as follows: Cash, $1376.50; a three months' note of $250 made by S. Tarnow, due May 1; an account due from M. R. Leach, a neighbor, $72.50; a horse valued at $150; 10 cows worth $750; 100 hens worth $50; 2 pigs, $25; a tractor, $720; a truck, $550; miscellaneous farming implements, $960; farm of 120 acres worth $45 an acre. His debts were a note of $175 due June 1, in favor of T. Murray; an unpaid doctor's bill of $40; and a grocery bill of $23.50.

Set up a financial statement to show Moody's present worth.

Farm Records

2. A cash account should be started at once, and all receipts and payments of cash recorded as they occur. The following suggested form may be helpful.

CASH RECEIPTS					CASH PAYMENTS				
19—									
April	1	*Balance*	1376	50					

SUGGESTED CASH ACCOUNT FORM

Mr. Moody has a hired man whom he pays $45 a month. The 120 acres of Mr. Moody's farm are divided as follows:

Pasturage for the cows	40 acres
Woodland	10 acres
Ground occupied by the house, barn, garden, and fences	5 acres
Meadowland	20 acres
For cultivated crops	45 acres
Total	120 acres

COST AND PRODUCTION RECORD

Cost			Production		
Seeds Bushels Price			Grain Bushels Price		
Feeding and Care of Stock			Vegetables		
Horse			Bushels at		
Hay tons at					
Grain bushels at					
Shoeing					
Cows			Fodder Crops		
Ensilage tons at			Hay tons at		
Hay tons at			Ensilage tons at		
Feed tons at					
Grinding tons at					
Poultry			Milk Pounds Test Price		
Feed tons at					
Grinding tons at					
Other feed					
Eggs for hatching doz. at					
Labor					
Produce Used in House			Poultry		
Eggs doz. at			Eggs doz. at		
Milk qt. at			Broilers at		
			Fowls lb. at		
Machinery			Miscellaneous		
Tractor			Man and Tractor days at		
Gas gal. at					
Oil gal. at					
Repairs					
Truck					
Gas gal. at			Wood		
Oil gal. at			cords at		
Repairs					
Insurance					
Buildings			Milk Used in House		
Contents					
Taxes					
Miscellaneous					
Depreciation					
Horse					
Cows					
Tractor					
Truck					

3. A Cost and Production Record should be kept, and items of cost and production entered as they occur. In the Cost and Production Record, enter the cost of every item of grain, hay, or feed used for seed or for feeding the stock; enter as cost the value of all eggs and milk used in the house, and all money spent for running the tractor and truck, for wages, taxes, insurance, etc. Enter as income or production the value of all crops raised, whether sold or not, wages received for use of tractor on neighbors' farms, etc.

4. April 15. Moody paid the doctor and the grocer for the items shown in his list of liabilities. Record payment.

5. May 1. S. Tarnow paid his note and M. R. Leach paid his bill to Moody. Enter these items in the cash book.

On this date, and on the first of each month during the year, Moody paid the hired man his wages of $45. These payments are to be entered without further mention in these problems.

6. During the months of May and June, Moody puts in the following crops, buying seed for cash as indicated. Find the cost of all the seed used.

Crop	No. of Acres	Seed per Acre	Pounds per Bushel	Price per Bushel
Barley	5	$1\frac{1}{2}$ bu.	48	$.64
Buckwheat . . .	7	1 bu.	48	.75
Corn (for ensilage)	3	12 quarts	56	.85
Corn (for ears) .	5	6 quarts	56	.85
Oats	15	3 bu.	32	.52
Potatoes	10	$7\frac{1}{2}$ bu.	60	.60

7. June 1. Moody paid his note in favor of T. Murray.

8. During June and July the hay was gathered. The crop averaged $1\frac{3}{4}$ tons to the acre. At $14 a ton, how much was the hay worth?

9. During August, September, and October, the following crops were gathered:

Barley	130 bushels	Corn	300 bushels
Buckwheat	160 bushels	Oats	475 bushels
Ensilage	36 tons	Potatoes	625 bushels

Using the prices paid for seed, except for ensilage, which may be reckoned at $6 a ton, find the value of the crops raised. (See Problem 6 for other prices.)

10. October 20. Moody sold 500 bushels of potatoes at $.60 a bushel, and 140 bushels of buckwheat at $.75 a bushel. How much did he receive for them?

11. To feed the horse for a year requires $3\frac{1}{2}$ tons of hay and 90 bushels of oats. The horse needs three new sets of shoes for the year, at $.35 a shoe. Find the cost of keeping the horse for a year. (The shoes have to be paid for in cash; hay and oats are taken from the stock on hand.)

12. To feed each cow, in addition to pasturage, requires

40 lb. of ensilage per day for 5 months (use 30 days to a month).

4 quarts of feed a day, the year round (365 days).

1 ton of hay for the year.

The feed consists of a mixture of 3 bu. of oats, 2 bu. of corn, and 1 bu. of barley ground together. Cost of grinding is $.15 per cwt. Find the cost of feeding the cows, including the cost of grinding the feed, for a year.

13. March 5. (Late winter) Moody sold the hay not needed for the horse or the cows at $14 a ton. How much did he receive for it?

During the year Moody sold milk to one of the large milk companies. Milk is sold by the hundred weight. The price received for the milk depends in part on the quality of the milk — that is, on the percentage of butter fat in it. 100 pounds of milk of standard quality is considered to have in it $3\frac{1}{2}$ pounds of butter fat (that is, $3\frac{1}{2}$ lb. of butter). The price of milk is based on the quality.

Some herds of cows produce milk richer than 3.5%. For each .1% of butter fat above 3.5% the dairyman receives an additional $.04 per hundred weight. If the quality of his milk falls below 3.5%, he receives $.04 per hundred weight less than the price of 3.5% milk. Thus if the price of 3.5% milk is $1.52 per hundred weight, and milk tests 3.8%, the dairyman would receive \$.12 per hundred weight above the standard price of \$1.52, or \$1.64. If his milk tests 3.3%, he would receive \$.08 less than \$1.52, or \$1.44 per hundred weight of milk.

Using \$1.50 as the price of 3.5% milk, find the price paid for milk testing as follows:

14. 3.7%

15. 3.9%

16. 3.2%

17. 4%

Normally a cow will give milk about ten months of the year. The quantity and quality of milk a cow will give vary with the cow and with the kind of feeding she receives.

18–29. The quantity of milk sold by Moody month by month, together with the per cent of butter fat, and the price received for it, is shown below. Find the amount of the monthly milk check, and the total for the year.

RECORD OF MILK SOLD

Month	*Weight*	*Test*	*Price of 3.5% milk*
April	6790 lb.	3.7	\$1.56
May	7385 lb.	3.7	1.56
June	8571 lb.	3.8	1.50
July	8469 lb.	3.8	1.50
August	7957 lb.	3.8	1.50
September	7409 lb.	3.8	1.55
October	7211 lb.	3.8	1.55
November	7113 lb.	3.8	1.55
December	6956 lb.	3.7	1.60
January	6754 lb.	3.7	1.60
February	6387 lb.	3.7	1.60
March	6742 lb.	3.7	1.60

30. Two quarts of milk were used daily in the house. At \$.03$\frac{1}{4}$ a quart, find the value of the milk used in the house.

31. If the average profitable producing life of a cow is 8 years, at the end of which time she may be sold for \$20, how much should be allowed annually for depreciation on the herd of cows?

32. Find the year's profit on the herd of cows. (Include the milk used in the house.)

33. To feed the chickens, Moody bought 50 bushels of wheat at $1 a bushel. He mixed the wheat with 90 bushels of oats, 30 bushels of corn, and 30 bushels of barley, and had it all ground. The cost of grinding was $.15 a hundred pounds. Other expenses of care and feeding the hens and chickens amounted to $17.60. Find the total cost of caring for and feeding the hens and chickens.

34. The average number of eggs laid per hen was 153. How many dozen eggs were laid by all the hens?

35. If 75 dozen eggs were used in the house, 50 dozen were used for hatching chickens, and the remaining eggs sold for $.30 a dozen, how much was received for the eggs sold?

36. From the 50 dozen eggs there were hatched 523 chickens. Of that number 496 lived. When they had grown to weigh 2 lb. each, 450 of them were sold at $.40 each. How much was received for them?

37. From the flock of hens 25 were culled out as being inferior as egg producers. They were dressed and sold to the local market at $.16 a pound. Their average weight was $4\frac{1}{2}$ lb. when dressed. How much was received for them?

38. During the year, Moody's hired man worked with the tractor for neighboring farmers a total of 17 days, for which Moody was paid $10 a day. How much was received for this work?

39. During the winter months Moody and the hired man cut and delivered 75 cords of wood at $5.50 a cord. How much was received for the wood?

40. To run the tractor and the truck for the year required gasoline and oil as follows:

For the tractor 660 gallons of gasoline and 32 gallons of oil. For the truck 225 gallons of gasoline and 6 gallons of oil. Gasoline cost $.19, and oil $.75, a gallon. Repairs for the truck cost $17.40, and for the truck, $11.60. Find the cost of running both for the year.

41. If the profitable working life of a horse is 15 years, and at the end of that time he can be sold for $25, how much should be allowed annually for depreciation on the horse?

42. Find the annual depreciation on the tractor and on the truck if each can be used for 7 years, after which time the tractor can be traded in for $75, and the truck for $50.

43. The farm is assessed at $3600. The tax rate is $1.3875 per $100. The taxes are due March 31, but a discount of $\frac{1}{2}\%$ is allowed if paid on or before February 1. Moody paid the tax on January 31. How much did he pay?

44. The farm buildings are insured for $2500 at $2 per $100 for 3 years. The contents of the barns are insured for $750 at $.75 per $100 for 1 year. Find the annual cost of insurance.

45. Check up on the "Farm Cost and Production Record" to see if all items have been entered. Find the total income from, and the total cost of operating, the farm. From the net income deduct the several items of depreciation mentioned in the problems, to show the net profit on the farm business.

46. Balance and close the cash account.

Moody's cash on hand and in the bank amount to only $1895.76. There are no checks outstanding and his check book balance agrees with the bank statement. Varying amounts of cash have been spent for family and household purposes. He is able to account for only $930 of this discrepancy.

To avoid a repetition of this situation he and Mrs. Moody decide to prepare a family budget for the coming year. They are agreed that, exclusive of milk, eggs, fruit, vegetables, poultry, etc., from the farm and garden, they should be able to live comfortably on $900 a year. They have two children, a girl 11 years old, and a boy 14 years old.

Preparing a family budget requires careful study of the needs of the family. Much attention has been given to the subject, and fairly well-defined principles of budget making have been established. One of the first things to do, after having determined the amount of the budget (in this case $900) is to make a list of the necessary types of expenditure such as food, clothing, doctor and dental bills, education, benevolence, etc., and allow to each type of expenditure a certain percentage of the whole budget. (For an average percentage of distribution of expenditures based on experience, see page 270.

47. Remembering that the Moodys have no rent to pay, and that their fuel comes from the wood lot, and much of their food comes from the farm and garden, draw up a budget totaling $900, showing the amount to be spent for each type of expenditure decided upon.

48. At the end of the next year, Mrs. Moody had the following amounts recorded as spent under the budget plan:

Food	$185.92	Recreation, vacations, etc.	$117.90
Clothing	201.60	Miscellaneous expenses	17.86
Household expenses	111.57	Benevolence	102.50
Doctor's bills, etc.	7.40		
Dental bills	25.50		
Education (including magazines and newspapers)	102.75		

Compare these amounts with the budget you prepared and note in which accounts you differ.

PART FOUR

REMEDIAL PROBLEMS AND TESTS

REMEDIAL PROBLEMS

The remedial problems in Part Four are grouped under appropriate headings to permit one to select readily the type of exercise or problem needed.

ADDITION AND SUBTRACTION

In each of the following, find (*a*) the total debits, (*b*) the total credits, and (*c*) the balance for each debit and credit. Check the results by adding the balances to see if the sum of the balances agrees with the difference between the total debits and credits.

	Debits	*Credits*	*Balances*
1.	$371.40	$125.20	$??? ??
	128.90	47.60	??? ??
	50.60	42.50	??? ??
	18.75	11.85	??? ??
	??? ??	??? ??	??? ??
2.	$115.00	$107.10	$??? ??
	84.10	68.50	??? ??
	9.16	7.25	??? ??
	75.09	25.80	??? ??
	??? ??	??? ??	??? ??
3.	$34.88	$9.34	$??? ??
	91.75	17.56	??? ??
	37.10	32.10	??? ??
	7.15	5.08	??? ??
	??? ??	??? ??	??? ??
4.	$11.52	$9.38	$??? ??
	196.84	117.56	??? ??
	39.76	37.24	??? ??
	27.81	19.58	??? ??
	??? ??	??? ??	??? ??

	Debits	*Credits*	*Balances*
5.	$39.87	$19.30	$??? ??
	184.93	52.45	??? ??
	210.50	175.30	??? ??
	9.11	8.33	??? ??
	??? ??	??? ??	??? ??
6.	$58.13	$8.17	$??? ??
	29.17	13.24	??? ??
	111.10	91.27	??? ??
	91.90	64.38	??? ??
	??? ??	??? ??	??? ??
7.	$77.25	$44.50	$??? ??
	62.88	51.39	??? ??
	36.66	28.50	??? ??
	44.26	18.88	??? ??
	??? ??	??? ??	??? ??
8.	$63.74	$39.24	$??? ??
	179.47	84.19	??? ??
	248.50	127.10	??? ??
	9.11	8.41	??? ??
	??? ??	??? ??	??? ??
9.	$118.75	$13.18	$??? ??
	19.18	18.19	??? ??
	21.50	17.42	??? ??
	39.27	16.43	??? ??
	??? ??	?? ??	??? ??
10.	$24.87	$8.47	$??? ??
	36.47	16.47	??? ??
	92.13	31.29	??? ??
	100.10	60.10	??? ??
	??? ??	?? ??	??? ??
11.	$324.56	$53.78	$??? ??
	85.68	31.45	??? ??
	251.97	163.88	??? ??
	569.66	348.98	??? ??
	??? ??	??? ??	??? ??

CASH ACCOUNT

A **cash account** is a record of cash received and cash paid out; it is one of the most important accounts in a business.

Following is a cash account showing the amount (balance) of cash on hand at the beginning of business on May 1, and the several amounts of cash received and paid out during the month. On the left-hand side of the cash account are written the amount of cash on hand at the beginning of the business period, and all items of cash received during the period. On the right-hand side of the account are recorded all items of cash paid out during the business period.

The prime purpose of presenting the cash account at this place is to provide a practical exercise in addition and subtraction. For the method of proving cash, see page 149.

Cash Account

19—						19—					
May	1	Balance		150	00	May	3			19	64
	6			125	50		7			21	35
	9			52	75		15			112	38
	11			5	28		23			72	90
	16			17	50		27			13	34
	24			116	36					239	61
	31			81	90						
				549	29						

As each amount column of cash is added the total is written in small figures as shown in the illustration. To find the **balance** of the cash account at the end of a day, or the end of a month, the total of the cash payments is subtracted from the total of cash receipts including the balance on hand at the beginning of the day or the month, as the case may be. The difference between the two sides of the cash account is called the **balance.** It is given the name *balance,* because the amount of the balance is written into the account on the right-hand side to make the whole account balance; that is, to make both sides add to the same amount. The cash account balanced and closed is shown in the form on page 412.

CASH ACCOUNT

19—					19—				
May	1	Balance	150	00	May	3		19	64
	6		125	50		7		21	35
	9		52	75		15		112	38
	11		5	28		23		72	90
	16		17	50		27		13	34
	24		116	36				239	61
	31		81	90		31	*Balance*	309	68
			549	29					
			549	29				549	29
June	1	Balance	309	68					

To balance and close the cash account means to find the balance of cash on hand, enter the amount as in the illustration, and then rule the account as shown. The balance is then brought down below the closing rulings to show the amount of cash with which to begin a new business period.

Study the form of closing the cash account. Then copy the following accounts on ledger paper, and close each account in a manner similar to the foregoing illustration.

12. CASH

19—				19—			
June	1	Balance	309.68	June	2		137.64
	4		425.16		6		25.37
	7		27.85		12		238.46
	11		375.81		20		721.59
	19		1238.93		28		522.77
	26		841.07				

13. CASH

19—				19—			
July	1	Balance	1572.67	July	2		15.00
	6		721.33		4		117.28
	14		208.07		13		364.78
	17		9.83		18		1369.86
	21		17.38		23		248.71
	24		218.49		25		17.36
	28		.74		30		9.48
	30		19.42		31		43.97

14. CASH

19—			19—	
August 1	Balance	581.49	August 4	250.00
8		175.65	6	75.45
15		1132.78	9	112.50
21		1375.90	11	132.47
29		2168.55	13	9.54
			16	38.67
			19	396.77
			25	74.33
			29	456.32
			31	99.75

MULTIPLICATION AND DIVISION

1. For four years a man planted corn as follows: first year, 23 A.; second year, 18 A.; third year, 24 A.; and fourth year, 17 A. His average yield was 53 bu. per acre. At $.72 a bushel, find the value of the corn crop for the four years.

2. Each of 3 men set 5 fence posts per hour. If they worked 8 hr. each day for 6 da., how many posts were set?

3. An automobile tire that costs $12.40 runs 21,500 mi. and one that costs $9.92 runs 16,000 mi.

(*a*) Which is the cheaper tire for the motorist? (*b*) How much more per mile does it cost the motorist for tires, if he uses the tires that give the lesser mileage? (Carry the answer to the nearest sixth decimal place.) (*c*) In driving 75,000 mi. how much more will the poorer tires cost than the better tires?

4. At a counter in a department store there are four clerks. Each clerk fills out a sales slip for each sale. The sales slips are numbered consecutively. On a given day the slips turned in were numbered as follows:

Miss Brown, Slips 56 to 73 inclusive
Miss Everett, Slips 117 to 141 inclusive
Miss Hammond, Slips 215 to 243 inclusive
Miss Norton, Slips 296 to 322 inclusive

(*a*) Find the number of sales slips used by each clerk.

(*b*) At an average price of 79¢ per sale, find the total amount of sales for the four clerks.

5. A man's wages are \$5.50 a day. He works 22 da. a month. His living expenses are \$2.75 a day. How much is he able to save from April 1 to September 30, inclusive?

6. A woman bought a turkey weighing $11\frac{3}{4}$ lb. at \$.36 a pound. She gave a five-dollar bill in payment. How much change did she receive?

7. A man exchanged $7\frac{1}{2}$ dozen eggs at \$.36 a dozen for $\frac{3}{4}$ of a pound of tea at \$.60 a pound, $2\frac{1}{2}$ lb. butter at \$.38 a pound, and sugar for the rest at \$.05 a pound. How many pounds of sugar did he receive?

8. You have a news route and deliver 125 papers a day at \$.03 each. Your profit on each paper is \$.01$\frac{1}{4}$. How much is your profit for 6 days?

9. Referring to Problem 8, how much would your net profit be if two customers who each received a paper a day failed to pay their bills?

10. Oranges that cost \$.32 a dozen are sold at the rate of 4 for \$.15. Find the profit on 12 dozen oranges.

11. If lemons are sold 4 for \$.10, how many lemons can be bought for \$.25?

12. There are 30 dozen eggs in a crate. If they cost \$.24 a dozen, and sell at the rate of 4 for \$.10, find the profit on a crate of eggs, if 8 eggs are broken and have to be thrown away.

13. A stenographer earned \$16.50 a week the first year, \$19 a week the second year, and \$22 a week the third year. Her normal living expenses were \$11.50 a week. Owing to illness, she lost 4 weeks' wages the second year and had to pay a doctor's bill of \$68.75. How much was she able to save in the course of 3 yr.?

14. Emerson Orvis had \$750 for a vacation and fishing trip in Canada. Before starting, he purchased travelers' checks as follows, paying the \$.75 fee for each \$100: 3 checks of \$100 each, 4 checks of \$50 each, and 10 checks of \$10 each. When he returned home, he had left one \$100 check, one \$50 check, three \$10 checks, and \$17.64 in cash. How much did his trip cost him?

15. In a large mail-order house the mail clerks are on duty at 8:30 A.M. If each clerk can distribute 120 letters in an hour, how many clerks will be required to distribute 810 letters by 9:15 A.M.?

16. A stationer bought $3\frac{1}{2}$ gross lead pencils at $\$.37\frac{1}{2}$ a dozen. He sold the pencils at $.05 each. How much was his gross profit?

RETAILING

There is no single business operation in which more people engage than in buying at retail. Food, clothing, medicines, jewelry, household appliances, and all the numerous items used in everyday life are the things purchased at retail.

Every person, therefore, whether in business or not, should be able to perform the arithmetical operations for the daily purchases required in his home.

Sales Slips

The Sales Slip shown below is typical of those used when a customer buys on credit; that is, when she has the amount of the purchase charged to her account, to be paid for later. A

SALES SLIP

H. HARVARD AND SON

Retail Grocers

88 Yale Street **Pittsburgh, Pa.**

May 23, 19—

Sold to **Mrs. A. R. Bostwick**
Address **32 Lake Ave., City**

10 lb. sugar	$.05\frac{1}{2}$		55
$1\frac{1}{2}$ lb. coffee	.23		35
$\frac{1}{2}$ doz. oranges	.30		15
3 lb. bananas	.06		18
6 cans corn	.08		48
		1	71
Charge			

customer who buys on credit should keep the sales slips till a settlement is made, so as to check the total charge made by the merchant.

If a customer pays cash for a purchase she may receive a small slip printed in the cash register where the amounts of the purchases are entered and totaled, similar to the one shown here.

In either case the customer should check the calculations to insure accuracy in the amount charged.

May 23	323
$	0.35
$	0.09
$	0.06
$	0.10
$	0.09
$	0.24
$	0.23
$	0.19
$	0.09
*$	1.44

Problems

Rule sales slips similar to the one shown on page 415 and enter the following purchases. Date the sales slip the day you work these exercises. Use any street address and the name of your own town or city as the place of the seller and buyer.

1. Mrs. Harriet Woodrow bought on credit from the Grisbrow Brothers Grocery the following items:

6 cakes Fairy soap	at 3 for 10¢
8 cans tomato soup	at 2 for 15¢
18 oranges	at 30¢ a dozen
6 lemons	at 4 for 10¢
½ lb. tea	at 60¢ a pound
10 lb. granulated sugar	at 5½¢ a pound

2. Mrs. Amy Lester bought on credit from the City Market:

2½ doz. eggs	at 28¢ a dozen
15 oranges	at 35¢ a dozen
8 cans evaporated milk	at 4 for 19¢
1½ lb. bacon	at 17¢ a half pound
5 lb. apples	at 3¢ a pound
10 lb. potatoes	at 30¢ a peck *

3. Wesley Brown purchased for cash at the General Store, the following supplies for school; he paid a 2¢ tax on

* A peck of potatoes weighs 15 lb.

each article that cost over 12¢ and less than 63¢; and 3¢ for each article costing over 62¢. Find the total amount he paid for his purchases:

2 notebooks and fillers	at 25¢ each (1 purchase)
A ruler for	10¢
A bound notebook for	15¢
A brief case for	75¢
A fountain pen for	$1.10
A typewriter ribbon for	.50

4. Helen Bowers made the following purchases for cash:

1 pair of shoes		$3.75
3 pair stockings	at	.69
1 pair of gloves		1.25
$4\frac{1}{2}$ yd. ribbon	at	.19
$3\frac{1}{4}$ yd. lace	at	.33
$\frac{1}{2}$ dozen handkerchiefs	at	.22 each

If she paid a 2% sales tax on the entire purchase, find the total cost of her purchases.

5. You bought the following items for cash at the Ames Hardware Store:

$3\frac{1}{2}$ lb. 10d nails	at 6¢ a pound
3 panes of glass	at 18¢ each
1 lb. putty	10¢
1 lb. 4 oz. shingle nails	at 8¢ a pound
$2\frac{1}{2}$ gal. paint	at $3.50 a gallon

You were charged a sales tax of 3% on the entire amount of the bill. How much change should you receive from a ten-dollar bill?

6. Grace Lannon bought from the Variety Store the following items for cash:

30 inches of ribbon	at 48¢ a yard
3 yd. 18 inches of cheesecloth	at 6¢ a yard
2 yd. 9 inches of edging	at 20¢ a yard
4 yd. 18 inches of toweling	at 22¢ a yard

A sales tax of 2% was charged on the total of the bill.

How much change should she receive from a five-dollar bill?

7. Mrs. Harding buys her groceries and meats at the West End Market. She receives a sales slip with each purchase, which she keeps till the end of the month. During the month she makes some payments on account, and at the end of the month, pays the balance due on the month's purchases. From the following record of purchases and payments find the amount due at the end of the month.

March 2. Purchases were:

$4\frac{1}{4}$ lb. roast beef	at 29¢ a pound
$1\frac{1}{2}$ doz. eggs	at 26¢ a dozen
4 oz. pepper	25¢
6 cans vegetable soup	at 2 cans for 13¢
$1\frac{1}{2}$ lb. butter	at 34¢ a pound

March 6. The following purchases were made:

1 lb. 10 oz. beef steak	at 28¢ a pound
1 lb. 8 oz. bacon	at 36¢ a pound
2 loaves of bread	at 9¢ a loaf
8 lemons	at 30¢ a dozen
1 lb. 12 oz. cheese	at 36¢ a pound

Mrs. Harding paid $2 on account.

March 12. Purchases were made as follows:

1 pkg. shredded wheat	12¢
10 lb. granulated sugar	at $5\frac{1}{4}$¢ a pound
9 oranges	at 25¢ a dozen
5 lb. potatoes	at 30¢ a peck (15 lb.)
4 lb. sweet potatoes	at $3\frac{1}{2}$¢ a pound
$1\frac{1}{2}$ lb. smelts	at 12¢ a pound
2 lb. 8 oz. walnuts	at 22¢ a pound
6 grapefruit	at 2 for 15¢

March 20. Mrs. Harding made the following purchases:

2 loaves bread	at 9¢ a loaf
$5\frac{1}{2}$ lb. chicken	at 25¢ a pound
18 eggs	at 28¢ a dozen
8 cans noodle soup	at 2 cans for 17¢
2 lb. 4 oz. cheese	at 36¢ a pound
3 pints of milk	at 12¢ a quart
2 lb. 8 oz. bacon	at 34¢ a pound
$6\frac{1}{2}$ lb. bananas	at $5\frac{1}{2}$¢ a pound

$3 was paid on account.

March 30. The following purchases were made:

$2\frac{1}{2}$ lb. brown sugar	at 5¢ a pound
$1\frac{1}{2}$ doz. oranges	at 4¢ each
6 cans of peaches	at 2 for 29¢
1 lb. 8 oz. cookies	at 22¢ a pound
20 eggs	at 32¢ a dozen

FRACTIONS

1. In 3 hr. a boy rode his bicycle $28\frac{1}{2}$ mi. What was his average speed per hour?

2. A man sowed $22\frac{3}{4}$ bu. of oats on 8 A. of land. How many bushels of oats did he sow per acre? If he paid $.80 a bushel for the seed oats, find the cost of seed for 1 acre.

3. A girl cut $3\frac{3}{4}$ yd. of ribbon into 5 equal lengths. How long was each piece?

4. A man put $118\frac{3}{4}$ bu. of wheat into 50 bags. Find the average number of bushels per bag.

5. From a piece of cloth containing $13\frac{1}{8}$ yd., a tailor made 5 overcoats. What was the average number of yards to a coat? At $4.25 a yard, find the cost of the cloth for 1 overcoat.

6. Six bags of grain weighed $131\frac{1}{2}$ lb., $128\frac{3}{4}$ lb., $129\frac{1}{2}$ lb., $133\frac{3}{4}$ lb., $127\frac{3}{4}$ lb., and $136\frac{1}{2}$ lb., respectively. Find their average weight.

7. Divide $4\frac{3}{8}$ into 7 equal parts.

8. A square flower bed is enclosed by a low wire fence $42\frac{2}{3}$ ft. long. What is the length of each side of the flower bed?

9. A board $14\frac{2}{3}$ ft. long is to be cut into 4 equal pieces for shelves. How long is each shelf?

10. If 5 tons of coal cost $$68\frac{3}{4}$, find the cost of 12 tons.

11. A baseball team of 14 players bought balls for $5, a mask for $$2\frac{3}{4}$, mitts for $$5\frac{1}{2}$, a protector for $$3\frac{1}{4}$, and bats for $$4\frac{1}{4}$. In their treasury they had $$10\frac{1}{4}$. They agreed to contribute equally to make up the balance of the money needed. How much did each player contribute?

12. A city lot having a frontage of 75 ft. was sold for $2156\frac{1}{4}$. What was the price per foot of frontage?

13. When tea is selling at $.65 a pound, how much will $\frac{3}{4}$ of a pound of tea cost?

14. In one week a man worked $38\frac{3}{4}$ hours at $.42$\frac{1}{2}$ an hour. How much did he earn?

15. If it takes $\frac{5}{8}$ of a yard of ribbon to tie one package, how many yards will be required to tie 38 packages?

16. A gift shop prepared fancy boxes of Christmas gifts by wrapping each box in cellophane. If it takes $\frac{1}{6}$ of a square yard for each package, how many packages could be wrapped in $12\frac{1}{2}$ square yards of cellophane?

17. On an automobile trip to Florida and return, covering 3741 miles, the average number of miles of gasoline per gallon was $14\frac{1}{2}$. If the average cost of gasoline was $.18$\frac{1}{2}$ a gallon, find the cost of the gasoline for the trip.

18. Find the total cost of the following:

$43\frac{1}{4}$ yd. taffeta	at	$1.65
$23\frac{1}{2}$ yd. lace	at	$ .75
$38\frac{3}{4}$ yd. muslin	at	$ .17$\frac{1}{2}$
$26\frac{1}{2}$ yd. flannel	at	$ .21$\frac{1}{2}$

19. Water weighs $62\frac{1}{2}$ lb. per cubic foot. Gold weighs $1203\frac{5}{8}$ lb. per cubic foot. Gold is how many times as heavy as water? (The result is known as the specific gravity of gold.)

20. Cork weighs 15 lb. per cubic foot. Find the specific gravity of cork. (See preceding problem.)

21. 4 pieces (bolts) of cloth contain $34\frac{1}{2}$ yd., $37\frac{1}{4}$ yd., $39\frac{3}{4}$ yd., and $43\frac{1}{4}$ yd. respectively. At $.37$\frac{1}{2}$ a yard, find the value of the cloth.

22. A fruit grower fertilizes his trees with $2\frac{1}{2}$ lb. of fertilizer per tree. If he has 3600 trees, find the cost of the fertilizer at $57 a ton.

TELEPHONE PROBLEMS

1. A man pays $48 a year for telephone service. He is entitled to 66 local calls each month. Extra calls cost $.05 each. In one month he made 79 local calls and had long-distance calls for which the toll charge was $1.47. Find the amount of his telephone bill for that month.

2. Henry Hall pays $48 a year for a private telephone wire. He is entitled to 66 local calls a month. Local calls in excess of the contract number are $.05 each. He has an extension for which he pays $.50 a month. In one month he made 84 local calls, 13 calls which cost $.10 each, and a long-distance call which cost $.74; he also sent a 16-word telegram at the rate of $.48 for the first 10 words and $.035 for each additional word. If the taxes were $.07, find the amount of Mr. Hall's telephone bill for the month.

3. Mr. Hammond pays $32.50 a year for his telephone. He is entitled to 75 local calls a month. For each local call over 75, he is charged $.05. He has two extensions, for each of which he pays $6 a year. He has an extra listing in the telephone book at $3 a year. During the month of May he made 113 local calls, 8 calls at $.10 each, and 7 calls at $.15 each; he also had a long-distance call at $1.36, including tax, and he sent two telegrams, one of 17 words at the rate of 72–5 (72¢ for the first 10 words and 5¢ for each additional word) and the other of 24 words at the rate of 42–2.5. The tax on the telegrams was $.05 on the first and $.04 on the second. The telegraph charges were added to his telephone bill. Find Mr. Hammond's total telephone bill for May.

4. The regular charge per month for telephone in a man's residence is $4. He has the following additional charges for a month: 1 call at $.05; 3 calls at $.10; 4 calls at $.15; 3 calls at $.20; 1 call at $.25; 1 long-distance call at $.40; and 1 long-distance call at $.65, with a $.10 tax added. Find his telephone bill for the month.

RAILROAD PROBLEMS

Revenue per Ton Mile

Railroad companies keep a careful record of *revenue per ton mile* received for carrying freight and of *revenue per passenger mile* for carrying passengers. *Ton miles* are found by multiplying the number of tons carried by the number of miles they are carried. *Passenger miles* are found by multiplying the number of passengers carried by the number of miles they are carried. The revenue per ton mile or per passenger mile is found by dividing the earnings by the total mileage.

In each of the following, find the revenue per ton mile:

1. 13.8 T. were carried 375 mi. at earnings of $347.60.

2. 7.9 T. were carried 256 mi. at earnings of $152.27.

3. 142.4 T. were carried 1715 mi. at earnings of $5984.50.

4. 75.1 T. were carried 913 mi. at earnings of $1956.08.

Revenue per Passenger Mile

In each of the following, find the revenue per passenger mile:

5. 173 passengers were carried 206 mi. at earnings of $1104.78.

6. 416 passengers were carried 137 mi. at earnings of $1852.24.

7. 571 passengers were carried 611 mi. at earnings of $9594.23.

8. 203 passengers were carried 84 mi. at earnings of $545.66.

Freight

9. Find the total freight charge on the following: 14,968 lb. at $.415 per hundred weight; 22,708 lb. at $2.43 per net ton (2000 lb.); and 57,846 lb. at $2.17 per gross ton (2240 lb.).

If a shipment of freight is carried by more than one railroad (or other common carrier), the revenue received for carrying it is prorated in proportion to the number of miles each road carries it.

10. A quantity of freight was carried over three railroads for $105.75. Railroad A carried it 107 mi.; railroad B, 238 mi.; and railroad C, 78 mi. What amount should each railroad receive?

11. Copy the following tables and complete them, finding the revenue received by each road:

	Roads	*Miles Carried*	*Total Revenue*
12.	X	154	
	Y	382	
	Z	960	
			$78.54
13.	D	716	
	E	45	
	F	194	
			$131.79
14.	M	1146	
	N	271	
	O	88	
			$228.76

PAY ROLL

1. From the following time sheet, find the total hours worked by each employee for the week ended Feb. 20, the wages earned, the old age benefit tax, and the wages due each employee.

Pay Roll for the Week Ended February 20, 19—

Names	M	T	W	Th	F	S	Total Hours	Rate per Hour	Wages	O.A.B. Tax	Wages Due
Arthur Field	7	7	7	6	7	4		$.33			
Ben Gomer	7	6	6	7	7	4		.38			
Andrew Hood	7	7	7	5	4	4		.35			
Charles Karl	6	7	7	6	3	2		.42			
David Noonan	7	7	7	7	7	0		.43			
Harry Perkins	7	7	5	7	0	4		.38			
							Total Wages		$		

2. For each hour worked over 6 hours per day, wages were reckoned at double the regular rate. Using the data given below, complete the pay roll sheet.

Pay Roll for the Week Ended March 6, 19—

Names	M	T	W	Th	F	S	Reg. Time	Overtime	Rate per Hour	Reg. Wage	Overtime Wage	Total Wage	O.A.B. Tax	Wages Due
A. Arden	6	6½	7	6	6	3			$.36					
C. Brooks	7	6	6	6	7	3			.37½					
N. Connelly	7	7	8	6½	6	0			.40					
W. London	6	6	6	7	8	3			.33½					
B. Lumley	7	7	6	7¼	6	3			.35					
D. Nast	6	6	6	6	7	3			.31¼					
E. Potter	6	6¼	7	7	5	2			.37½					
H. Rabideau	7	6	7	7	4	3			.42					
E. Werner	8½	6¼	6	6	5	3			.45					
R. Yoder	7	0	7½	6¾	5	3			.42					
									Totals					

3. Prepare a change memorandum for the pay roll in problem No. 2.

4. Write a check on The Crescent Bank payable to E. C. Rogers for Pay Roll, for the total amount of wages due the employees in problem No. 2.

5. In a certain factory the wages are paid on the differential piecework plan. The standard number of pieces for a day's work is 30, and the standard rate is $.25 per piece. Employees who do more or less than the standard day's work are paid according to the following schedule of rates, page 425.

Illustration. An employee who completes 30 pieces a day at $.25 a piece will earn $7.50 a day. If he can complete 35 pieces a day, he will be paid $.26 a piece, and his earnings will be $9.10 a day. If he completes 25 pieces a day, he will receive only $.22 a piece, and his earnings will be $4.50 a day. The difference in the price per piece is based on the fact the overhead expense in the factory is greater per piece when only a few pieces are completed in a day, and is less per piece when more pieces are completed in one day. This is briefly the meaning of the "differential piecework plan" of compensation.

Piecework and differential rates are based on predetermined standards — the amount of time required by a capable workman to do a specific amount of work. If a workman requires two hours to accomplish a task that he should finish in one hour, he accordingly increases the cost of the product he is working on. And this inefficiency ultimately raises the cost to the consumer.

SCHEDULE OF RATES FOR PIECEWORK

Pieces per Day	Rate per Piece
Up to 19	$.20
20 to 22	.21
23 to 26	.22
27 to 29	.23½
30 to 32	.25
33 to 35	.26
36 to 38	.27½
39 to 41	.29

Using the rates stated above, find the daily wages for each employee, and the total wages for the week, if work was completed as follows:

Names	No. of Pieces Completed						Daily Wages						Total Wages
	M	T	W	Th	F	S	M	T	W	Th	F	S	
A. Bannister	23	22	24	20	21	13*							
T. Goddard	25	27	26	25	28	15							
F. Hartley	30	32	33	29	31	16							
G. Jones	33	34	31	35	36	19							
M. Oncken	36	39	40	37	38	20							
					Totals								

* Use the rate per piece for double the number completed on Saturday.

ALIQUOT PARTS

Halves, Quarters, Eighths, and Sixteenths

A careful study of the following table will help you to remember the sixteenths and their relation to the eighths, the quarters and the halves.

	Halves	Quarters	Eighths	Sixteenths	
1				$.06\frac{1}{4}$	$= \frac{1}{16}$
2			$.12\frac{1}{2}$	$.12\frac{1}{2}$	$= \frac{2}{16} = \frac{1}{8}$
3				$.18\frac{3}{4}$	$= \frac{3}{16}$
4		.25	.25	.25	$= \frac{4}{16} = \frac{2}{8} = \frac{1}{4}$
5				$.31\frac{1}{4}$	$= \frac{5}{16}$
6			$.37\frac{1}{2}$	$.37\frac{1}{2}$	$= \frac{6}{16} = \frac{3}{8}$
7				$.43\frac{3}{4}$	$= \frac{7}{16}$
8	.50	.50	.50	.50	$= \frac{8}{16} = \frac{4}{8} = \frac{2}{4} = \frac{1}{2}$
9				$.56\frac{1}{4}$	$= \frac{9}{16}$
10			$.62\frac{1}{2}$	$.62\frac{1}{2}$	$= \frac{10}{16} = \frac{5}{8}$
11				$.68\frac{3}{4}$	$= \frac{11}{16}$
12		.75	.75	.75	$= \frac{12}{16} = \frac{6}{8} = \frac{3}{4}$
13				$.81\frac{1}{4}$	$= \frac{13}{16}$
14			$.87\frac{1}{2}$	$.87\frac{1}{2}$	$= \frac{14}{16} = \frac{7}{8}$
15				$.93\frac{3}{4}$	$= \frac{15}{16}$
16	1.00	1.00	1.00	1.00	$= \frac{16}{16} = \frac{8}{8} = \frac{4}{4} = \frac{2}{2}$

The numbers at the left are the numerators of fractions whose denominator is 16. To illustrate:

$.37\frac{1}{2}$ is on line 6, hence $.37\frac{1}{2}$ is $\frac{6}{16}$, or $\frac{3}{8}$ of 1.00; $.56\frac{1}{4}$ is on line 9, hence $.56\frac{1}{4}$ is $\frac{9}{16}$ of 1.00; $.87\frac{1}{2}$ is on line 14, hence $.87\frac{1}{2}$ is equal to $\frac{14}{16}$, or $\frac{7}{8}$ of 1.00, etc.

The ratio, or relation of one value to another, in the table is the ratio of the numerators at the left. To illustrate:

The ratio of $.43\frac{3}{4}$ to .50 is the same as the ratio of 7 to 8, or $\frac{7}{8}$; the ratio of $.56\frac{1}{4}$ to .50 is the same as the ratio of 9 to 8, or $\frac{9}{8}$; the ratio of $.18\frac{3}{4}$ to .75 is the same as the ratio of 3 to 12, or $\frac{1}{4}$, etc.

Multiplication by any of the sixteenths is made easy and rapid by following the principles illustrated in the following solutions:

Illustration. Find the value of $143\frac{3}{4}$ yd. at $\$.56\frac{1}{4}$ a yard.

\$143	75	= value at \$1 a yard
71	875	= value at \$.50 a yard
8	9843	= value at $\$.06\frac{1}{4}$ a yard ($\frac{1}{8}$ of \$71.875)
\$80	8593	= value at $\$.56\frac{1}{4}$ a yard

Illustration. Find the value of $49\frac{1}{4}$ yd. at $\$.18\frac{3}{4}$ a yard.

\$49	25	= value at \$1 a yard
12	3125	= value at \$.25 a yard
3	0781	= value at $\$.06\frac{1}{4}$ a yard ($\frac{1}{4}$ of \$12.3125)
\$9	2344	= value at $\$.18\frac{3}{4}$ a yard

Problems

Using the plan of solution shown in the foregoing illustrations, find the value of each of the following:

1. $43\frac{1}{2}$ yd. at $\$.18\frac{3}{4}$
2. $67\frac{1}{4}$ yd. at $\$.43\frac{3}{4}$
3. $85\frac{3}{4}$ yd. at $\$.31\frac{1}{4}$
4. $91\frac{3}{4}$ yd. at $\$.18\frac{3}{4}$
5. $79\frac{1}{3}$ yd. at $\$.56\frac{1}{4}$
6. $235\frac{1}{2}$ yd. at $\$.31\frac{1}{4}$
7. $342\frac{1}{4}$ yd. at $\$.56\frac{1}{4}$
8. $437\frac{1}{4}$ yd. at $\$.43\frac{3}{4}$
9. $572\frac{1}{2}$ yd. at $\$.68\frac{3}{4}$
10. $837\frac{1}{4}$ yd. at $\$.68\frac{3}{4}$
11. $317\frac{1}{4}$ yd. at $\$.18\frac{3}{4}$
12. $416\frac{3}{4}$ yd. at $\$.31\frac{1}{4}$
13. $199\frac{1}{2}$ yd. at $\$.43\frac{3}{4}$
14. $919\frac{1}{4}$ yd. at $\$.56\frac{1}{4}$
15. $713\frac{1}{2}$ yd. at $\$.68\frac{3}{4}$
16. $487\frac{3}{4}$ yd. at $\$.81\frac{1}{4}$
17. $743\frac{1}{4}$ yd. at $\$.68\frac{3}{4}$
18. $117\frac{3}{4}$ yd. at $\$.56\frac{1}{4}$
19. $219\frac{1}{4}$ yd. at $\$.43\frac{3}{4}$
20. $333\frac{3}{4}$ yd. at $\$.31\frac{1}{4}$

Halves, Quarters, Thirds, Sixths, and Twelfths

	Halves	Quarters	Thirds	Sixths	Twelfths	
1					$.08\frac{1}{3}$	$= \frac{1}{12}$
2				$.16\frac{2}{3}$	$.16\frac{2}{3}$	$= \frac{2}{12} = \frac{1}{6}$
3		.25			.25	$= \frac{3}{12} = \frac{1}{4}$
4			$.33\frac{1}{3}$	$.33\frac{1}{3}$	$.33\frac{1}{3}$	$= \frac{4}{12} = \frac{2}{6} = \frac{1}{3}$
5					$.41\frac{2}{3}$	$= \frac{5}{12}$
6	.50	.50	.50	.50	.50	$= \frac{6}{12} = \frac{3}{6} = \frac{2}{4} = \frac{1}{2}$
7					$.58\frac{1}{3}$	$= \frac{7}{12}$
8			$.66\frac{2}{3}$	$.66\frac{2}{3}$	$.66\frac{2}{3}$	$= \frac{8}{12} = \frac{4}{6} = \frac{2}{3}$
9		.75			.75	$= \frac{9}{12} = \frac{3}{4}$
10				$.83\frac{1}{3}$	$.83\frac{1}{3}$	$= \frac{10}{12} = \frac{5}{6}$
11					$.91\frac{2}{3}$	$= \frac{11}{12}$
12	1.00	1.00	1.00	1.00	1.00	$= \frac{12}{12} = \frac{6}{6} = \frac{3}{3} = \frac{4}{4} = \frac{2}{2}$

A study of the table on this page will show the relation of any part to any other part as well as to 1.00. To illustrate:

$.33\frac{1}{3}$ is not only $\frac{1}{3}$ of 1.00, but it is also $\frac{2}{3}$ of .50; it is also $\frac{4}{5}$ of $.41\frac{2}{3}$, and $\frac{4}{3}$ of .25. $.16\frac{2}{3}$ is $\frac{1}{6}$ of 1.00; $\frac{1}{2}$ of $.33\frac{1}{3}$, and $\frac{1}{3}$ of .50, etc.

Practice in using these parts is the only way to become familiar with them. Apply the aliquot-part principle at every opportunity.

Illustration. Find the value of 738 yards of cloth at $\$.41\frac{2}{3}$ a yard.

\$738	00	= value at \$1 a yard
369	00	= value at \$.50 a yard
61	50	= value at $\$.08\frac{1}{3}$ a yard ($\frac{1}{6}$ of \$.50)
\$307	50	= value at $\$.41\frac{2}{3}$ a yard

A ready knowledge of twelfths is important because so many things are bought by the dozen and sold singly.

Problems

Find the net cost of each of these groups:

21.	72 yd. @ $16\frac{2}{3}$¢	**22.**	96 yd. @ $33\frac{1}{3}$¢	**23.**	36 yd. @ $41\frac{2}{3}$¢
	54 yd. @ $33\frac{1}{3}$¢		87 yd. @ $33\frac{1}{3}$¢		48 yd. @ $58\frac{1}{3}$¢
	48 yd. @ $8\frac{1}{3}$¢		81 yd. @ $16\frac{2}{3}$¢		60 yd. @ $91\frac{2}{3}$¢
	84 yd. @ $41\frac{2}{3}$¢		102 yd. @ $33\frac{1}{3}$¢		84 yd. @ $8\frac{1}{3}$¢
	45 yd. @ $66\frac{2}{3}$¢		108 yd. @ $8\frac{1}{3}$¢		120 yd. @ $41\frac{2}{3}$¢
	Less 3%		Less 2%		Less 5%
24.	51 yd. @ $16\frac{2}{3}$¢	**25.**	123 yd. @ $33\frac{1}{3}$¢	**26.**	144 yd. @ $66\frac{2}{3}$¢
	55 yd. @ 25¢		123 yd. @ $16\frac{2}{3}$¢		156 yd. @ $33\frac{1}{3}$¢
	57 yd. @ $33\frac{1}{3}$¢		123 yd. @ $8\frac{1}{3}$¢		168 yd. @ $8\frac{1}{3}$¢
	60 yd. @ $41\frac{2}{3}$¢		135 yd. @ $66\frac{2}{3}$¢		144 yd. @ $91\frac{2}{3}$¢
	78 yd. @ $66\frac{2}{3}$¢		150 yd. @ $16\frac{2}{3}$¢		150 yd. @ 75¢
	Less 2%		Less 3%		Less 4%

Division by Aliquots

To divide by aliquot parts:

1. Express the aliquot part as a fraction.
2. Write the reciprocal of the fraction.
3. Multiply the number to be divided by the reciprocal of the fraction. (The reciprocal of a fraction is the fraction inverted.)

Problems

Find the quantity that can be bought for:

27. \$5 at 25¢ each.

28. \$4 at $12\frac{1}{2}$¢ each.

29. \$7 at 50¢ each.

30. \$9 at $37\frac{1}{2}$¢ each.

31. \$12 at 75¢ each.

32. \$16 at 25¢ each.

33. \$4.50 at $12\frac{1}{2}$¢ each.

34. \$7.25 at 25¢ each.

35. \$15 at $37\frac{1}{2}$¢ each.

36. \$18 at 75¢ each.

37. \$25 at $62\frac{1}{2}$¢ each.

38. \$4.50 at 75¢ each.

39. \$21 at $87\frac{1}{2}$¢ each.

40. \$28.84 at $87\frac{1}{2}$¢ each.

41. \$37.50 at $62\frac{1}{2}$¢ each.

42. \$47.50 at $62\frac{1}{2}$¢ each.

43. At 50¢ a pound, how many pounds of tea can be bought for $2? for $3? for $5?

44. At 25¢ a pound, how many pounds of coffee can be bought for $1? for $2? for $3? for $10?

45. At 25¢ each, how many arm bands can be bought for $6?

46. At $37\frac{1}{2}$¢ a dozen, how many dozen eggs can be bought for $3?

MISCELLANEOUS REVIEW PROBLEMS

1. The regular time schedule for a train to make a run of 228 mi. was 6 hr. On a certain day, after running 1 hr., the train was delayed 1 hr. before continuing. At what average rate of speed must the remainder of the trip be made for the train to reach its destination on schedule time?

2. A painter offered to furnish materials and decorate a room for $22 or to do the work at 75¢ an hour if the owner furnished the materials. The owner decided to buy the materials and employ the painter by the hour. Varnish cost $4.50, paint $4, and other materials $1.50. The painter worked 6 hr. on Monday, 5 hr. on Tuesday, and 7 hr. on Wednesday. (*a*) Find the total cost. (*b*) How much more or less than $22 was this?

3. For gas for household purposes a gas company charges $.72 for the first 100 cu. ft. and $1.20 per 1000 cu. ft. for all over 100 cu. ft. If a man's bill shows 2100 cu. ft. of gas consumed in the month, how much is his gas bill?

4. An electric-lighting company charges 8¢ per kilowatt hour for the first 20 kilowatts of current a month, 7¢ per kilowatt hour for the next 10 kilowatts, and $6\frac{1}{2}$¢ per kilowatt for the next 70 kilowatts. Find the cost of 87 kilowatt-hours of current.

5. Toilet soap costs $6 a gross. In handling 3 gross a grocer sold 228 cakes at 5¢ each and the remainder at a sale at 6 cakes for 25¢. How much did he make?

6. A retail merchant had on hand $1\frac{5}{12}$ doz. shirts, size $15\frac{1}{2}$. He bought $5\frac{1}{4}$ doz. at $18.60 a dozen. He sold $4\frac{1}{3}$ doz. at $1.95 a shirt and cleared out the remainder of his stock at a

sale at 4 shirts for $6.80. If the shirts he had on hand cost the same as those he bought, find his profit on all the shirts.

7. A man gave his son a patch of ground on which to raise potatoes. The boy paid $2 for seed potatoes and $4 for fertilizer. He harvested 56 bu. of potatoes, which he sold at 60¢ a bushel. He paid his father $9 for the use of horses for cultivation and for hauling potatoes to market. If the boy put in 60 hr. of labor on the crop, how much per hour did his profit net him?

8. The power of an engine is measured in what is called *horsepower*. One horsepower is the power that will lift 550 lb. 1 ft. in 1 sec. How many pounds will a 1-horsepower engine lift 1 ft. in 1 min.?

9. A stock trader bought 150 sheep at $3.50 each. Before he could sell them, 5 of the sheep died. The remaining sheep were sold at $4.25 each. Feed cost $25, and labor and incidental expenses were $12.25. Find his net profit.

10. A contractor employed 20 men at $3 a day, 15 men at $3.75 a day, and a foreman at $58.50 a week. What was the average daily wage paid to his men?

11. On Monday morning a man's bank balance was $2175.50. During the week he deposited money in the bank and drew checks against his account as follows: Monday, deposited $375. Tuesday, drew checks for $340.50 and $3.64. Wednesday, deposited $972.60. Thursday, deposited $420; drew checks for $5.75, $16.47, and $101.75. Friday, drew checks for $57.68 and $119.18. Saturday, deposited $1281.62. Find his bank balance at the end of the week.

12. An agricultural experiment station recommends from 5 lb. to 10 lb. of ammonium sulphate as a fertilizer for 1000 sq. ft. of lawn. A man has a lawn containing 9000 sq. ft. He decides to use 8 lb. of fertilizer for each 1000 sq. ft. of lawn. At $7.50 a hundredweight, how much will the fertilizer cost?

13. In a diagram of a schoolyard, 1 in. on the diagram represents 2 rd. If the yard is 16 rd. long and 12 rd. wide, what are the dimensions of the diagram?

14. To be on the honor roll, Mary had to have an average of 85 in all her work. In three subjects she received 83, 85, and 80. What mark must she receive in her fourth subject to make the honor roll?

15. A haberdasher bought ties at $1.65 a dozen. He sold them at 20¢ each. Find his profit on 12 doz. ties.

16. A grocer bought eggs from a farmer at 35¢ a dozen. He sold them at the rate of 3 for 10¢. How much did he make on 8 doz. eggs?

COUNTING TIME
(Between Two Dates)

Problems

Find (*a*) the compound time, (*b*) the bankers' time, and (*c*) the exact time between the following dates:

1. From May 3 to Dec. 9
2. From Mar. 30 to Nov. 4
3. From Feb. 27 to Dec. 8
4. From Dec. 17 to June 1
5. From Sept. 25 to May 1
6. From Aug. 6 to Feb. 1
7. From April 15 to Nov. 30
8. From July 31 to Nov. 30
9. From Oct. 24 to Feb. 13
10. From July 17 to Oct. 2

Counting Forward

Counting forward a given number of days is an important operation in many problems. In counting forward a stated number of days, it is understood that exact time will be used.

Illustration. Count forward 70 days from October 18.

From the total number of days,	70 da.
Subtract the remaining days in October,	13
Leaving,	57 da.
Then subtract the days in November	30
Leaving the number of days in December,	27 da.

Therefore, 70 days after October 18 is December 27.

Problems

Count forward:

11. 50 days from May 1

12. 80 days from Aug. 18

13. 66 days from Jan. 27

14. 90 days from Aug. 10

15. 116 days from Sept. 30

16. 85 days from Dec. 15

17. 75 days from Nov. 24

18. 100 days from Jan. 3

Counting Back

Illustration. Count back 72 days from July 18.

From the total number of days,	72 da.
Subtract the days in July to July 18,	18
Leaving,	54 da.
Then subtract the days in June,	30
Leaving,	24 da.

Subtract 24 days from the 31 days in May, leaving 7 days.

Therefore, 72 days back from July 18 is May 7.

Problems

Count back:

19. 38 days from May 12

20. 49 days from June 1

21. 76 days from Oct. 15

22. 110 days from Nov. 22

23. 90 days from Dec. 25

24. 88 days from Feb. 28

25. 68 days from June 27

26. 120 days from July 4

27. A note dated May 2 was paid 75 days later. On what date was it paid?

28. Mr. Harding paid for a bill of goods on April 16. Because the bill was overdue, he was charged interest for 68 days. On what date should he have paid the bill?

NOTES. 1. The term *month* means the time from a given date in one month to the same date in the next month, except in such cases as "1 month from May 31," in which case the time is June 30; or "1 month from January 31," which is February 28 (or February 29 in a leap year).

2. "One half month" is 15 days.

3. From the standpoint of time, "one month" and "30 days" are not always equal periods of time.

1 month from May 1 is June 1.
30 days from May 1 is May 31.
1 month from January 31 is February 28 (or February 29).
30 days from January 31 is March 2 (or March 1, in leap year).

4. From the standpoint of interest calculation by what is called the "ordinary" interest method, "one month" and "30 days" are equal periods of time.

Find the due dates of the following notes:

	Date	*Time to Run*		*Date*	*Time to Run*
29.	May 1	1 mo.	**32.**	July 1	30 da.
30.	March 18	$\frac{1}{2}$ mo.	**33.**	July 1	1 mo.
31.	Jan. 31	3 mo.	**34.**	Aug. 30	$\frac{1}{2}$ mo.

PERCENTAGE PROBLEMS

Type I — Finding a Per Cent of a Number

1. Express as decimals: 5%; $7\frac{1}{2}$%; $\frac{1}{2}$%; $\frac{1}{4}$%; $\frac{1}{8}$%.

2. Find the value of each of the following:

$3\frac{3}{4}$% of \$16.80 $\qquad$ $\frac{1}{10}$% less than \$1500
125% of \$3640 $\qquad$ $1\frac{1}{8}$% of \$3200
.5% of \$13,750

3. What is the difference in commission between $3\frac{1}{2}$% of sales and \$.03 a bushel on a sale of 650 bushels of potatoes at \$.85 a bushel?

4. A merchant marked his goods 25% above cost. In a one-day sale he reduced prices 20%, thinking he was then making a profit of 5% of cost. Was he right? How much did he make or lose if his sales for the day amounted to \$450? (Disregard overhead expenses.)

5. On a factory building which cost \$35,000, depreciation at the rate of $2\frac{1}{2}$% is written off each year. Find the first year's depreciation.

6. Last year's sales were \$27,642.50. This year's sales are $3\frac{3}{4}\%$ less than last year's sales. Find the amount of the sales for the two years.

7. If woolen cloth shrinks 3% of its length in sponging, find the shrinkage in yards, feet, and inches in sponging 125 yards of cloth.

8. A salesman's commission was 8% of all his sales. He was offered an additional 3% of all sales if he increased his sales by 25%. His sales had been averaging \$6600 a month. Find the average monthly sales required to receive the extra rate of commission. If he increased his sales by 30%, find the total commission for a year.

9. Prime cost of purchases in a hardware store were \$46,196.54, and the buying expenses were $4\frac{1}{4}\%$ of prime cost. Find the buying expenses.

10. A man bought an iron tank priced, "Regular \$20; special \$18." By mistake the seller quoted the price as "\$18 less 10%" instead of "\$20 less 10%." The seller, however, sold the tank at his quoted price. How much less than the regular price did the purchaser pay?

Type II — Finding What Per Cent One Number Is of Another

11. An article which sold for cash at \$45 was sold on the installment plan as follows: \$3 down, and \$3 weekly for 15 weeks. The installment price was what per cent greater than the cash price?

12. The gross cost of an article is \$13 and it is sold for \$20. The selling expenses are 25% of the selling price. Find (*a*) the gross profit; (*b*) the net profit; and (*c*) the per cent of net profit based on sales.

13. The cost of food for a family of four persons increased from \$41.75 a month to \$45.09 because of advancing prices. How much should a monthly income of \$160 be increased if it increases at the same rate as the cost of food increases?

14. Four salesmen reported sales for November as follows:

B. Elger	$2721.38	S. Gilmartin	$2643.88
R. Dilworthy	$3132.64	T. Longfellow	$3502.10

Find, to the nearest whole per cent, the per cent of total sales made by each. How can you check the accuracy of the rates?

15. A fur coat bore a price tag reading, "Was $175; now $139.50." The reduction in price was what rate per cent?

16. A man paid $755.25 on a debt of $1987.50. What per cent of his debt does he still owe?

17. Johnson bought a motor boat for $380. He was told that the depreciation for the first year would be 25%. He estimated it would cost $15 a month to run the boat and to provide a place to anchor and store it during the winter. Other incidental expenses were reckoned at $3 a month. Johnson's salary was $150 a month. Find to the nearest whole per cent what part of his salary it would cost to run and care for the boat and provide for the depreciation, for the first year. Was it a wise investment?

18. In a factory there are employed 350 men and 210 women. Find the percentage of men employed. Of women.

19. A baseball team won 15 games. They lost 9 games. The games won was what per cent of all the games played?

20. Mr. Hanks bought a vacant lot for $1050 and erected a house costing $5950 on it. The cost of the lot was what per cent of the total cost?

Type III — Finding a Number When a Per Cent of It Is Known

21. Find the amount of which

(*a*) $750 is 150% (*c*) $1250 is 125%

(*b*) $900 is 180% (*d*) $14.40 is $\frac{1}{4}$%.

22. (*a*) \$1400 is 40% greater than how many dollars?
(*b*) \$1875 is 25% greater than how many dollars?
(*c*) \$1575 is 5% greater than how many dollars?
(*d*) \$2650 is 6% greater than how many dollars?

23. (*a*) 34 is 15% less than what number?
(*b*) 56 is what per cent less than 80?
(*c*) \$1498.50 is $\frac{1}{10}$% less than what value?
(*d*) \$2864.82 is $\frac{1}{4}$% less than what value?

24. On a 25%-discount sale a coat was sold for \$42.60. What was the price of the coat before the discount was allowed?

25. One number is 18% greater than another number. The sum of the two numbers is 490.5. What are the numbers?

26. One number is 22% less than another number. The sum of the two numbers is 489.5. What are the numbers?

27. A young man sold his car for \$943, which was 18% less than he paid for it 6 months ago. How much was the depreciation on the car?

28. A bankrupt company can pay only 43% of its debts, out of its available resources of \$5697.50. How much are its debts?

29. The sales in a grocery store were 19% greater one year than they were the preceding year. The second year's sales were \$69,853. What were the sales the first year?

30. A stock of goods was sold at a gross profit of \$11,500, which was 23% of the cost of the goods. For how much did they sell?

COMMISSION PROBLEMS

1. The Northern Woolen Company pays its salesman a salary of \$175 a month, and a commission of $2\frac{1}{2}$% on all sales over \$2500 a month, to and including \$3500 a month. For all sales over \$3500 in a single month, the agent receives 3% commission. For two months the sales were \$3375 and \$3950, respectively. Find the agent's average monthly earnings for the two months.

2. A commission merchant received a carload of potatoes, weighing 34,200 lb. He paid the freight, amounting to \$65.70, and charged \$25 for storage. He sold the potatoes at \$.75 a bushel of 60 lb., and charged $3\frac{1}{2}\%$ commission. Find the proceeds of the sale.

3. An agent purchased for the Empire Grocery Company 600 bbl. of sweet potatoes at \$2.10 a barrel. Commission was $2\frac{1}{2}\%$. The agent prepaid the freight, amounting to \$240. Find the total cost of the potatoes.

4. An agent charged 3% commission for purchasing a quantity of merchandise for a client. If the commission amounted to \$49.50, find the total cost of the merchandise.

5. Find the total commission on the following:

A sale amounting to \$3450, commission $2\frac{1}{4}\%$
A sale amounting to \$1430, commission $3\frac{1}{2}\%$
A sale amounting to \$3275, commission $1\frac{1}{8}\%$

6. A sales clerk receives weekly wages of \$15, and a commission of $2\frac{1}{2}\%$ for all sales over a minimum of \$300 a week. Her sales for four weeks were \$390, \$425, \$372.50, and \$543.75. Find her average earning for the four weeks.

7. A traveling salesman receives a salary of \$25 a week and a commission of $1\frac{1}{2}\%$ on all sales. He drives a car. His employer pays for gas and oil and pays his hotel bills. In 4 weeks the salesman drove his car 1300 mi., using 98 gal. of gasoline at \$.18 a gallon and 5 qt. of oil at \$.30 a quart. His hotel bills averaged \$3 a day. His sales amounted to \$17,450.60. The merchandise sold at a gross profit of 10% of sales.

(*a*) Find the total amount of wages and commission paid the agent.

(*b*) Find the total traveling expenses.

(*c*) What profit did the company make after paying the selling costs?

(*d*) What per cent of the total sales were the selling costs?

(*e*) What per cent of the gross profits were the selling costs?

8. A commission merchant had 360 bags of onions to sell for a client. He sold $\frac{3}{8}$ of them at $1.10 a bag; $\frac{4}{5}$ of the remainder at $1.15 a bag, and what was then left at $1.20 a bag. He charged $3\frac{1}{2}\%$ commission. Find the amount received for all, the average price per bag, and the proceeds of the sale.

9. A farmer had 750 bushels of potatoes to sell. He was offered $.68 a bushel for them at his door. The city price was $.80 a bushel. He decided to send them to a commission merchant, who sold them as follows: 500 bushels at $.81 a bushel, and the remainder at $.78 a bushel. The charges were freight, $46.50; cartage in the city, $31.50; commission, $.02 a bushel. Did the farmer gain or lose, and how much, by sending his potatoes to the commission merchant to be sold?

10. A salesman's sales for one week were as follows: Monday, $375.50; Tuesday, $219.80; Wednesday, $481.90; Thursday, $301.75; Friday, $750; Saturday, $417.10. His wages were $21 a week plus a 2% commission on all sales over $200 a day. Find (*a*) his commission for each day; (*b*) his total commission for the week; (*c*) his average daily earnings.

11. Roger Wilson, a commission merchant in Chicago, sold for a client, Duncan Wood, of Terre Haute, Indiana, the following quantities of cabbage: On August 3, 12,500 lb. at $1.10 per cwt.; on August 5, 16,000 lb. at $1.08 per cwt.; and on August 6, 9500 lb. at $1.05 per cwt. He paid the following expenses: freight $37.50, and cartage, $25. Commission was 4%. Set up an account sales.

12. A buyer purchased for his firm, the Elton Grocery Company, Louisville, Ky., the following: 100 tubs, 5000 lb., butter, at $.24\frac{1}{2}$ a pound; 75 crates eggs, 2250 doz., at $.26 a dozen; and 6400 lb. cheese at $.21\frac{1}{4}$ a pound. He prepaid the freight, $175, and charged $3\frac{1}{2}\%$ commission. Set up an account purchase. Use your own name as buyer.

COMMERCIAL DISCOUNT PROBLEMS

At a special sale, a grocer reduced prices thus:

Items	*Usual Price*	*Sale Price*
Evaporated milk	$.07 a can	3 cans for $.17
Macaroni	$.05 a package	$.04 a package
Oatmeal	$.09 a package	2 packages for $.15
Breakfast cereal	$.15 a box	2 boxes for $.25
Catsup	$.15 a bottle	2 bottles for $.25
Tomatoes	$.10 a can	3 cans for $.25
Corn	$.15 a can	2 cans for $.25
Peaches	$.17 a can	2 cans for $.29
Pineapple	$.22 a can	2 cans for $.35
Baked beans	$.10 a can	3 cans for $.23

1. Mrs. Gale bought 12 cans of evaporated milk, 4 packages of oatmeal, 12 cans of tomatoes, 6 cans of peaches, and 6 cans of pineapple. How much did she save?

2. Mrs. Weston, who runs a boarding house, bought 24 packages of macaroni, 12 packages of breakfast cereal, 24 bottles of catsup, 36 cans of corn, 24 cans of peaches, 12 cans of pineapple, and 24 cans of baked beans. How much did she save? What per cent of the usual cost of the articles was this?

3. A case of corn (24 cans) sells for $2.65. How much is saved by buying a case at a time instead of buying it at 15¢ a can? What per cent is saved?

4. The Eastern Refrigerator Company sold refrigerators for $160 less 25%. To meet competition the net price of refrigerators was reduced to $110.40. This reduction was equal to what additional rate of discount?

5. In a store window a suit is marked "$17.50 — formerly $25." At what rate was the price reduced?

6. A city employee, who is paid monthly, receives an annual salary of $2640. He agrees to return to the city 10% of his salary for 1 year. How much will his net monthly salary be?

7. A dealer marked goods 40% above cost. (*a*) Find the marked price of a desk for which he paid $32.40 and on which he paid freight charges of $2.60. (*b*) Find his net selling price if he allows 10% discount to customers.

8. Find the net cash required to pay the following bills:

(*a*) $450, less 25% and 20%, terms 3/10, N/60

(*b*) $543.50, less $33\frac{1}{3}$% and 25%, terms 2/10, N/30

(*c*) $2750, less $16\frac{2}{3}$% and 10%, terms 5/10, N/60

(*d*) $2475, less 20% and 10%, terms 4/10, N/60. Anticipation, interest 6%. (Date of invoice Jan. 4.)

(*e*) $3500, less 30% and $14\frac{2}{7}$%, terms 3/10, E. O. M. Anticipation, interest 6%. (Date of invoice March 27; date of payment April 4.)

9. What single discount is equivalent to a series of 20%, $16\frac{2}{3}$%, and 10%?

10. On a machine listed at $450, a manufacturer offered a discount of $33\frac{1}{3}$%. To meet competition he reduced the price of the machine to $270. The final reduction in price was equal to what additional rate of discount?

PROFIT AND LOSS PROBLEMS

Find (*a*) the gross cost; (*b*) the gross profit; (*c*) the net profit; and (*d*) the rate of net profit based on the sales:

	Prime Cost	*Buying Expenses*	*Selling Price*	*Selling Expenses*
1.	$ 6.25	4%	$10	25%
2.	$ 9.00	5%	$13.50	20%
3.	$14.40	$6\frac{1}{4}$%	$20	15%
4.	$15	8%	$22.50	$16\frac{2}{3}$%
5.	$22.50	8%	$32	15%
6.	$25	10%	$40	20%

7. Mr. Nelson's buying expenses are 5% of the prime cost of the goods. He buys coats from a manufacturer at $40 each, less 25% and 20%. Find the gross cost of each coat.

8. A wholesale merchant paid $16.20 for an article. He sold it for $30, less 25% and 10%. Find his profit.

9. A radio sells for $17.50. The rate of profit is 20% of the selling price. Find the cost.

10. A dealer sold an electric clock for $12.60, thereby making a gross profit of 20% of the cost. Find the cost.

11. Mr. Bates bought an automobile robe for $6.80. The dealer made a gross profit of 15% of the selling price. How much did the robe cost the dealer?

12. A grocer mixed equal quantities of coffee costing 18¢, 20¢, and 22¢ a pound. What per cent of cost was gained by selling it at 25¢ a pound?

13. A shoe dealer sells shoes at an advance of 30% of the cost. (*a*) How much does he pay for a pair of shoes that he sells for $6.50? (*b*) If his overhead expenses are 10% of his sales, find the per cent of net profit based on the cost.

14. A wholesale clothing manufacturer made 1200 suits of clothes to be sold for $27.75 per suit. The manufacturing costs were distributed as follows: material, $12,842.11; salaries and wages, $10,986.57; and overhead expense, $2811.32. What per cent of the manufacturing cost was the gross profit?

Make a circle graph, showing the share of each part of the expense and the profit.

15. A dealer estimates that his selling and overhead expenses amount to 16% of his sales. If he buys a rug for $66, less 10% and 10%, at what price should he sell the rug to clear 18% of the selling price?

16. Hobbs and Son, hardware merchants, on January 1, 19—, had on hand merchandise valued at $17,500; furniture and fixtures worth $1200; and trucks worth $2200. Their purchases for the next year amounted to $78,500, and their net sales were $117,560. Overhead expenses were rent, $4500; salaries, $8500; heat and light, $1950; insurance, $75; office and general supplies, $1150; miscellaneous supplies, $1750. At the close of the year their inventories were merchandise, $14,500; furniture and fixtures, $1000; and trucks, $1750. Set up a statement of profit and loss,

and indicate what per cent of the sales is each of the following: cost of goods sold, gross profit on sales, total operating expenses, net profit. What per cent of the total operating expenses is each of the items of expense?

17. My sales for two years were $73,443.14. The sales for the second year exceeded the sales for the first year by 15%. Find the sales for each year.

18. Adams and Adams bought 3 dozen lamps at $43.20 a dozen, less $16\frac{2}{3}$%. At what price should they sell each lamp to make a gross profit of 50% of the cost?

19. A shoe company bought 400 pairs of shoes for $1250, less 20%. 150 pairs of the shoes were sold at $3.50 a pair. At what price per pair must the remaining shoes be sold to make a gross profit of $17\frac{1}{2}$% on the cost of all the shoes?

20. A dealer bought washing machines at $70 less 20%. Freight and other buying expenses amounted to $2.80 per machine. At what price should he sell each machine to make a profit of 10% of the selling price after allowing $2\frac{1}{2}$% of sales for bad debts, and $17\frac{1}{2}$% of sales for selling expenses?

21. An article cost $32.40. The selling expenses are 25% of the sales. Find the selling price to make $12\frac{1}{2}$% of cost.

22. An electrical company purchased a quantity of fixtures for $1480 less 20% and $12\frac{1}{2}$%. The fixtures were priced to sell at a profit of 14% of the sales and to cover selling expenses of 16% of sales. Find the amount for which the entire stock should sell.

23. A dressing table listed at $64 was sold by the manufacturer subject to trade discounts of $33\frac{1}{3}$%, 25%, and 10%. The furniture dealer who bought it reckons his selling expenses at 19% of his sales. If he sells the table to net a profit of $12\frac{1}{2}$% of his cost, at what price should he sell it?

24. A retail merchant bought a stove for $25 less 20% and 10%. He sold it at a price which covered $16\frac{1}{2}$% overhead expenses, $3\frac{1}{2}$% bad debts, and which netted him a profit of 8% of his sales. Find the selling price.

63

25. The wholesaler's list price of a refrigerator was $120. He allowed a trade discount of $12\frac{1}{2}\%$. The retailer who bought it sold it to net him a profit of 9% of sales, after allowing 18% for overhead expenses and 3% for bad debts. For what price did the retailer sell it?

INTEREST PROBLEMS

Find (*a*) the date of maturity, (*b*) the interest, and (*c*) the amount due at maturity on each of the following notes:

	Date of Note	*Face of Note*	*Time*	*Rate of Interest*
1.	May 4	$4340	80 da.	6%
2.	Feb. 15	$3275	90 da.	4%
3.	June 15	$2792.25	60 da.	5%
4.	Aug. 25	$ 975.50	4 mo.	3%
5.	May 4	$1150.60	30 da.	$3\frac{1}{2}\%$
6.	Jan 11	$1975.80	60 da.	$3\frac{1}{2}\%$
7.	Dec. 7	$2590	3 mo.	$4\frac{1}{2}\%$
8.	Oct. 31	$3685	5 mo.	5%
9.	June 20	$7500	3 mo.	4%

In some cases the exact number of days is counted when reckoning interest.

In the following exercises find: (*a*) the exact number of days from the date of the loan till it was paid; (*b*) the interest on the loan; (*c*) the amount required to repay the loan at maturity:

	Amount Loaned	*Date Loaned*	*Date Repaid*	*Rate of Interest*
10.	$ 575	Aug. 10	Sept. 15	$3\frac{1}{2}\%$
11.	$ 500	July 1	Aug. 17	$3\frac{1}{4}\%$
12.	$1000	May 28	July 15	3%
13.	$ 250	April 15	Aug. 1	$4\frac{1}{2}\%$
14.	$ 360	March 1	July 1	5%
15.	$ 450	Jan. 20	March 4	5%

16.	$ 580	Oct. 10	Dec. 1	4%
17.	$1250	June 5	Oct. 1	2%
18.	$1375	Aug. 10	Nov. 11	$2\frac{1}{2}$%
19.	$1450	Feb. 18	March 18	$3\frac{1}{2}$%
20.	$1675	April 30	June 5	$4\frac{1}{2}$%

21. A man owns $10,000 worth of bonds paying 4% interest. He sells the bonds and buys a 2-family house for $10,000. Each part of the house rents for $35 a month. The taxes are $246.50; insurance costs $13.50 a year; water rent is $10.50 for each family; and other expenses and upkeep amount to $150 a year. Based on these figures (*a*) find if his income is increased or decreased for the year. (*b*) Would you think it a wise investment considering the possibility of part of the house being vacant occasionally? (*c*) Discuss the question of time and attention required by the purchaser as compared with the time and thought required to be given to the investment in the bonds.

22. A real estate dealer bought a plot of ground for $27,500, on April 1. On May 1 he paid $1500 for materials used in building sidewalks and curbing on two sides of the lot. On July 1 he paid $2100 for labor. On August 1 he paid $60 for advertising the property for sale, and on Sept. 1 he paid the taxes amounting to $450. On June 1, the following year, he sold the property for $36,500. In his schedule of costs he included interest at 6% on all payments from the time the payment was made till the date of sale. Find his net profit or loss on the transaction.

23. To pay cash for a purchase of merchandise valued at $1750, terms 5% for cash, net 90 days, Mr. Abeles discounted his personal note of $1750 for 90 days at 6%. The proceeds of the note were how much more than the net amount of the bill of goods?

24. Mr. Woodale had been successful in business and at age 50 had $250,000. He debated whether he would continue in business thus giving employment to 50 worthy people, or whether he should retire and invest his money in government securities, and take his ease. What arguments have you in favor of either of his proposed courses?

RATIO PROBLEMS

Illustration. Three men agreed to buy a motor boat as follows: For each dollar paid by A, B was to pay \$2, and C was to pay \$4. If the boat cost \$280, how much should each pay?

$\$1 + \$2 + \$4 = \$7.$
A paid \$1 out of every \$7, or $\frac{1}{7}$ of \$280 = \$40
B paid \$2 out of every \$7, or $\frac{2}{7}$ of \$280 = \$80
C paid \$4 out of every \$7, or $\frac{4}{7}$ of \$280 = \$160
Check: \$40 + \$80 + \$160 = \$280.

1. What amount of money should each person receive if \$3600 is divided among three persons in the ratio of 3, 4, and 5?

2. The profits of a certain business were divided among the partners in the ratio of 5, 6, and 7. If the net profits amounted to \$16,200, how much should each partner receive?

3. Four men invested the following amounts in business: Burke invested \$4000; Case, \$5000; Daly, \$6000; and Evans, \$10,000. Express, in simplest term, the ratio of their investments to each other.

4. A merchant's assets total \$15,500. He owes three creditors amounts as follows: A, \$4500; B, \$5000; and C, \$7500. In view of his insolvency he becomes bankrupt. To settle his affairs costs \$500. The balance of his assets is distributed among his creditors in proportion to their claims. How much should each receive?

5. Three men agree to build a piece of highway for \$27,500. A employed 20 men for 32 days; B employed 25 men for 28 days; and C employed 43 men for 20 days. Of the total amount received for building the highway, \$5500 was used for materials. The balance was to be divided in proportion to the time and labor furnished by each of the contractors. How much should each contractor receive?

STENOGRAPHIC PROBLEMS

Many stenographers do not realize how much it costs to produce a well-written letter.

The average number of letters that a stenographer can write in a day has a considerable bearing on office expenses.

For a stenographer to make mistakes in taking dictation, or in transcribing her notes, is costly for her employer. Following are some of the facts revealed by a recent investigation of costs of business correspondence.

Average time required to dictate letter	7.6 minutes
Average time required to transcribe letter . . .	8.7 minutes
Average length of letter	292 words
Average monthly wage of dictator	$213.50
Average monthly wage of transcriber	$102.50
Number of hours worked . .	8 hr. per day, 40 hr. per week

Using the information given above, solve these problems:

1. What was the average transcription rate per minute (*i.e.*, the number of words written per minute)?

2. What was the average number of letters dictated per hour?

3. Reckoning 22 working days per month, find the average wage per hour for each, the dictator and the stenographer.

4. Using the results found in problems 2 and 3, find the cost per letter of dictating the letters and taking the dictation.

5. What was the time required to transcribe the 8 letters taken in dictation in one hour? (State the time in nearest whole minute.)

6. What was the cost of transcribing the 8 letters taken in an hour's dictation? (State in nearest whole cent.)

7. Find the average cost per letter of dictating, taking the dictation, and transcribing the eight letters.

Note. In addition to the costs indicated in the foregoing problems, there are other items which serve to increase the cost of correspondence. Some of those items are use of the typewriter, typewriter ribbons, stationery, and carbon paper.

8. As an experiment have someone dictate to you for an hour (or a half hour). Then transcribe your notes, making note of the time required for transcription. Compare your results with those stated on page 447. How many words a minute did you take in dictation? How many words a minute did you write in transcription? How many typing errors did you make in transcription? Is your record equal to, better than, or poorer than the average reported on page 447?

9. Two stenographers were engaged by a firm at a wage of $17.50 per week of 40 hours. Miss A took dictation at the rate of 12 letters in 30 minutes, the letters averaging 175 words each. In making her transcription, she had to rewrite three letters, and spent ten minutes consulting the dictionary for correct spelling of words. Her total time for transcription was 2 hours.

Miss B took dictation at the rate of 9 letters in 30 minutes, the letters averaging 300 words each. She made no mistakes in transcription and did not have to consult the dictionary. She transcribed the letters in 1 hour and 30 minutes.

If Miss A's work was equal to that of the average stenographer, was Miss B's work better or worse than the average? What was the average number of words taken in dictation and transcribed per minute by each stenographer?

10. Using the results obtained in problem 9, and assuming that Miss A's wages were fair for the amount and quality of work she did, how much should Miss B's wages be if she were paid in proportion to the amount of work she did?

11. In 1 hour an executive, whose wages were $5000 a year (reckoned as 12 mos. of 22 days each, and 8 hours a day), dictated 18 letters averaging 150 words each, to a dictating machine. A stenographer, whose wages were $22.50 per week of 40 hours, typed the letters in 2 hours. Find the average cost per letter of dictating and typing the letters.

12. In one week a firm dictated to stenographers 320 letters at the rate of 8 letters per hour. The average time per letter for transcription was 6.4 letters per hour. The average wage of the dictators was $352 per month (22 days of 8 hours each) and that of the stenographers was $18 a week of 40 hours. Find the total direct labor cost of the week's correspondence. What was the average cost per letter?

13. The following week the firm referred to in problem 12 experimented with dictating machines. The same persons dictated to the machines 480 letters at the rate of 12 letters per hour. The stenographers transcribed the letters from the machine at the rate of 7.5 letters per hour. Find the average cost per letter.

A stenographer should be word-conscious. There are many words in English which are similar, or identical, in sound which differ widely in meaning. The successful stenographer recognizes the difference in spelling and meaning of words.

14. A stenographer, whose normal rate of transcription is 30 words a minute, wrote the word "tenor" for the word "tenure" in a letter of 360 words. Her employer detected the error and asked to have the letter rewritten. If the stenographer's wages were $20 for a week of 40 hours, how much did the transcription of the letter cost? The actual cost of transcription was how many times as great as it should have been?

15. An office manager, whose salary is $10 a day of 8 hours, spends 2 hours dictating 20 letters to his secretary. The secretary, who receives $4 a day of 8 hours, spends 4 hours transcribing the letters. Find the average direct labor cost of each letter.

16. If the office manager referred to in problem 15 had used a dictating machine, his dictation time might have been reduced to 1 hour and 30 minutes. The secretary's time in transcribing the letters might have been reduced to 3 hours. Find the direct labor cost of producing each letter.

17. In a typing contest three stenographers made the following records:

Miss A wrote from

Shorthand notes	66 words a minute
Dictation machine	93 words a minute

Miss B wrote from

Shorthand notes	35 words a minute
Dictation machine	80 words a minute

Miss C wrote from

Shorthand notes	36 words a minute
Dictation machine	58 words a minute

The number of words transcribed from the dictating machine was what per cent greater than from shorthand notes

(*a*) For each contestant?

(*b*) For all three contestants, expressed as an average?

18. A survey covering over 700 stenographers reveals that the average number of words per minute taken in shorthand and transcribed on the typewriter is 24. The range in the number of words so taken and transcribed was from 10 words to 39 words. The average is what per cent greater than the smallest number of words per minute? The highest number of words is what per cent greater than the average number?

19. If the average wage of the stenographers in problem 18 is $18 a week, what should be the weekly wage, based on the amount of work accomplished, of stenographers whose average number of words was 39 per minute? Of those whose average was 10 words per minute?

20. If you are a prospective applicant for a position as stenographer and typist, you should make a survey of your own capacity, and chart the results. You will then have an exhibit of what you can do to present to a prospective employer. Take dictation for a half hour, as fast as you can write legibly. Then transcribe your notes as fast as you can without errors. Keep an accurate record of your time. Count the words you have written and then chart the results as follows:

Minutes Dictating	No. Words Dictated	Time Transcribing	Words per Minute

To find the number of words per minute divide the total number of words by the total number of minutes occupied in both taking dictation and transcribing your notes. Is your average better or worse than the average noted in problem 18? How many errors did you make in transcription? If your record is not better than the average, you should practice diligently until you can do much better than the average before applying for a position as stenographer and typist.

PROBLEMS IN THE HOME

1. Mrs. Tanner receives an allowance of $50 a month for household expenses. The rent, fuel, gas, and electric bills are paid by Mr. Tanner. Mrs. Tanner does not budget her household expenses, but keeps a strict account of all her expenditures, which are as follows: 4 qt. of milk per week at 13¢ a quart, ½ pint of cream at 24¢, 2 days a week. (In a month there would be 2 extra quarts of milk and 1 extra half pint of cream, because a month is more than 4 weeks.) Other items are eggs, 4 dozen a month, at 35¢; butter, 4 lb. a month, at 35¢; groceries, $21 a month; meat, $9 a month; fruits, $.50 a month. Carfares average 70¢ a month; postage stamps, 50¢ a month; laundry, $4 a month; and amusements, $2 a month. Mrs. Tanner plans to buy a new radio for $62.50. She can turn in her old radio for $7.50. How much can she pay out of her allowance each month? How long will it take her to pay for the radio?

2. Two young men earning $35 a week each decided to reduce their living expenses by hiring a small furnished apartment at $40 a month. Their room rent had previously been $30 a month each. Their board bill had been $38 a month. Their place of business was near their room, so they planned to get their own meals. Their first month's bills were as follows: Food, $48, gas, $3.60, electricity, $3, laundry, $4, and the services of a woman to clean their apartment, $8. They purchased a used car for $250, agreeing to pay $12.50 a month from their housekeeping savings. After paying all the above-mentioned bills, how much was left from their savings to apply to the running and upkeep of the car?

3. Mr. Jones purchased a car for $960. He paid for the

first year, for insurance, \$36; license plates, \$14.50, garage rent, \$8 a month, repairs and greasing, \$27.50, gasoline, 350 gal. at 20¢ a gallon, and 30 qt. of oil at 25¢ a quart. If he averaged 15 miles to the gallon of gasoline, find the cost of gasoline and oil per mile. The company for whom he worked allowed him 5¢ a mile for use of his car. Depreciation on the car for the year was \$160; loss of interest on the cost of the car at the rate of 3%. At the end of the year he entered into partnership with a man who ran a garage, and turned in his car for \$800. Find his gain or loss on the entire transaction for the year.

4. A farmer's wife preparing to stock her kitchen with supplies applied to the manager of a large store for prices of the following items, if bought in quantity.

Items	Price in Small Quantity	Price in Larger Quantity
Flour	7# bag, 35¢	$24\frac{1}{2}$# sack, \$1.08
Evaporated milk	3 cans for 19¢	Case, 24 cans, \$1.40
Sugar	5# sack, 26¢	100# sack, \$4.80
Prunes	2# box, 15¢	25# box, \$1.48
Rice	1# package, 6¢	5# package, 24¢
Tea	$\frac{1}{4}$# box, 15¢	1# box, 48¢
Coffee	2# for 35¢	10 lb. sack, \$1.50
Canned pears	2 cans, 35¢	Case, 24 cans, \$3.60
Canned peaches	2# cans, 37¢	Case, 24 cans, \$3.80
Canned cherries	3 cans for 25¢	Case, 24 cans, \$1.80
Soap	6 cakes for 25¢	4 dozen cakes for \$1.65
Salmon	2 cans for 35¢	Dozen cans, \$1.90

She purchased 4 $24\frac{1}{2}$# sacks of flour, 2 cases evaporated milk, 100# sugar, 1 large box of prunes, 5# rice, 3# tea, 10# coffee, 1 case of pears, 1 case of peaches, 1 case of cherries, 4 doz. cakes of soap, and a dozen cans of salmon. How much did she save on the whole order, by buying in quantity?

5. Mr. Hadley earns \$1800 a year. He owns a car for which he paid \$400. During the year he drove his car 5276 miles. He bought 351 gallons of gasoline at an average price of 18¢ a gallon, and 18 quarts of oil at 25¢ a quart. Garage rent cost him \$4 a month, and insurance \$44 a year. His driving license and license plates cost him \$14.50. His greasing and repair bills for the year were $24.50. Depreciation on the car was estimated at $65. Allowing $2\frac{1}{2}\%$ interest on the cost of the car, find the total cost of running the car for one year. Find, to the nearest tenth of a cent, the cost per mile of running his car.

6. Mr. Hadley (see problem 5) pays $4 a week for room rent, and $8 a week for board. In addition to the clothing he has on hand, he estimates he will need for the coming year 2 new suits of clothes costing $52; a hat, shirts, and other miscellaneous items of clothing, $35. His laundry, dry cleaning, and incidental repair bills he estimates at $1.25 a week. For other expenses, such as hair cuts, dental and medical care, personal advancement (magazines, books, lectures, etc.), amusements, presents, he allows $2 a week. He carries a $3000 life insurance policy on which he pays a premium of $74.40. He contributes $90 to religious and charitable objects. Disregarding the Federal and State income taxes, find the amount by which his salary exceeds his total expenditures, as estimated, including the cost of running his car, as stated in problem 5.

7. Mr. Hunter is working only four days a week, and has a monthly wage of $80 a month. He has a wife and one child, a boy, 10 years old. On the days he works he carries his lunch from home. Mrs. Hunter tries to put up not only a tasty lunch, but one that is satisfying both as to quantity and nourishment. His lunch for one day consisted of 2 meat sandwiches, an orange, a half pint of milk, and a piece of homemade cake. The prices of the various items in the lunch were as follows:

Loaf of bread, 20 slices	$.08 a loaf
Butter, 40 sandwiches to the pound	.32 a pound
Meat, 25 sandwiches to the pound	.25 a pound
Milk	.12 a quart
Oranges	.30 a dozen
Cake, to cut 20 portions	.20 a loaf

Using these prices, find the cost of the lunch Mr. Hunter carried with him.

8. Referring to problem 7, Mrs. Hunter also puts up a lunch for the boy to carry to school. His lunch one day consisted of 1 egg sandwich, 1 peanut butter sandwich, 4 graham crackers, an apple, and 2 ginger cookies. Using the following prices (bread and butter as in problem 7), find the cost of the lunch the boy had.

Eggs, one for a sandwich	$.30 a dozen
Peanut butter, enough for 40 sandwiches	.15
Graham crackers, 30 to a box	.10 a box
Apples	3 for 5¢
Ginger cookies	.15 a dozen

9. Mrs. Preston in preparing a vegetable soup for her family of 6 persons, used the following ingredients. Using the quantities and prices indicated, find the cost per portion of the soup:

Ingredients	*Quantity*	*Cost*
Beef stock —	a portion of the juices from a roast	Cost included in cost of the roast
Potatoes —	1 cup (half pound) diced	5# for 15¢
Tomatoes —	$\frac{1}{2}$ of a #2 can	$5\frac{1}{2}$¢ a can
Onions —	1 medium size ($\frac{1}{4}$ lb.)	4¢ a pound
Carrots —	1 medium size	4¢ a bunch of 6
Rice —	1 tablespoon ($\frac{1}{2}$ ounce)	8¢ a pound
Celery —	1 cup, tops were used	Considered as of no cost as otherwise they would be thrown away
Water —	1 quart	Cost not estimated
Salt —	$\frac{1}{2}$ teaspoon	Cost not estimated

If a No. 2 can of vegetable soup will make three portions of soup, compare the cost of the home-made soup made by Mrs. Preston, with the cost of canned soup.

Table of Weights and Measures (Level, not heaped measures)	
3 teaspoons	= 1 tablespoon
4 tablespoons flour	= 1 ounce
16 tablespoons	= 1 cup
2 tablespoons butter	= 1 ounce
2 cups fat (butter, lard, etc.)	= 1 pound
4 cups flour	= 1 pound
2 cups granulated sugar	= 1 pound
$2\frac{2}{3}$ cups brown sugar	= 1 pound
$2\frac{2}{3}$ cups powdered sugar	= 1 pound
$1\frac{7}{8}$ cups rice	= 1 pound
$4\frac{1}{3}$ cups coffee	= 1 pound
2 cups meat, chopped fine	= 1 pound
2 cups liquid	= 1 pint
4–6 medium size onions	= 1 pound

Referring to the Table of Weights and Measures, and using local prices of the food items mentioned, find the cost of the following: (Cost of salt and pepper is negligible, and not reckoned in the cost.)

10. Cream of Celery Soup

3 cups celery, cut fine — 2 tablespoons flour
2 cups boiling water — 2 tablespoons fat
$\frac{1}{2}$ teaspoon salt — 2 cups milk
$\frac{1}{8}$ teaspoon pepper

Compare the cost of this soup with an equal quantity of canned soup.

11. Cream of Tomato Soup

1 pint of tomatoes — 1 quart milk
2 teaspoons sugar — 1 slice of onion
$\frac{1}{4}$ teaspoon soda — $\frac{1}{4}$ cup flour
1 teaspoon salt — $\frac{1}{4}$ cup butter
Pepper to taste

In comparing the cost of this soup with canned tomato soup it is well to remember that to the canned soup milk has to be added to make cream of tomato soup.

12. VEAL LOAF

2 pounds veal
$\frac{1}{4}$ pound fat salt pork
1 tablespoon parsley, chopped fine
$\frac{1}{2}$ cup dry bread crumbs
2 tablespoons tomato catsup
$\frac{1}{4}$ cup milk
1 medium size onion
1 egg
2 teaspoons salt
Pepper to taste

Weigh the loaf when it is cooked, and compare its cost with the cost of an equal weight of veal loaf bought at the store.

13. APPLE PIE (2 CRUST)

For the crust:

$1\frac{1}{2}$ cups flour
$\frac{1}{2}$ teaspoon salt
$\frac{1}{2}$ cup shortening
$\frac{1}{4}$ cup cold water

For the filling:

4 or 5 sour apples
1 teaspoon butter
$\frac{1}{4}$ teaspoon cinnamon
1 teaspoon lemon juice
$\frac{1}{8}$ teaspoon salt
$\frac{1}{8}$ teaspoon nutmeg
$\frac{1}{2}$ cup sugar

14. Two neighbors have homes of equal size and of similar construction. A heats his house and hot water for the kitchen and bathroom with an oil burner. The average annual quantity of oil used is 2250 gallons, at $6\frac{1}{4}$¢ a gallon. He pays \$12 a year for burner service. B heats his house with coal fire, using 12 tons of coal at an average cost of \$7.50 a ton. From October 15 to April 15 hot water for the kitchen and bathroom is furnished by the coal furnace. For the remainder of the year hot water is furnished by a gas heater at a cost of \$3 a month. For the six months the furnace is used B pays a man \$2 a week to care for the fire. He also pays a boy \$.25 a week to remove the ashes from the basement. Which man pays the less for heating his house? How much? If B cared for his own furnace and ashes, which man would pay the less for heating? How much less?

MISCELLANEOUS PROBLEMS

1. To how many decimal places is the per cent sign (%) equivalent?

2. Explain how to find to the nearest tenth per cent the per cent equivalent of $\frac{5}{16}$. Illustrate.

3. Explain how to change 2.75% to a common fraction in its lowest terms. Illustrate.

4. What is meant by depreciation as applied to furniture or other office equipment?

5. If an answer is desired in the nearest cent value, may the correct value be obtained in the following indicated operation by dropping the fraction in the rate before multiplying? Illustrate.

$$13\tfrac{1}{4}\% \text{ of } \$763.75$$

6. Using the following problem as a sample, formulate a simple problem to show the correct use of each of the following expressions:

Sample: "Arthur paid $4.50 for a pair of shoes; he paid 20% as much for a pair of rubbers. How much did he pay for both?"

"5% less than"; "diminished by 15%"; "16% larger than"; "increased by 4%"; "6% more than"; "decreased by 25%"; "4% better than"; "shrinkage of 7%"; "shortened by 40%"; "exceeded by 4%"; "lengthened by 10%"; "increased by 6% of itself"; "diminished by 4% of itself"; "exceeds itself by 8%."

7. A taxicab driver's receipts for six days were: Monday, $8.50; Tuesday, $7.90; Wednesday, $9.90; Thursday, $11.60; Friday, $12.75; and Saturday, $14.85. During the week he drove 468 miles. He used 52 gallons of gasoline at $.17 a gallon, and a quart of oil at $.25. Find (*a*) the average daily receipts; (*b*) the average daily cost of operating the taxicab; (*c*) the average net earnings per day; and (*d*) the average number of miles he drove per gallon of gasoline.

8. A stenographer's salary is $2160 a year. Her living expenses are $75 a month. What per cent of her salary can she save?

9. A merchant's gross sales were $19,681.30. The returns and allowances were $1416.38. Find to the nearest tenth per cent the per cent of the returns.

10. The gross profit of the Herzog Company was $28,725.38, and the operating expenses were $18,384.24. The net profit was what per cent of the gross profit?

11. A dealer bought a floor lamp for $13.20, less $16\frac{2}{3}\%$ and 10%. If he sells the lamp at the list price of $13.20, what rate of gross profit, based on cost, will he make?

12. A retailer sold a bicycle for $22.50. His gross profit was 50% of the cost. (*a*) How much did he pay for the bicycle? (*b*) If the cost of doing business was 20% of the sales, find his net profit. (*c*) What per cent of the cost was the net profit?

13. A clothier bought men's suits for $40 less 35%. When selling them for $38.50 each, he sold 14 suits a day. By reducing the price to $32.50, his sales increased to 30 suits a day. What per cent were his daily profits increased or decreased by reducing the price of the suits?

14. A radio cost a dealer $250 less 40%. The dealer sold it for $200, receiving $130 in cash, and an old radio for which he allowed the purchaser $70. He sold the old radio for $45. What per cent, based on cost, did the dealer make on the transaction?

15. The Traders Gas Range Company offers a gas range for $65 cash, or for $5.50 down and 12 monthly payments of $5.50. The installment price is what per cent greater than the cash price?

16. A clothier purchased 400 men's suits at $21.50 a suit. He marked them to sell at $32.25, and sold on the average 12 suits a day. To move the suits faster, he reduced the price to $27.50 each, and his sales increased to 25 suits a day. Was his daily gross profit increased or diminished, and how much?

17. Mr. McCarthy bought a new truck for $1600. During the first year he had it he had an accident. Repairs cost

$250. He was insured and the insurance company paid the repair bill. Later in the year he bought a set of new tires for $95. Gas and oil for the year cost him $275. At the end of the year he estimated the depreciation at 30% of the cost of the car. (*a*) What amount was allowed for depreciation? (*b*) Including depreciation, what was the total cost of running the truck for the year? (*c*) What was the value of the truck at the end of the first year?

18. A mechanic bought a house for $4250. Soon after buying it he discovered the roof leaked and he had a new roof put on the house at a cost of $175. He also spent $150 in redecorating the interior of the house. Do these expenditures increase the asset value of the house? Assume a new glass-enclosed sun porch, costing $500, is added to the house. What effect does this item have on the value of the house?

19. L. B. Forsman expects to live in a certain city for 3 years. He can rent a furnished apartment for $1400 a year, or he can rent an unfurnished apartment for $65 a month. Furniture will cost $1650, which he feels sure he can sell at the end of three years for $375. Which is the better plan for Mr. Forsman to follow? What per cent of the total cost of the more expensive plan is the saving by adopting the cheaper plan?

20. A salesman receives a salary of $50 a month and a commission of 4% on all sales. What must be the amount of his sales each month in order that his total monthly income may be $200?

21. To provide ready funds for paying for an invoice of merchandise valued at $7485.80, terms 5/10, N/60, a merchant wrote his 50-day note for the amount of the invoice and discounted it at his bank, at 6%. The cash discount was how much more than the bank discount?

22. On June 15, Mr. Barlow received word that he had overdrawn his bank account by $76.50. To meet the overdraft he took to the bank a 3-months' note of $850, dated May 26, and had it discounted at 6%. When the proceeds were deposited, how much was Mr. Barlow's bank balance?

23. Compare the bank discount with the true discount on $7500 for 90 days, at 6%. Which is greater? How much greater?

24. Mr. Light invested $11,792.50 in some store stock at 47, which he bought through a broker, paying $.17 a share for brokerage.

(*a*) How many shares of stock did he buy?

(*b*) If the stock paid dividends of $2.40 a share, what income did Mr. Light receive?

(*c*) What rate of income did he receive on his investment?

In ex. 25 to 27 find (*a*) the number of shares bought, (*b*) the amount of the dividend, and (*c*) the rate of income, to the nearest tenth per cent, allowing for brokerage.

25. Mr. Hines paid $3933.60 for Illuminating Gas stock at $16\frac{1}{4}$. The dividend was $1.20 a share, brokerage $.14 a share.

26. Mr. Abbott paid $33,372 for United Telephone stock at 111. The dividend was $9 a share, brokerage $.24 a share.

27. Frank Miller paid $16,041.30 for Southern Can at 97, when it was paying dividends of $4 a share, brokerage $.22 a share.

28. A man bought 350 shares of Payne and Whitlock stock at $33\frac{1}{8}$. Three months later he sold it at $36\frac{7}{8}$. While he owned the stock, he received a semiannual dividend of $.75 a share. Allowing brokerage of $.16 a share for both buying and selling, find his total profit on the transaction.

29. A man had $2800 in a savings bank paying $3\frac{1}{2}$% interest, compounded semiannually. He drew out $2446 and bought Midwestern Railroad stock at $48\frac{3}{4}$ plus brokerage at $.17 a share, paying dividends of $1 a share each six months. Was his annual income increased or decreased? by how much? Assume that when the semiannual dividend is received, it is put into the savings bank and draws interest for the second half year.

30. A merchant retired with $30,000, which he invested as follows: five $1000 Paragon Soap 6% bonds at 90, ten $1000 United Telephone 5% bonds at 106, and the rest of the funds in Vermont Railroad stock at $74\frac{1}{2}$, paying dividends of $5 a share. Disregard interest and brokerage charges.

(*a*) Find the cost of the Paragon Soap bonds.
(*b*) Find the cost of the United Telephone bonds.
(*c*) How many shares of railroad stock did he buy?
(*d*) Find the total annual income.

31. If bonds are bought at par (that is, at a price of 100, which means at $1000 each), how many dollars' worth of 5% bonds will yield $200 interest annually?

32. Henry Hammond sold through his broker 200 shares of Camden Camera stock at 96, paying dividends of $4 a share. Brokerage was $.22 per share. He invested the proceeds in Vermont Railroad 5% bonds at $105\frac{1}{2}$, paying brokerage of $2.50 on each bond.

(*a*) How many bonds did he buy?
(*b*) How much cash had he left?
(*c*) By how much was his annual income increased or diminished?

TESTS

The following groups of tests are provided as a basis for determining how thoroughly pupils have mastered the principles and problems of business arithmetic. The tests cover principles and subject matter used by insurance companies, department stores, the Joint Committee on Tests of the National Office Management Association and the National Council of Business Education, the University of the State of New York (Regents Examinations), and original tests prepared by the author.

INSURANCE EXECUTIVE'S TEST

The following short test was given by an insurance executive to a group of candidates for a clerical position. Less than 20% of the group passed the test.

1. Find $16\frac{2}{3}\%$ of \$16,472.50
2. Find $17\frac{1}{2}\%$ of \$10,953.80
3. Add:

\$4.75
13.25
.56
191.72
832.07
1.035
2.006

TESTS FOR ACCURACY OF OBSERVATION

(Given by a Large Insurance Company)

Below are two columns of numbers. Copy them and put an × as illustrated, after each pair of numbers *not* alike.

3458653	3458653
5437391	5437319×
2105476	2105476
1005040	1004050
9567892	9567892
2468024	2468204
4056782	4065782
6199753	6199763
2010567	2001567
3452468	3452468
9876345	9876245
4573809	4573809
6457381	6458371
5390609	5390609
2010102	2010102
2938475	2938745
6457234	6457234
9090190	9091090
3155432	3155432
5133423	5133423
4721564	4721564
7415462	7451462
5791357	5791357
1020304	1030204
7628577	7628577
8643217	8642317
9145142	9145142
2242322	2224322

Copy the two columns of numbers given below, inserting in exact numerical order the following eight numbers:

34,200,450	33,596,800
30,045,010	32,705,989
33,956,080	32,700,100
30,607,007	34,200,449
********	********
30,045,009	32,745,789
30,134,756	32,754,342
30,507,009	32,800,909
31,456,899	32,945,091
31,979,675	33,345,767
31,993,999	33,435,234
31,998,009	33,595,800
32,234,596	33,596,801
32,235,773	33,876,452
32,325,895	33,900,542
32,400,500	33,965,080
32,457,887	34,000,004
32,499,862	34,050,400
32,501,700	34,159,944
32,503,606	34,199,949
32,530,605	34,201,456
32,596,800	34,750,500
32,645,750	35,200,400
32,699,001	35,200,452
32,710,001	35,301,153

DEPARTMENT STORE TEST

A large department store gives its prospective sales people the following test:

1. Add:	2. Add:	3. Subtract:	4. Multiply:	5. Add:
$.34	$1.47	$568.43	$37.84	$5.07
.68	4.09	91.84	.63	3.76
				.67
				15.48
				1.91
				.07
				23.65
				9.74
				?? ??

6. Find the total cost of:

3 books at $.69	= ???
4 books at $.87	= ???
Total	= ???

7. Find the total cost of:

3 pkg. soap flakes	at $.28	= ??
5 bars soap	at $.04	= ??
7 cakes bluing	at $.07	= ??
8 bottles ammonia	at $.13	= ??
Total		= ??

Find the value of each of the following:

8. 8 oranges	@ $.27 a dozen
9. 6 yd. ribbon	@ $.29 a yard
10. 3 doz. bars soap	@ 3 bars for $.10
11. $1\frac{1}{4}$ yd. lace	@ $.49 a yard
12. 15 cups and saucers	@ $1.08 a dozen

13. A customer made a purchase amounting to $5.31, plus a sales tax of 2%. She gave a ten-dollar bill in payment. Indicate the kind and number of coins and bill she received in change.

14. A customer returned a dress for which she had paid $5.89 plus sales tax of 2%. In exchange she took a dress worth $7.94. After making adjustment in the price and sales tax, how much change should the customer receive from a five-dollar bill?

15. A suit of clothes for which a man paid $26.75, plus sales tax of 2%, was returned and in exchange the man selected a suit priced at $22.75. Making allowance for the sales tax and the difference in price, find how much money should be returned to the customer.

16. A customer bought an article for $4.44. She handed the clerk $5. Calculate the sales tax at 2% and indicate how much change should be returned.

The following operations are to be made without the use of pencil and paper, except to tabulate the results:

17. Add 48 + 87

18. Subtract 143 − 79

19. 46 + 69 − 87

20. 113 − 56 + 32 − 29

NATIONAL CLERICAL ABILITY TEST *

A

In this section are presented fifteen problems dealing with business arithmetic. On your answer paper write in a vertical column the numbers from 1 to 15. Compare your answer to each problem with the four answers furnished. If one of the answers is correct, place its number after the number of the problem on your sheet. If none of the answers is correct, write the correct answer after the number of problem, on your sheet.

1. Add:

```
49562
81935
 4621
 8367
75294
 2438
 1785
68419
 9382
37928
```

1. (1) 349731
(2) 338731
(3) 339731
(4) 339721
(N)

2. If insulators are $32\frac{1}{2}$¢ a pair, how many pairs can be purchased for $19.50?

2. (1) 62
(2) 60
(3) 59
(4) 120
(N)

* This test is a part of the National Clerical Ability Testing Program (1940 series). It is but one section of a test covering such fundamentals as grammar, choice of words, spelling, punctuation, business information, and arithmetic. It is reproduced by courtesy of the Joint Committee on Tests representing the National Office Management Association and the National Council for Business Education.

3. If a bill of goods amounting to $4638 is delivered to X on April 27 and paid for on May 1, how much would X pay? The terms are 3/5, N/30.

3. (1) $4499.86
(2) $4498.76
(3) $4498.86
(4) $4638.00
(N)

4. How much would the interest on $760 be for 15 days at 6%?

4. (1) $1.91
(2) $4.56
(3) $1.70
(4) $3.80
(N)

5. If a profit of $76 is wanted on the sale of an article costing $304, what per cent higher than cost will you have to charge?

5. (1) 35%
(2) 25%
(3) 20%
(4) $33\frac{1}{3}$%
(N)

6. X purchased a truck seven years ago for $847. If he sells it now at 42% of the cost, what will the average annual depreciation have been?

6. (1) $71.16
(2) $52.80
(3) $70.18
(4) $50.82
(N)

7. If a profit of $35.55 is made on an article which cost $158, what is the rate of profit? Compute on cost.

7. (1) $19\frac{1}{2}$%
(2) 21%
(3) $22\frac{1}{2}$%
(4) 18%
(N)

8. A shipment of goods was paid for immediately on arrival on a discount basis of 40/10/2 on list price. The list price on the shipment was $175. How much was paid?

8. (1) $93.61
(2) $93.71
(3) $91.61
(4) $91.00
(N)

9. A married man with two children earns $3700 annually. According to the income tax law he is allowed exemption of $2500 as head of the family, and $400 for each child. He has no other exemptions. Compute his tax on a basis of 4% for the first $100 of taxable income and $3\frac{1}{2}$% for each additional 100 dollars.

9. (1) $145
(2) $109
(3) $14.50
(4) $28.50
(N)

10. If X brand of coffee is worth 50¢ per lb. and Y brand is worth 25¢ per lb., what proportion of each should a mixture contain to be worth 35¢ per lb.?

10. (1) X–40% Y–60%
(2) X–50% Y–50%
(3) X–60% Y–40%
(4) X–25% Y–75%
(N)

11. A note for $1000 is to be paid in five annual installments of $200 each, plus accrued interest. The first payment is to be made one year after the date of the note. What is the total amount paid, interest at 6% per annum?

11. (1) $260
(2) $1200
(3) $1260
(4) $1060
(N)

12. A series of ten prizes was offered. The prizes were $1, $2, $4, $8, etc. Find the total amount awarded in prizes.

12. (1) $1123
(2) $511
(3) $1023
(4) $101
(N)

13. A towel is to be made from a piece of crash $28\frac{7}{8}''$ long. If $\frac{5}{16}$ of an inch is used at each end for a hem, how long will the finished towel be?

13. (1) $28\frac{1}{4}''$
(2) $28''$
(3) $29\frac{1}{2}''$
(4) $28\frac{1}{8}''$
(N)

14. Forty hats were bought for $148. At what price should they be sold to make 50¢ on each hat?

14. (1) $3.70
(2) $4.20
(3) $3.20
(4) $4.00
(N)

15. A grocer bought goods to the amount of $9000. He paid out $4365 in salaries and $850 for rent. For how much must he sell the goods in order to clear $2500?

15. (1) $15,215
(2) $15,940
(3) $16,715
(4) $11,500
(N)

B

Following is a series of problems based on a test submitted by the Joint Committee on Tests of the National Office Management Association and the National Council of Business Education.

After each of the following problems three answers are submitted. Indicate which of these answers is correct, if any. If none of the answers is correct, give the correct answer. Submit all work necessary to obtain results.

1. A merchant received a bill of merchandise on August 4, amounting to \$3732.64. The terms were 3/10, N/60. If the bill was paid on Aug. 14, find the amount paid.	**1.** \$3721.44 **2.** \$3359.38 **3.** \$3620.66 ?
2. Find the interest on \$1125 at 6% for 22 days.	**1.** \$4.19 **2.** \$41.25 **3.** \$0.41 ?
3. A retailer purchased a stove for \$45. At what per cent above cost should he sell the stove to make a gross profit of \$12.60?	**1.** 25% **2.** 28% **3.** 30% ?
4. You purchase a new automobile for \$1150, use it for 5 years, and then sell it for 30% of what you paid for it. What was the average annual depreciation on the car?	**1.** \$160 **2.** \$69 **3.** \$151 ?
5. An article cost \$245. It was sold at a profit of \$44.10. What per cent of the cost was gained?	**1.** 18% **2.** 82% **3.** 15.3% ?
6. You pay \$17.60 for a chair and sell it to gain \$4.40. What per cent of the selling price was gained?	**1.** 25% **2.** $33\frac{1}{3}$% **3.** 20% ?
7. A bill of merchandise listed at \$560 was subject to a trade discount of 25%, 20%, and 10% (usually written as 25/20/10). Find the net amount of the invoice.	**1.** \$252 **2.** \$308 **3.** \$313.60 ?

8. A man has a salary of \$4900. The income tax law permits him to deduct \$2500 as head of a family, and \$400 for each of 3 children. On the balance of his income he must pay 2% of the first \$1000, and 3% of the next \$1000 or fraction thereof. How much income tax did he pay?	1. \$60 2. \$34 3. \$30 ?

		35¢ Tea	*60¢ Tea*
9. A merchant mixes tea selling at \$.35 a pound with tea selling at \$.60 a pound to make a mixture to sell at \$.40 a pound. What proportion of each kind of tea should he use in the mixture?	1.	80%	20%
	2.	75%	25%
	3.	20%	80%
	?		

10. In purchasing an automobile a man paid \$500 down, and gave four notes of \$250 each, payable with interest, in 3 mo., 6 mo., 9 mo., and 12 mo., respectively. Find the total cost, including interest, of the car.	1. \$1037.50 2. \$1503.75 3. \$1375.00 ?
11. A man seeking work offered to work ten weeks for wages as follows: the first week for \$.01; the second week, for \$.03; the third week, for \$.09; and so on, his wages to be trebled each week for the 10 weeks. If the offer was accepted, find the total amount of his wages.	1. \$196.83 2. \$590.48 3. \$295.48 ?
12. A piece of curtain material 74″ long was hemmed by making a hem of $2\frac{3}{4}$ inches at one end and $1\frac{7}{8}$ inches at the other. Find the length of the curtain when it was finished.	1. $73\frac{1}{2}$ inches 2. $69\frac{1}{2}$ inches 3. $69\frac{1}{8}$ inches ?
13. A dealer bought 24 lamps for \$216, less 25%. Find the price each to gain \$2.25 on each lamp.	1. \$7.50 2. \$9.25 3. \$8.75 ?

		(a)	(b)
14. A bill of goods cost a merchant $6975. To sell them cost him $1150 in wages and $575 in other expenses. If he sold the goods to make a net profit of $695, find (*a*) the selling price, (*b*) the gross profit.	1.	$8125	$1270
	2.	$8700	$1725
	3.	$9395	$1845
	?		

15. Add:

```
 3925
  247.50
  308.25
    9.758
 4821.6
   59.64
  407.00
 7826.03
  391.607
   48.98
```

1. 17,605.365
2. 17,505.565
3. 17,503.365
?

16. At $.39$\frac{3}{4}$ a yard, how many yards of cloth can be bought for $34.98?

1. 880
2. 88
3. 86
?

17. At $.42$\frac{1}{4}$ a yard, find the cost of 178$\frac{3}{4}$ yd. of linen.

1. $75.52
2. $75.08
3. $75.21
?

18. An article which cost $21.48 was sold to gain $7.16. The gross profit was what part of the selling price?

1. 20%
2. 25%
3. 33$\frac{1}{3}$%
?

19. A wholesaler who paid $17.50 for an article marks it so he can make a profit of $5 after allowing his customers a 10% discount on his marked price. Find his marked price.

1. $24.50
2. $25.00
3. $19.75
?

20. A watch was sold for $38.70, which was 20% more than it cost. Find the gross profit on the watch.

1. $7.74
2. $6.45
3. $7.50
?

The following series of 6 tests, known as Regents Examinations, were prepared by the University of the State of New York. Each test consists of two units — "Rapid Calculation" and "Business Arithmetic."

RAPID CALCULATION TEST NO. 1

(June 18, 1940)

1–2. (*a*) Complete the following record of cash receipts: **(5)**

	Bills	Specie	Total
Monday	$48	$135	$???
Tuesday	152	710	???
Wednesday	50	79	???
Thursday	95	187	???
Friday	106	42	???
Saturday	753	156	???
Total	$???	$???	$???

(*b*) Compute the interest: **(5)**

$720 for 66 days at 6%
$600 for 72 days at 3%
$240 for 20 days at $4\frac{1}{2}$%
$360 for 3 months at 6%
$480 for 45 days at 6%

(*c*) Compute the following: **(5)**

80 bushels @$2.50
160 pieces @ $7\frac{1}{2}$¢
200 pounds @ 18¢
$87\frac{1}{2}$ gallons @ 24¢
492 articles @ $16\frac{2}{3}$¢

(*d*) Complete *each* of the following: **(5)**

80 decreased by $\frac{3}{4}$ of itself is ?? 500 lb. at 40¢ per cwt. is $??
A tax rate of $.286 per $100 is equivalent to $?? per $1000
45.68% expressed as a decimal is ?? $\frac{3}{8}$% of $96 is equal to $??

BUSINESS ARITHMETIC TEST NO. 1

(June 18, 1940)

1–2. Rapid Calculation Test No. 1. **(20)**

3. Answer all parts of this question. **(10)** [Two credits are assigned to each correct answer. Answers only are required in this question.]

(*a*) The freight rate between New York and Chicago on a certain class of merchandise is $1.25 per 100 pounds. What would be the total freight charges on a shipment of goods of the foregoing class, consisting of 2 barrels weighing 380 pounds each, and 3 cartons weighing 200 pounds each?

(*b*) What will be the amount of the check sent in payment of an invoice amounting to $660, terms 3/10, 1/20, N/30, dated April 27, and paid May 15?

(*c*) The employees of a radio factory were paid 60 cents an hour for a 44-hour week. If John Kingsley worked 44 hours in one week, what was the amount of his pay check after deducting 1% social-security tax?

(*d*) A mortgage amounting to $7800 bears interest at $4\frac{1}{2}$%, payable quarterly. What would be the amount of interest due each quarter?

(*e*) The tax rate for 1940 in a certain community is $25.22 per $1000. If property worth $3800 is assessed for 80% of its value, find the amount of the tax bill.

4. A clothier purchased topcoats for $24.50 and sold them for $36. In order to increase his sales, the clothier advertised the topcoats as follows: "Sale of Topcoats — Formerly $36 — Now $31.50."

(*a*) What was the per cent of discount offered on the topcoats during the sale? **(4)**

(*b*) If the clothier sold 12 topcoats a day before the sale, but sold 26 topcoats the day of the sale, what was the amount of the increase or decrease in the daily profit during the sale? **(6)**

5. The meter rate for filtered water in a certain city is 8 cents per 100 cubic feet for the first 20,000 cubic feet, 7 cents per 100 cubic feet for the next 30,000 cubic feet, and 5 cents per 100 cubic feet for all over 50,000 cubic feet. On January 3, 1940, the Western Laboratories received a bill for 58,000 cubic feet of filtered water. If 1% cash discount was allowed for paying the bill on or before February 2, 1940, what was the amount of the check sent in payment of the bill on February 1, 1940? **(10)**

6. Answer both (*a*) and (*b*):

(*a*) Personal property valued at $5000 was insured for 80% of its value at the three-year rate of $5 per thousand. Find the average yearly cost of the insurance. **(4)**

(*b*) The Atlas Corporation insured its building valued at $10,000 in three companies as follows: Star Insurance Company $4500; Western Indemnity Company $3500; United Insurance Company $2000. A fire resulted in a partial loss of $3600. For how much was each company liable? **(6)**

7. In 1939 the Zazijian Rug Company determined the selling price of its goods by basing the gross profit of 40% on the cost. In 1940 the company decided to base the 40% gross profit on the selling price.

(*a*) If a rug cost $66, what was the selling price of the rug in 1939? **(2)**

(*b*) If the cost of the rug remained the same, what was the selling price of the rug in 1940? **(4)**

(*c*) By what per cent was the gross profit on the rug increased or decreased in 1940 as compared with 1939? **(4)**

8. A firm in Boston offers you an invoice of merchandise for $480, less 20%, 10%, and 10%, f. o. b. your city. Another company in Chicago offers similar merchandise at $500, less 25% and 20%. The freight charges from Chicago to your city are $18.75.

(*a*) Find a single discount equivalent to the trade discount series offered by the company in Boston. **(2)**

(*b*) How much is saved by taking advantage of the better offer? **(8)**

9. Davidson and Lee entered into a partnership, investing $8000 and $4000 respectively. At the end of the year the total sales amounted to $18,525, cost of goods sold was $12,200, and overhead expenses were $1522. If the profit was to be divided according to the investment, find each partner's share of the profit. **(10)**

10. L. W. Webster purchased a house and lot for $6800, paying $1800 in cash and giving a $4\frac{1}{2}$% mortgage for the remainder. The expenses for the year, in addition to the interest on the mortgage, were as follows: taxes $128, insurance $35, repairs $69, water bill $15, depreciation $104, interest lost on the cash invested $36.

(*a*) What was the annual interest charge on the mortgage? **(2)**

(*b*) What were the total expenses for the year? **(2)**

(*c*) If Mr. Webster rented the house for $60 a month, what was his net income for the year? **(2)**

(*d*) What was the rate of net income on the investment? **(4)**

11. The cash price of a certain grade of coal purchased during the summer months is $9.75 a ton. The same grade of coal purchased after October 1 costs $10.85 a ton. Mr. James needed 12 tons of coal. In order to take advantage of the summer price of coal, he borrowed the necessary money on his 90-day note at 6% interest. How much was saved by borrowing the money and purchasing the coal at the reduced price? (10)

12. The Anderson Corporation purchased a new truck for $980. They estimated the life of the truck would be three years, at the end of which time the truck would have a trade-in value of $125. For the first year, the expenses of operating the truck, in addition to the depreciation, were as follows: insurance $148, repairs $18, gasoline and oil $236.20, license plates $19.

(*a*) What is the annual depreciation of the truck? (2)

(*b*) What was the total cost of operating the truck the first year? (4)

(*c*) If the car was driven 21,400 miles the first year, what was the average cost per truck mile to the *nearest tenth of a cent?* (4)

RAPID CALCULATION TEST NO. 2

(January 23, 1940)

1–2. (*a*) Complete the following sales record: (4)

	Cash	Credit	Total
Monday	$92	$85	$???
Tuesday	121	246	???
Wednesday	279	334	???
Thursday	82	98	???
Friday	293	402	???
Saturday	389	591	???
Total	???	???	???

(*b*) Compute the interest: (5)

$150 for 96 days @ 6%
$800 for 27 days @ 3%
$269 for 4 months @ 6%
$18.60 for 50 days @ 6%
$270 for 120 days @ 2%

(*c*) Compute the following: (5)

268 articles @ $2\frac{1}{2}$¢
440 bu. @ $1.25
750 bu. @ 44¢
298 yd. @ $33\frac{1}{3}$¢
1200 lb. @ $25 a ton

(*d*) Complete *each* of the following: (6)

$1\frac{1}{2}$¢ a pound is equivalent to $?? a ton 48 is $\frac{1}{3}$ larger than ??
$\frac{1}{4}$% of $240 is $?? 1.5 divided by 30 equals ??

The exact number of days from October 4, 1939, to January 2, 1940, is ?? days

.0125 is equivalent to ??%

BUSINESS ARITHMETIC TEST NO. 2

(January 23, 1940 — 9:15 A.M. to 12:15 P.M.)

1–2. Rapid Calculation Test No. 2. **(20)**

3. Answer all parts of this question. (**10**) [Two credits are assigned to each correct answer. Answers only are required in this question.]

(*a*) A farmer sold $\frac{3}{8}$ of his potatoes for \$60. At that rate, what would he receive for the remainder of his crop?

(*b*) In November, Jones & Smith had goods on hand amounting to \$9225. During the month they purchased goods worth \$6878. If at the end of the month the goods on hand amounted to \$5269, find the cost of the goods sold during November.

(*c*) For how much must goods that cost \$147 be sold to gain $16\frac{2}{3}\%$ of the selling price?

(*d*) After allowing discounts of $12\frac{1}{2}\%$ and 10% on an article listed at \$60, a dealer made a gross profit of \$9. Find the cost of the article.

(*e*) In a 10-day trip to the Gaspé Peninsula, we traveled 2280 miles. If we drove an average of 6 hours a day, what was our average hourly rate of travel?

4. Gasoline which was purchased for 13¢ a gallon was sold at 17.5¢ a gallon. At this price 500 gallons a day were sold. During a gasoline war the sales price of the same gasoline was reduced to 6 gallons for 99¢. At this price 660 gallons were sold in a day. Was the profit decreased or increased, and how much? **(10)**

5. (*a*) A building was insured in three companies as follows: National Co. \$8000; Standard Co. \$9000; Mutual Co. \$3000. If a fire loss of \$1620 occurred, find each company's share of the loss. **(5)**

(*b*) A building valued at \$12,000 is insured for \$8000 under a policy containing an 80% coinsurance clause. What amount must the company pay in case of a fire loss of \$1800? **(5)**

6. If discounted at 6% on August 29, 1939, what were the proceeds of a 90-day note for \$526.10, dated July 15, 1939, with interest at 5%? **(10)**

7. The assessed valuation of taxable property in a certain school district is \$9,446,190. The gross cost of operating the schools amounts to \$300,669.21. The school district's income from state moneys and nonresident tuition fees is \$126,623.97.

(*a*) Find the tax rate. [Carry the decimal to *five* places.] **(6)**

(*b*) Express your answer to (*a*) as the tax rate per \$1000. **(1)**

(*c*) Find the amount of John Smith's school tax if his property is valued at \$12,000 and assessed at 75% of its value. **(3)**

8. A merchant buys gloves at \$18 a dozen pairs. During a special sale he desires to offer a discount of 20% from the marked price and still make a profit of $33\frac{1}{3}$% on the cost. At what price must each pair be marked? **(10)**

9. The Eastern Electric Company pays its employees time and a half for overtime. Regular factory hours are 8 hours a day from Monday to Friday inclusive. All other working time is considered to be overtime. During the week of January 8, James Jones was employed as follows: Monday 7 hours, Tuesday $8\frac{1}{2}$ hours, Wednesday 9 hours, Thursday $10\frac{1}{2}$ hours, Friday 6 hours, Saturday 5 hours.

(*a*) If his wage rate was 75¢ an hour, what was the amount of his wages for the week? **(6)**

(*b*) If Jones spent 28% of his earnings for rent and 23% for food, how much money did he have left out of his earnings for the week? **(4)**

10. Brown, a salesman, is paid \$120 a month and a 4% commission on all sales in excess of \$25,000 for the year. During 1939, Brown's sales amounted to \$32,680.

(*a*) How much commission was Brown entitled to receive? **(4)**

(*b*) What was Brown's total income for the year? **(4)**

(*c*) What was Brown's average monthly income for the year? **(2)**

11. In 1937, Merrill used 8.4 tons of coal in his furnace. Coal was \$11 a ton and Merrill figured that his depreciation was \$5 and service costs \$2 a year. He then installed an automatic stoker at a cost of \$235. In 1938, his annual expenses were as follows: interest at 6% on his investment in the stoker; depreciation \$24; 7.5 tons of coal at \$7.50 a ton; service costs \$8; 108 kilowatt hours of electrical energy at 5¢ a kilowatt hour.

(*a*) What was Merrill's heating cost in 1937? **(2)**

(*b*) What was Merrill's heating cost in 1938? **(4)**

(*c*) What was the per cent of increase or decrease? **(4)**

12. Smith purchased ten \$1000 railroad bonds bearing 5% interest, at \$450 each, brokerage \$2.50 a bond, and 40 shares of

Eastern Electric stock at 42, brokerage 17¢ a share. The stock pays a quarterly dividend of 25¢ a share.

(*a*) Find the total cost of the bonds and stock. **(5)**

(*b*) Find Smith's annual income from these investments. **(3)**

(*c*) Find the rate of income to the *nearest tenth of a per cent.* **(2)**

RAPID CALCULATION TEST NO. 3

1–2. (*a*) Complete the following summary of sales: **(4)**

Department	Sales for April	Sales for May	Total
A	$291	$184	$???
B	712	697	???
C	342	288	???
D	164	129	???
E	159	108	???
F	204	271	???
Total	$????	$????	$????

(*b*) Compute the following: **(5)**

$33\frac{1}{3}$ bu. @ $1.08
16 oz. @ $2\frac{1}{2}$¢
36 cows @ $25
96 lb. @ 1.12\frac{1}{2}$
124 lb. @ 75¢

(*c*) Compute the interest: **(4)**

$6000 for 91 days @ 6%
$320 for 30 days @ $4\frac{1}{2}$%
$128 for 15 days @ 3%
$500 for 4 mo. @ 2%

(*d*) How many yards can be bought for **(2)**

$15 @ $33\frac{1}{3}$¢ $60 @ $62\frac{1}{2}$¢

(*e*) Complete *each* of the following: **(5)**

$\frac{1}{3}$% of $630 is ??
40 increased by 20% of itself is ??
36 divided by 1.8 is ??
.05 × 4.8 equals ??
$50 per ton is equivalent to $?? per pound

BUSINESS ARITHMETIC TEST NO. 3

1–2. Rapid Calculation Test No. 3. **(20)**

3. Answer all parts of this question. **(10)** [Deduct 2 credits for each incorrect answer. Answers only are required in this question.]

(*a*) By selling a car for $1500, a man lost $300. What per cent of the cost of the car did he lose?

(*b*) An investor pays $80 for a $100 bond bearing interest at 5%. What will be the rate of income on his investment?

(*c*) If the tax rate in a certain city is $25.40 per $1000, what amount of tax must be paid on property assessed at $8000?

(*d*) Find the single discount equivalent to a series of discounts of 20%, $12\frac{1}{2}$%, and 5%.

(*e*) An automobile that cost $630 four years ago can be traded in today for $150. What is the average annual depreciation?

4. On April 1, 1938, Brown deposited $500 in his savings bank. The interest rate is $1\frac{1}{2}$% per annum and the bank adds the interest to the depositors' accounts on April 1 and October 1 of each year. On April 1, 1939, Brown had to pay the semiannual interest at the rate of 5% per annum on a $3500 mortgage on his home. He withdrew the necessary amount from his savings account to make this payment.

(*a*) How much did Brown have on deposit in the savings bank on April, 1939, before making the withdrawal? **(5)**

(*b*) What was his bank balance after the withdrawal? **(5)**

5. Mrs. Bush, who conducts a ladies' apparel shop, has fixtures valued at $1000 and a stock of merchandise valued at $4500. She has the fixtures and stock insured at 80% of their value, paying 30¢ a hundred for one year on the fixtures and $1.80 a hundred for three years on the stock.

(*a*) Find the premium on the fixtures. **(4)**

(*b*) Find the premium on the stock. **(4)**

(*c*) Find the total yearly cost of insurance. **(2)**

6. Henry Clark is paying $35 a month rent for a one-family house. He can purchase the house for $4900 by paying $490 cash and giving a mortgage at 5% for the remainder. The estimated annual expenses that he would have as an owner are: taxes $125, water charge $25, repairs $50, insurance $9. If he can earn 2% on his money by investing it in government securities, will it be cheaper to buy or to rent, and how much? **(10)**

7. Smith wishes to purchase a car which sells for $756 cash. However, if he buys it on the installment plan, the dealer wants a down payment of $300 and the remainder in 12 equal monthly installments of $42.64 each. According to either plan, the dealer will allow Smith $200 for his used car to be applied on the down payment.

(*a*) How much money will be paid if the car is bought for cash? (2)

(*b*) What will be the total amount of cash paid if the car is bought on the installment plan? (4)

(*c*) By what per cent will the amount of cash paid on the installment plan exceed the amount of cash paid on the cash plan? (4)

8. The Acme Sales Company conducted a contest for its salesmen. Potter's average sales for the last nine weeks of 1938 were $379.65. For the first four weeks of 1939 his sales amounted to $376.14, $625.32, $429.53, and $374.52 respectively. Find Potter's average weekly sales for the 13 weeks. (10)

9. A commission merchant was ordered by a confectioner to purchase 275 bags of sugar, each containing 100 pounds. The commission merchant purchased the sugar at 3.5 cents a pound and charged 4% commission. He paid the freight at the rate of 53 cents a bag and a handling charge of $32.50.

(*a*) Find the total cost of the sugar to the confectioner. (8)

(*b*) Find, to the nearest tenth of a cent, the cost to the confectioner of a pound of sugar. (2)

10. Peter Small submitted the following facts on his New York State income-tax blank for the year 1938: salary for the year $4500; interest on savings account $48; profit on sale of stocks $75. The law entitles him to an exemption of $2500 as a married man and $400 for a dependent son. He is also permitted to deduct his contributions to church and community chest, which total $65. What will be the amount of his normal income tax if the rate is 2% on the first taxable $1000 and 3% on the next taxable $1000? (10)

11. Write the letters *a*, *b*, *c*, *d*, *e* on your answer paper. After *each* letter write "True" if the corresponding statement is true; if the statement is false, write the amount that should be substituted for the underscored amount to make the statement correct. [Deduct 2 credits for each incorrect answer.] (10)

(*a*) The net price of a refrigerator listed at $130, less 20% and 5%, is <u>$98.80</u>.

(*b*) On November 20, <u>$245</u> should be accepted in full payment of a bill for $250 worth of goods bought October 18 at the following terms: 4/10, 2/30, N/60.

(*c*) If a dealer bought belts at $15 a dozen and sold them for $2 each, his rate of gain on the selling price was $\underline{37\frac{1}{2}\%}$.

(*d*) In computing the discount on a note the exact number of days from November 25, 1938, to March 1, 1939, is $\underline{95}$.

(*e*) If the selling price of an article is $540 after a discount of 10% from the list price has been given, the list price of the article must have been $\underline{\$620}$.

12. On June 1, James Scribner received his bank statement, which showed a bank balance of $127.89. His checkbook balance on that date was $82.50. On comparing the statement with the checkbook, Scribner found that the following items had not been recorded in the checkbook: a canceled check for $15.92, a deposit of $21.36, and a service charge of $1. The following checks were outstanding: $20.00, $4.95, $16.00.

(*a*) Reconcile the balances. **(8)**

(*b*) On the reconciliation statement that you have prepared, indicate clearly the amount that represents the correct checkbook balance. **(2)**

RAPID CALCULATION TEST NO. 4

1–2. (*a*) Compute the following: **(5)**

80 bu. @ $1.75
12 yd. @ $3\frac{1}{3}$¢
90 lb. @ $66\frac{2}{3}$¢
64 yd. @ $87\frac{1}{2}$¢
360 lb. @ $16\frac{2}{3}$¢

(*b*) Compute the interest on *each* of the following: **(5)**

$840 for 40 days at 6%
$900 for 22 days at 6%
$150 for 36 days at 3%
$200 for 120 days at $4\frac{1}{2}$%
$36 for 60 days at 5%

(*c*) Complete *each* of the following: **(6)**

A tax rate of $18\frac{1}{2}$ mills on $1 is equivalent to $? ? per $1000

$\frac{3}{4}$% expressed as a decimal is ? ?

The number that will give 24 when increased by $\frac{1}{3}$ of itself is ? ?

80 is 25% of ? ?

A table that was listed at $50 was sold for $40; the rate of discount was ? ?%

2 yd. 1 ft. 6 in. is equal to ? ? inches

(*d*) Complete the following record of insurance policies written: **(4)**

	Albany Branch	Buffalo Branch	Total
January	81	102	???
February	108	99	???
March	95	85	???
April	67	76	???
May	122	116	???
June	73	93	???
Total	???	???	???

BUSINESS ARITHMETIC TEST NO. 4

1–2. Rapid Calculation Test No. 4. **(20)**

3. Answer all parts of this question. **(10)** [Deduct 2 credits for each incorrect answer. Answers only are required in this question.]

(*a*) A garage is 20′ × 18′. Give the dimensions of a diagram of the garage if a scale of $\frac{1}{4}$ inch to a foot is used.

(*b*) Pigskin gloves selling at $2.50 a pair advanced in price to $3 a pair. What is the per cent of increase?

(*c*) G. E. Getman gave an agency an account amounting to $500 to collect. The agency collected 75% of the account and charged 5% for collecting. How much did Getman receive?

(*d*) When potatoes sell for $.90 a bushel, which is better for the agent, a commission of 3% or a commission of 3¢ a bushel?

(*e*) A desk that cost $35 has been selling for $45.50. The same type of desk costs $37.50 today. At what price should it be sold to make the same rate of profit on the cost?

4. A commission merchant purchased for Walker & Son a carload of potatoes, containing 40,200 pounds, at 75¢ a bag. The net weight of each bag was 100 pounds. The commission merchant's expenses and charges were $65.57 for freight, $14.75 for sacks, $18.50 for labor, and 5% commission.

(*a*) How much did the potatoes cost Walker & Son? **(8)**

(*b*) What price per bushel (60 pounds) did Walker & Son pay? **(2)**

5. A dealer estimates that his selling and overhead expenses amount to 20% of his total sales. If he buys a radio for $64, less 25% and 10%, at what price must he sell it in order to gain $12\frac{1}{2}\%$ on the selling price? **(10)**

6. On December 5, Lenz & Company had a checkbook balance of $462.38. They wished to pay Maxson & Son for goods purchased on November 25 for $1375, less 20% and 10%, terms 2/10, N/30. To raise additional funds for the bank account, they discounted Hale & Company's three-months' interest-bearing note for $750, dated October 14. They then mailed their check to Maxson & Son.

(*a*) For how much did Lenz & Company write their check in payment of the bill on December 5? **(2)**

(*b*) What were the proceeds of the note that was discounted at the bank? **(6)**

(*c*) What was the balance in the checkbook after the check was issued? **(2)**

7. You wish to borrow $300 on a note and pay it back in installments of $75 each month on the principal. The total interest and other charges made by a bank for this loan will be $5.75. A loan company will charge 3% a month on that part of the loan which does not exceed $150 and $2\frac{1}{2}\%$ a month on that part of the loan which exceeds $150.

(*a*) Find the total interest cost that would be charged by the loan company. [In your solution show the interest to be paid each month.] **(8)**

(*b*) From which concern would it be better to borrow? How much better? **(2)**

8. A merchant bought 6 dozen blankets at $6 a blanket and marked them up 50% for regular sale. At the close of the season 18 blankets remained unsold. If the merchant wished to realize a profit of 40% on the cost of the 6 dozen, at what special price must he mark each of the remaining blankets? **(10)**

9. The semiannual rates for water in a certain city are as follows: 25¢ per 100 cubic feet for the first 5000 cubic feet or less; 20¢ per 100 cubic feet for the next 5000 cubic feet or less; 15¢ per 100 cubic feet for the next 5000 cubic feet or less. Find the amount of Mr. Anderson's water tax for six months if his meter showed 12,200 cubic feet used and if he took advantage of the 20% discount allowed for payment within 30 days. **(10)**

10. Williams was considering the purchase of real estate priced at $10,000 and subject to a mortgage of $5000. It was assessed at $7500 and insured for $6000. The interest rate on the mortgage was 5%, the tax rate $23.75 per thousand, and the insurance rate 80¢ per $100 for three years. The annual expense for repairs was estimated to be 2% of the purchase price.

(*a*) What was the amount of the annual interest charge? **(2)**

(*b*) What were the annual taxes? **(2)**

(*c*) What was the annual cost of insurance? **(2)**

(*d*) What minimum monthly rental will Williams have to receive for the property in order to cover expenses? **(4)**

11. Answer both (*a*) and (*b*):

(*a*) The four departments of a glove factory occupy floor space as follows: cutting department 2000 square feet, making department 3800 square feet, examining department 1500 square feet and shipping department 2200 square feet. The yearly heating cost for the entire factory is $2185. If this expense is divided among the several departments according to floor space, find the amount that should be charged to each department. **(5)**

(*b*) In addition to the heating cost, the expenses in operating this factory for the year were: rent $2760, insurance $424.50, miscellaneous expenses $3794.50. The goods manufactured during the year amounted to $192,000. What per cent of this output were the total factory expenses? [Express your answer to the *nearest tenth* per cent.] **(5)**

12. On December 15, 1937, a trucking company equipped each of two trucks of the same make and size with four new tires. On September 10, 1938, the tires had to be replaced. The speedometer readings and the costs were as follows:

Truck	Speedometer Reading		Tire Cost
	Dec. 15	Sept. 10	
A	96,482	146,482	$90 each (Grade 1)
B	36,785	76,785	$82 each (Grade 2)

(*a*) What was the cost per mile for each tire on truck A? **(3)**

(*b*) What was the cost per mile for each tire on truck B? **(3)**

(*c*) Supplying *two* reasons for your answer, state which was the more economical tire to buy. **(4)**

RAPID CALCULATION TEST NO. 5

1–2. (*a*) Solve by aliquot parts: **(4)**

144 yd @ $33\frac{1}{3}$¢
120 lb. @ $7\frac{1}{2}$¢
50 bu. @ $1.25
64 doz. @ $37\frac{1}{2}$¢

(*b*) Compute the interest on *each* of the following: **(4)**

$300 for 84 days at 6%
$1200 for 25 days at 6%
$480 for 30 days at 4%
$64 for 15 days at $4\frac{1}{2}$%

(*c*) Complete the following record of packages delivered: **(4)**

	Route 1	Route 2	Total
Monday	105	69	???
Tuesday	98	134	???
Wednesday	57	88	???
Thursday	124	107	???
Friday	218	175	???
Saturday	170	93	???
Total	???	???	???

(*d*) Complete *each* of the following: **(8)**

$\frac{2}{3}$% of $450 is ??
A tax rate of $9.50 per $1000 is equivalent to $?? per $1
The exact number of days from March 11, 1938, to June 9, 1938, is ??
150 divided by 7.5 is ??
24 increased by $16\frac{2}{3}$% of itself is ??
.025 is equivalent to ??%
A chair that cost $20 was sold for $30; the rate of gain on the selling price was ??
A lamp that cost $16 was sold for $24; the rate of gain on the cost was ??

BUSINESS ARITHMETIC TEST NO. 5

1–2. Rapid Calculation Test No. 5. **(20)**

3. Answer all parts of this question. **(10)** [Deduct 2 credits for each incorrect answer. Answers only are required in this question.]

(*a*) The discount at 4% on an invoice of goods is $16. What is the net cost?

(*b*) A man bought an automobile for $845. Five years later he was allowed $225 for it toward the purchase of a new car. What was the average annual depreciation?

(*c*) Find the single discount which is equivalent to a series of discounts of 20% and 5%.

(*d*) A bedroom suite that had been selling at $300 was offered during a special sale for $250. What rate of discount was allowed?

(*e*) The May reading of a gas meter was 45,600 cubic feet and the April reading was 42,800 cubic feet. At $.90 per thousand cubic feet, find the amount of the gas bill.

4. John Harper bought an invoice of goods for $3650, less 10% and 5%, on terms 2/10 N/60. In order to take advantage of the cash discount, Harper borrowed the sum needed from Smith, agreeing to repay him in 50 days with 6% interest. How much did Harper gain by borrowing the money? **(10)**

5. A shoe store proprietor buys shoes at $7 a pair. He desires to make a profit of 20% on the selling price after offering a discount of $12\frac{1}{2}$% on the marked price. At what price must each pair be marked? **(10)**

6. While a certain lace curtain was selling at $3 a pair, a store sold an average of 10 pairs a day. By reducing the price to $2.50, the store increased its sales to 20 pairs a day with no increase in total selling expense. The curtains cost $1.75 a pair.

(*a*) What was the amount of increase or decrease in the daily profit? **(8)**

(*b*) What was the per cent of increase or decrease in the daily profit? **(2)**

7. The taxable property in a city is assessed at $31,406,800. The total amount necessary to meet the expenses of the school system for the coming year is $502,700. It is estimated that $230,400 will be received from the state and $18,200 will be received from other sources.

(*a*) Find the tax rate per $1000. [Carry the decimal to five places.] **(6)**

(*b*) What tax should Mr. Carter pay if his property is valued at $9000 and is assessed at 80% of its value? **(4)**

8. On June 1, 1937, Kennedy, Lane, and Allen entered into partnership. Kennedy invested $5000, Lane $7500, and Allen

$10,000. It was agreed that each partner should receive 6% annually on his investment and that the remaining profit should be divided equally among the partners. At the end of the year, the gross profit on sales amounted to $8690 and other income $735. The expenses for the year amounted to $2525.

(*a*) Find the firm's net profit for the year. **(1)**

(*b*) Find Kennedy's total income for the year. **(3)**

(*c*) Find Lane's total income for the year. **(3)**

(*d*) Find Allen's total income for the year. **(3)**

9. John Miller, a salesman, receives a monthly salary of $90 and a 5% commission on all sales. In addition, he receives a commission of 2% on sales in excess of $3000 in any single month. His sales in April amounted to $3850 and in May to $2700.

(*a*) Find Miller's total commission. **(6)**

(*b*) Find his average monthly income for the two months. **(4)**

10. On June 1, James Whitney received his bank statement, which showed a bank balance of $1032.53. His checkbook balance on that date was $744.18. The following checks were outstanding: $82.50, $20.75, $145.35. Comparing the statement with the checkbook, Whitney discovered that a canceled check for $35.85 was not recorded in the checkbook and that he had also failed to enter in his checkbook a deposit of $75.60.

(*a*) Reconcile the balances. **(8)**

(*b*) On the reconciliation statement that you have prepared, indicate clearly the amount that represents the correct checkbook balance. **(2)**

11. A businessman is paying $4800 a year rent for the first floor of a store building. He can buy the building for $60,000. He would then receive a total of $4000 annually in rent from the other two floors and he would have the following expenses: taxes $950, insurance $240, repairs $500, janitor service $1200. If money is worth 6% to him in his business, how much would he gain or lose by purchasing the building? **(10)**

12. On February 1, M. R. King bought 70 shares of stock at $98\frac{1}{2}$, brokerage 22¢ a share. On April 1 and again on October 1, he received a cash dividend of $2.50 a share on the stock. On November 1, he sold the stock at $110\frac{1}{4}$, brokerage 24¢ a share.

(*a*) How much did King gain on the sale of this stock? **(8)**

(*b*) How much did King make on the entire transaction? **(2)**

RAPID CALCULATION TEST NO. 6

1–2. (*a*) Add: (**4**)

$6.54
47.96
673.62
7.96
678.58
36.49
32.21
453.52
68.34
268.57
42.15
676.17
28.73
745.29
10.70
$??? ??

(*b*) Compute the following: (**4**)

48 yd. @ $1.12½
125 yd. @ 32¢
350 lb. @ $1.20 per C.
1500 lb. @ $28 per ton

(*c*) Compute the interest on *each* of the following: (**4**)

$160 for 30 days at 1½%
$270 for 4 months at 2%
$450 for 80 days at 4½%
$1200 for 25 days at 6%

[Footing not required]

(*d*) State the Rate of Gain on Selling Price, Rate of Gain on Cost, and Rate of Discount on Marked Price, for the two problems in (*d*): (**6**)

Marked Price	*Selling Price*	*Cost*
$80	$60	$50
$20	$18	$12

(*e*) How many articles can be bought for (**2**)

$18 at 33⅓¢ each? $24 at 25¢ each?

BUSINESS ARITHMETIC TEST NO. 6

1–2. Rapid Calculation Test No. 6. (**20**)

3. Answer all parts of this question. (**10**) [Deduct 2 credits for each incorrect answer. Answers only are required in this question.]

(*a*) If the tax rate is $21 on $1000, what is the rate, expressed in mills, on $1?

(*b*) When strawberries sell for $3.80 a crate, which is better for the agent, a commission of 5% or a commission of 15 cents a crate?

(*c*) A clerk saves 15% of his salary. If he earns $200 a month, in how many years can he pay for a house and lot costing $5400? [Disregard interest.]

(*d*) A pupil received the following grades: typewriting 75%, business arithmetic 81%, English 92%, drawing 83%. What per cent must he receive in shorthand in order that he may have an average of 85%?

(*e*) Ladies' hats costing $2.40 were sold for $6. If hats of the same grade cost $3.20 today, at what price should they be sold to make the same rate of profit on the selling price?

4. George Allen owned a building used for store purposes, valued at $18,000, and carried a stock of goods inventoried at $5250. He insured the building for 80% of its value at $1.65 per $100 for three years and the stock for the inventoried value at $1.20 per $100 for one year.

(*a*) Find the premium on the building. **(4)**

(*b*) Find the premium on the stock. **(4)**

(*c*) Find the total yearly cost of insurance. **(2)**

5. On December 1, A. B. Browne's bank statement showed a balance of $1245.27. His checkbook balance on that date was $1089.54. The following checks were outstanding: $125.10, $59.05, $118.08. Comparing the statement with the checkbook, Browne discovered that the following items had not been recorded in the checkbook: a service charge of $1, a note for $145.50 paid by the bank and charged to his account.

(*a*) Reconcile the balances. **(8)**

(*b*) Indicate clearly on your reconciliation statement the amount that represents the correct checkbook balance. **(2)**

6. A commission merchant received from a grower in Florida a carload of lettuce to be sold on commission. The car contained 670 crates and the shipping weight was 16,650 pounds. The freight was $1.30 per 100 pounds and the charge for icing was $63. The commission merchant sold 250 crates at $1.80, 220 crates at $1.70, and the remainder at $1.24 a crate. After deducting 5% commission and all charges, the commission merchant remitted the proceeds to the grower.

(*a*) What amount did the grower receive? **(8)**

(*b*) What was the average price per crate at which the agent sold the consignment? **(2)**

7. An electric refrigerator is billed to a dealer at $220, less 25%. The dealer's overhead expenses amount to 25% of the sales. At what price must he sell the refrigerator to gain 15% on the selling price? **(10)**

8. The employees of the Bedell Foundry Company are paid weekly on the basis of a 40-hour week with time and a half for overtime. During the month of November, 1937, George Mann worked 44 hours the first week, 36 hours the second week, 48 hours the third week, and 40 hours the fourth week. His regular rate of pay is 67 cents an hour.

(*a*) Find Mann's total wages for the four weeks. **(6)**

(*b*) The company deducted 1% from Mann's wages as his contribution to the Social Security fund. What was the net amount paid him for the four weeks? **(2)**

(*c*) The Social Security Act requires the employer to deduct 1% from the employees' wages and to make an equal contribution to the fund. The total pay roll for the four weeks was $20,000; what amount was paid to the Federal Government? **(2)**

9. A firm had bills amounting to $1275.50 to pay on January 5. Their checkbook balance was $1020.30. To raise additional funds, the firm discounted on January 4, 1938, Harry Brown's 60-day interest-bearing note for $500, dated December 20, 1937.

(*a*) Find the proceeds of the note. **(8)**

(*b*) What was the firm's balance on January 5, after the bills had been paid? **(2)**

10. A savings bank pays interest semiannually on deposits at the rate of $2\frac{1}{2}$% per annum. Interest is credited to the depositors' accounts on January 1 and July 1. On July 1, 1936, Bert Foster deposited $500. He withdrew $150 on July 1, 1937. How much did Foster have on deposit on January 1, 1938? **(10)**

11. David Baker owned 60 shares of State Electric stock. He authorized his broker to sell the stock at $108\frac{1}{2}$ and buy Arctic $1000 bonds at 98. The brokerage for selling the stock was $7.50 and for buying the bonds $2.50 for each bond.

(*a*) What amount was available for the purchase of the bonds? **(5)**

(*b*) How many bonds were purchased? **(2)**

(*c*) How much money was left to Baker's credit? **(3)**

12. If a charge of 6¢ a barrel for storage was made for the first 10 days and 2¢ a barrel for each succeeding 10 days or fraction thereof, find the total amount paid for storage on the following: (**10**)

Stored		*Withdrawn*	
October 2, 1937	125 barrels	October 20, 1937	150 barrels
October 16, 1937	50 barrels	December 18, 1937	125 barrels
December 9, 1937	100 barrels		

The preceding tests were of a general nature, covering a variety of subjects. The following tests prepared by the author are based on specific subjects.

Test in Percentage No. 1

1. What number is 15% more than 40?

2. 56 is 12% greater than what number?

3. 72 is $\frac{4}{5}$ of what number? 72 is 80% of what number?

4. 66 is $\frac{1}{3}$ less than what number? 66 is $33\frac{1}{3}$% less than what number?

5. Compare $\frac{1}{4}$% and $\frac{1}{4}$ of 1%.

6. Which is greatest, $\frac{1}{8}$%, $\frac{1}{8}$ of 1%, or .$12\frac{1}{2}$%?

7. A man's income exceeded his expenses one year by 15%. If his expenses were $2800, how much was his income that year?

8. Last year the number of men employed in a factory was 144. This year there are 168 men employed in the same factory. What is the per cent of increase over last year?

9. Last year Mr. Clark worked 48 hr. a week. This year he works only 40 hr. a week. Find the per cent of decrease in the number of hours Mr. Clark works each week.

10. Mr. Clark's wages last year were $.55 an hour. What must be his hourly wage this year to make his weekly wage the same as it was last year? (See Problem 9.)

Test in Percentage No. 2

1. Find, to the nearest tenth per cent, the rate of tax a man paid on property assessed at $3750 if he paid $85.05.

2. An employer has increased the number of his employees by 8%, adding 22 people to the force. How many employees had he at first? How many employees has he now?

3. State in words the meaning of $\frac{1}{2}$%; of 4%; of .12$\frac{1}{2}$%.

4. Mr. Drew's assets decreased 7% during last year. If his assets a year ago amounted to $17,400, what are his assets this year?

5. A discount of 3% is allowed on gas bills if they are paid before the tenth of the month. How much would be paid on a bill of $7.90 if paid on the eighth of the month?

6. How much would be saved in a year by prompt payment (see Problem 5) if the average monthly bill was $6.96?

7. The credit price of a dressing table is $19.75. The cash price is 8% less. Find the cash price.

8. A merchant's cash price for a chair is $8.50. His credit price is $9.18. What per cent of the cash price has been added to make the credit price?

Test in Percentage No. 3

1. In April a straw hat sells for $3.50. In August the same grade of hat sells for $2.10. For what per cent less does the hat sell in August than in April? Why?

2. A car was bought for $900. At the end of the year an allowance of $540 was made on it in a trade for a new car. What was the rate of depreciation?

3. A real-estate agent sold three lots of land for $975, $1150, and $1850, respectively. He received a commission of 2$\frac{1}{2}$%. How much did he earn?

4. A man paid $75 for a cow. For 9 mo. of the year the cow gave an average of 30 lb. of milk a day. The milk was sold at $1.65 a hundredweight. To feed the cow for a year cost $54.60. How much more was the milk worth than the cost of feeding the cow? (Reckon 30 days to a month.)

5. Allowing 6% interest on the cost of the cow in Problem 4 and 12$\frac{1}{2}$% depreciation on her value, find the owner's net profit for the year.

6. A merchant sold a suit of clothes for \$32.50. His profit was 12% of the selling price and his selling expenses were 18% of the selling price. Find (*a*) the profit; (*b*) the selling expenses; (*c*) the cost of the suit.

7. Mr. Bender's sales for a year were \$32,400. His overhead expenses, such as rent, heat, light, clerk hire, etc., were \$4374. What per cent of his sales were the overhead expenses?

8. A merchant who failed in business, owing \$27,984, had assets amounting to \$16,090.80. What per cent of his debts could he pay? How much would a creditor to whom he owed \$1148.80 receive?

Test in Percentage No. 4

1. Express each of the following fractions as a per cent:

a. $\frac{1}{4}$	*c.* $\frac{1}{8}$	*e.* $\frac{7}{8}$	*g.* $\frac{3}{10}$	*i.* $\frac{7}{16}$
b. $\frac{1}{3}$	*d.* $\frac{3}{5}$	*f.* $\frac{1}{6}$	*h.* $\frac{5}{12}$	*j.* $\frac{1}{40}$

2. Express each of the following rates per cent as a decimal; as a common fraction in its lowest terms.

a. $66\frac{2}{3}\%$	*c.* $2\frac{1}{2}\%$	*e.* $6\frac{1}{4}\%$	*g.* $\frac{1}{2}\%$	*i.* $\frac{1}{10}\%$
b. 75%	*d.* 15%	*f.* $\frac{1}{4}\%$	*h.* $\frac{1}{8}\%$	*j.* $\frac{3}{20}\%$

3. A bank charged $\frac{1}{10}\%$ collection on an out-of-town check of \$450. How much was the collection charge?

4. On a short-time loan of \$2500 a man paid $1\frac{1}{4}\%$ interest. How much interest did he pay?

5. On an investment of \$3500 a man received an annual return of \$157.50. What was the annual rate of return on the investment?

6. How much money must be invested at 5% to yield an annual income of \$1875?

7. A bookkeeper's wages were increased from \$20 a week to \$22.50 a week. What was the per cent of increase?

8. A stenographer who is now receiving \$27 a week said, "My wages this year are $12\frac{1}{2}\%$ greater than they were last year." How much were her weekly wages last year?

9. On an automobile costing \$2250 the depreciation for the first year was \$450. What was the rate of depreciation?

10. The furniture in a business office at the end of its first year of use was estimated to be worth \$350. If the rate of depreciation was reckoned at $12\frac{1}{2}\%$, what was the value of the furniture at the beginning of the year?

11. For collecting an out-of-town note of \$3280 for one of its depositors, a bank charged $\frac{1}{20}\%$. After deducting the collection charge, the balance of the note was placed to the credit of the depositor. With how much was the depositor credited?

12. Arrange the following in the order of size, beginning with the smallest: $\frac{1}{4}\%$, $12\frac{1}{2}\%$, 1.25%, $\frac{3}{10}\%$, 3%, $.12\frac{1}{2}\%$.

13. Three young men, Jarvis, Bullock, and Murphy, together bought a motor boat, paying \$75, \$125, and \$100, respectively. What per cent of the purchase price did each pay? They agreed to share the expenses of running and caring for the boat in the same proportion as each had paid to buy the boat. If the cost for the first year was \$120, how much of the cost should each pay?

14. Harry bought a set of golf clubs and a bag, agreeing to pay \$37.50 for them. He paid \$7.50 down, and three monthly payments of \$5 each. What per cent of the purchase price was then unpaid?

15. Find the following indicated products and the total of the products:

a. $2\frac{1}{2}\%$ of \$140	*c.* $62\frac{1}{2}\%$ of \$1200	*e.* $\frac{1}{10}\%$ of \$5000
b. $\frac{1}{4}\%$ of \$1600	*d.* $.12\frac{1}{2}\%$ of \$19,200	*f.* .3% of \$640

Test in Commission No. 1

Find the proceeds of each of the following sales:

1. Amount of sales, \$675; commission, 3%
2. Amount of sales, \$932; commission, 4%
3. Amount of sales, \$1155; commission, $2\frac{1}{2}\%$
4. Amount of sales, \$1630; commission, $1\frac{1}{2}\%$

5. Amount of sales, \$2140; commission, $2\frac{1}{2}\%$; cartage, \$18.75

6. Amount of sales, \$3275; commission, $3\frac{1}{2}\%$; freight, \$16.70

7. Sold 18 tubs of butter averaging 52 lb. to a tub, at \$.32 a pound; commission $4\frac{1}{2}\%$; freight, \$7.50

8. Sold 15 crates of eggs, 30 dozen to a crate, at \$.27½ a dozen; freight, \$6.75; cartage, \$3.50; commission 5%

Find the total cost of each of the following purchases:

9. Prime cost, \$1372.50; commission, 3%

10. Prime cost, \$4287.50; commission, $2\frac{3}{4}\%$

11. Bought 75 bbl. flour at \$7.25; commission, $2\frac{1}{2}\%$

12. Bought 2100 lb. coffee at \$.16¼; commission, 2%

13. Bought 15,000 bu. corn at \$.87½; commission, $\frac{1}{2}\%$; freight, \$75

14. Bought 25 M white pine lumber at \$77; commission, $2\frac{1}{4}\%$; freight, \$78.75

15. Bought 2870 lb. leather at \$.32½ per pound; commission, 4%; freight, \$14.35; guaranty, $1\frac{1}{2}\%$

Test in Commission No. 2

1. In what respect are problems in commission like the problems in percentage?

2. What term in commission corresponds to the base in percentage? to the rate? to the percentage?

3. What is the advantage to the employer in paying for work done on the commission basis? What disadvantage?

4. What advantage is it to the employee to be paid on the commission basis? What disadvantage?

5. A manufacturer employs an agent to sell his manufactured product under the following agreement: The agent is to receive \$100 a month and traveling expenses, plus a commission of 3% on all sales over \$2000 and not over \$2500 a month; 4% on all sales over \$2500 and not over \$3000 a

month; 5% commission on all sales over $3000 and not over $3500 a month, and so on, 1% being added to the rate of commission for each additional $500 (or fraction thereof) in the sales. Why can a manufacturer afford to increase the rate of commission as the amount of sales increases?

6. B. W. Hobson accepted a position as salesman at a monthly salary of $110 with 6% commission on all sales over $2000 a month. Mr. Hobson's sales in March amounted to $1950; in April, to $3250; and in May, to $3375. (*a*) What was the total commission that Mr. Hobson was entitled to receive? (*b*) What was Mr. Hobson's average monthly commission for the three months? (*c*) What was Mr. Hobson's total income for the three months?

7. Russell Green, a salesman, received a salary of $80 a month and a 5% commission on all sales. In addition, he received a commission of $1\frac{1}{2}$% on sales in excess of $2500 in any single month. His sales in November amounted to $3340 and in December to $2250.

(*a*) Find Mr. Green's total commission.

(*b*) Find his average monthly income for the two months.

8. A grower shipped to Chicago, to be sold on commission, 2 carloads of potatoes weighing respectively 34,500 pounds and 35,700 pounds. Freight charges paid by the commission merchant were $.23 per cwt. Before the potatoes could be sold they had to be graded and put into bags, 100 pounds to the bag. Sorting and sacking cost $.10 a bag. $66\frac{2}{3}$% of the potatoes were #1 grade and were sold at $.95 a bag. The remainder were #2 grade and were sold at $.70 a bag. The commission merchant charged 5% commission. Set up an account sales to show the proceeds of the sale.

9. R. R. Gridley of Cleveland, Ohio, bought for the Regal Grocers, Pittsburgh, Pa., the following quantities of cheese: 100 boxes averaging 60 pounds to the box, at $.15$\frac{1}{2}$ a pound, and 100 boxes averaging $62\frac{1}{2}$ pounds to the box, at $.18 a pound. Gridley paid a cartage charge of $12.50, prepaid the freight of $21.50, and charged $2\frac{1}{2}$% commission. Set up an account purchase to show the total cost of the cheese.

Test in Commercial Discount

1. What single discount equals a series of $33\frac{1}{3}\%$, 25%, and 10%?

2. One merchant offers a safe listed at $560, less 30% and 10%. A second merchant offers a safe of equal value for $575, less 20%, 20%, and 10%. Which is the better offer for the buyer, and how much better?

3. E. V. Dunkirk purchased an invoice of goods listed at $1641.50, less 20% and $12\frac{1}{2}\%$. The terms were 3/10, N/60. How much cash will be required to pay for the goods at the expiration of the discount period?

4. A wholesale dealer wishes to list a table in his catalogue so he can allow a trade discount of 20% and 10%, and still receive $21.60 for it after the discount has been deducted. Find the list, or catalogue, price of the table.

5. A manufacturer lists at $36 a radio which costs him $16.20. He allows a trade discount of 25% and 20%. To meet competition, he reduces the price of the radio to $18. This reduction in price is equivalent to what rate of discount in addition to the rates originally offered?

6. Write an original problem in which will be illustrated quantity discount, trade discount, and cash discount.

7. Solve the problem you wrote for Problem 6, and label each kind of discount.

8. A merchant received an invoice of goods worth $988.50, on June 13, terms 3/10, E. O. M., anticipate. Allowing interest at 6%, find the amount paid for the goods on June 15.

9. On August 25, the College Supply Company purchased from the Royal Paper Company a quantity of stationery and supplies for $1428.75, less 20% and $12\frac{1}{2}\%$, terms 5/10, 3/30, N/60. Find the amount of check required for settlement, Sept. 23.

10. During the month of October the sales of a wholesale house amounted to $98,796.40. Cash discounts amounting to $4928.62 were taken by customers. Find, to the nearest tenth per cent, what per cent of the sales was the cash discount.

INDEX